O, Georgia!

A Collection of Georgia's Newest
and
Most Promising Writers

Volume III

Humpus Bumpus Press
Cumming, Georgia
Terri Pepper Gavulic, Editor

© Copyright 1999 by Humpus Bumpus Press
First Printing - October, 1999

Published by
Humpus Bumpus Press
Cumming, Georgia 30040

ISBN: 0-9654624-5-5

Printed in the United States of America
Formatting and layout by TBI Creative Services
Cover illustration by Debrah Santini

For ordering information
Tel: (770) 781-9705
Toll Free: (800) 464-0683
Web: www.humpusbumpus.com
E-Mail: paulcossman@mindspring.com

Table of Contents

iv

Forward

As the publisher of O, Georgia! and the proprietor of an independent bookstore, I am immensely honored and privileged to be engaged in work which I love and for which I have great passion. One aspect of my work about which I feel passionate is the daily opportunity I have for creating a haven for readers and writers where each of us can speak in his/her own voice. An independent bookseller/publisher presides over a little island of civility and safety in an atmosphere in which no one has to be afraid to think and to share ideas openly and freely. Isn't this type of freedom what made our country great over 200 years ago?

In addition to fostering a free flow of ideas and discussion, I enjoy the struggle against the current trend toward uniformity in publishing. One of the most noble tasks an independent bookseller/publisher can perform is to promote diversity of thought by helping emerging authors give voice to new ideas and by enabling their voices to be heard.

Diversity of culture and thought keep our great land fresh and ever changing. Independent publishers are in a better position than almost anyone to promulgate a rich, intellectual stew by publishing budding authors. Those who have the greatest power to encourage diversity of ideas, however, are you, our readers. It is with exuberance and gusto that I invite you to dive into this refreshing pool of new talent and learn why the authors between these covers are, indeed, Georgia's newest and most promising writers!

Paul A. Cossman
Publisher

Acknowledgment

I wish to express gratitude to all the individuals who have helped make this year's O, Georgia! a reality. Our fiction and non-fiction judges are Donna Gessell, Ph.D., Eric Carl Link, Ph.D., and Alan Jackson. The poetry judges are John K. Ottley, Ethelene Dyer Jones, Margaret Langford and Dorothy Worth. Our judges are introduced at greater length in the *Biographical Notes* section of this book.

I would also like to thank Debrah Santini for creating and painting the delightfully whimsical work of art which graces the cover of this edition. Thanks to Terri Pepper Gavulic who read hundreds of submissions and edited the winning entries. My thanks to Janet Bolton and Paul Joffe of TBI Creative Services who rendered the book's format and layout. Special thanks go to my good friend and fellow bibliophile, Dennis Richards who, through a generous cash donation, helped to make this year's O, Georgia! possible.

To all the aforementioned people I offer that, without their enormous commitment of time, energy and expertise as well as their emotional investment in the O, Georgia! campaign, this fine literary achievement would never have found its way into your hands.

Finally, I thank all the enthusiastic writers who participated in this year's O, Georgia! and offer a hearty congratulations to those who were selected for publication. To all you writers everywhere, I invite you to submit your manuscripts today for the year 2000 O, Georgia! writing competition!

Paul A. Cossman
Publisher

x

The Acceptance
by Betsy McCall

Susan sat with Frances and Cynthia at the birthday party, taking in the surroundings. This marked the first time Susan and her family had come to an indoor playground like Sunset Zone. She felt at ease almost immediately in the large, well-lit room decorated in off-white, jade green, and mauve. Large plate glass windows punctuated the main room's front and back walls, adding to the room's sunny ambience.

The majority of the room's perimeter was loosely divided into sections devoted to miniature bowling, bumper pool, video games, basketball hoops, specially designed exercise areas, and a number of other activities Susan couldn't quite make out from where she sat. Along the remaining wall space stood a snack bar and a series of smaller enclosed rooms with long tables and chairs for private birthday parties. The sole entrance to the interior was designed so that patrons couldn't leave without paying or without the appropriate guardian. Patrons wore name tags around their wrists—akin to hospital bracelets—to ensure these results.

The only characteristic Susan found mildly annoying was the noise—the bells, the clangs, the hubbub of party-goers and others seeking amusement and recreation. Nonetheless, the activities looked inviting; she entertained the idea of returning by herself but dismissed it quickly. A participant her age would stand out by herself.

Like most of the adults chaperoning party-goers, the three women sat drinking various coffee beverages at one of the many tables which dotted the center of the main room. Susan added another Sweet 'N Low to her cappuccino, stirring it carefully to minimize spillage from the mountain of whipped cream on top.

"Well, how do you like being at home?" Cynthia asked Susan with a smile, as if there could only be one answer.

"Oh, it's nice." Susan tried to sound enthusiastic. She hadn't told Cynthia or Frances—neither of whom had worked a day of their married lives—about her recent job prospects or how they had evaporated one by one.

"Isn't it nice to relax and spend more time with the kids?" Cynthia pressed.

"Well, I'm not sure my kids are that relaxing. But it is nice." Frances gave a small sympathetic chuckle.

Cynthia pouted momentarily before asking, "So, have you been enjoying the Decapitator?" She kept her focus on Susan as she fingered her faux pearls. A few weeks earlier, Susan had bumped into Cynthia while browsing in a wine shop for a gift. Cynthia had insisted that Susan buy the Decapitator. "It will change your life," she had promised. Susan had reluctantly complied, even though she and her husband didn't drink much.

"What's a Decapitator?" asked Frances eagerly.

"Oh, it's a wonderful kind of wine bottle opener," Cynthia replied impatiently. "Isn't it fabulous, Susan? Didn't it change your life?"

"Well . . . we are enjoying it," Susan replied.

Cynthia gave a throaty laugh and nodded knowingly. Then she asked, "So how was your trip to Florida?"

"It was great!" replied Susan, this time with real enthusiasm. "We played golf and tennis and went swimming almost every day with my folks and the kids. And we all tried roller blading— even my parents! They also watched the kids a few nights so Derek and I could have some time to ourselves. It was a real vacation." She laughed. "For Derek and me, anyway."

"That sounds wonderful," purred Cynthia. She reminded Susan of her cat: trim, elegant and wearing a pretty collar.

"Wait, you mean your parents went with you?" asked Frances, a puzzled look pinching her thin face. "And they roller bladed?"

"Yeah. We go on a lot of trips together. They're fun."

"Wow. That's amazing," said Frances. "I can't imagine that."

At Susan's surprised look, Cynthia added, "It really is pretty remarkable, Susan."

Just then, their mutual friend Mary Ellen walked up and said in a voice commensurate with her ample size, "Hi girls. How are you?"

Murmurings of "Fine," "Well, thank you," and the like were exchanged. Never one for small talk, Mary Ellen said, "Cynthia, congratulations on your good news!"

Frances choked briefly on her cafe mocha and Susan tapped her cup with her spoon, making a loud clanging noise. Both women turned to Cynthia expectantly.

"Why, thank you," replied Cynthia, casting a brief, cautious glance at Frances while trying rather unsuccessfully to suppress a grin.

"What? What?" asked Frances. Her horned-rimmed glasses slipped off her nose and nearly fell into the whipped cream topping her drink. Susan wanted to know too, but said nothing. She used her spoon as a mirror to check if the cappuccino had stained her teeth.

"Well, Taylor got into Stonehurst," replied Cynthia with only slightly self-conscious pride as she fingered her pearls between her thumb and two slender fingers.

"Stonehurst! My God! Why didn't you tell me?!" cried Frances.

"Well . . . ." Cynthia shifted uncomfortably in her seat.

She was saved by Mary Ellen, who, ignoring Frances' question, said, "Now share your secrets, dearie. I told you all of mine when we went through this. I may need to use some of your tips in the near future, although it should be easier since we've got two in already." She pulled up a chair from another table and sat down, her purple silk top billowing briefly as she did so.

Apparently relishing the role of designated expert, Cynthia coyly complied. "Okay, okay. Well, first of all, he did well on the RCATs. Very well. He scored in the 96th percentile."

"Gosh," said Frances. She removed a packet of sugar from the black plastic container on the table and began to clean her fingernails with the packet corner.

"Wow," said Susan. She wondered what RCAT stood for.

"That's quite impressive," said Mary Ellen. "So the test-taking course really helped?"

"Yes, I highly recommend it," Cynthia said emphatically.

3

She tried her best to avoid looking at Frances.

"And," continued Cynthia, "Coming from a place like Washington Jefferson certainly helped."

"Of course. And Taylor having spent so many years there," said Mary Ellen.

"I think his community service and athletics helped a lot too. They really rounded out his resume."

Mary Ellen nodded. Frances threw down the sugar packet in disgust. She had ripped the packet and gotten some sugar granules under her nails. She tried removing the sugar with her other unaffected nails.

"The other thing we did—and we heard this from a number of friends—was we submitted the application several years in advance and got on the wait-list early."

"Hmmm," mused Mary Ellen. "I've heard that from a number of people too. It certainly helped us."

Frances sighed and took a sip of her cafe mocha.

"And then of course, we got the recommendation from Elliott," continued Cynthia.

"Did you know Elliott beforehand?" asked Mary Ellen, surprised.

"No, but Bill has a fraternity brother who did some plastic surgery for Elliot's wife."

The conversation paused as the women considered Cynthia's pearls of wisdom.

"We tried to get in to see Elliott but we just couldn't," whined Frances after a moment. "You have to have an appointment one year in advance. And we didn't know enough to apply early." Frances looked downright miserable. A faint whipped cream mustache had formed under her nose.

"And how goes your search anyhow, Frances?" asked Mary Ellen in a tone that suggested she already knew the answer.

"Well, All Saints wait-listed Jerry and Shirley. And we haven't heard from Hartford yet."

"Those are perfectly good places," said Cynthia with a touch of condescension. "They get pretty good ratings in the Barron's guide book. And the state-run institutions in your area are good, aren't they?"

"Yeah, I guess so, " said Frances. She stirred her coffee and stared into the cup. The whipped cream had now completely melted into the coffee, save for the remnants on her upper lip.

"Are your parents enjoying Evergreen Creek, Mary Ellen?" asked Cynthia.

"Oh yes. Immensely. We're thrilled to see them in such a good situation. They have art three times a week and music and dance twice a week. They can even take a foreign language if they want to. My mother won the talent show they had recently. She plays the piano quite well. She was once told she could have been a concert pianist if she was so inclined."

Unable to contain herself any longer, Susan blurted, "Who's Elliott?"

The three other women stopped and looked at her, amused surprise registered on their faces.

"Susan, what planet have you been on?" asked Cynthia.

"Now, now, I think we can forgive Susan," said Mary Ellen. "After all, she is just a teeny bit younger than us."

"Golden Years, Twilight and Retirement Today magazines only rank him the foremost retirement community psychologist in this area," said Frances, obviously happy to find someone who was more ignorant on the subject than she was.

"You know, really, Susan," said Cynthia, "You ought to start looking soon."

"Looking?" asked Susan.

"Yes, looking. The wait-list for some of these places is very long, several years in some cases. And with so many qualified applicants and so few spots, the best places are hard to get into."

"But our parents are fine," Susan protested. "Mine own their own condo and play golf and tennis every day."

"Oh, believe me, your parents and in-laws will reach that 'special age' before you know it," said Mary Ellen. "Have you at least talked to your parents about this?"

"No," said Susan, studying her spoon intently. Her parents

5

never liked to discuss financial matters with her. It irritated her, especially because she knew they discussed them with her brother, who as a doctor was neither more nor less qualified than she, an engineer.

"Well, we children have to be ready because we're the ones ultimately responsible," proclaimed Mary Ellen. After a pause she added, "You know, you should at least have them take the RCATs a few times, as practice, before the one that counts."

"RCATs?" Susan stared numbly at her parents who were bowling with some of the other party-goers.

"Retirement Community Achievement Test," the other three women said in unison, in an "everyone knows that" tone.

"There're some really good preparation courses out there," said Mary Ellen.

Cynthia nodded in agreement, and then asked, "Have you talked with an attorney?"

"No," replied Susan slowly. She felt her cheeks become flush. "Should I?"

"Well, an attorney can make sure all the correct papers are in place when the time comes to probate your parents' estates and can help minimize taxes. And he can help your parents qualify for Medicaid."

"Medicaid! My parents aren't poor. They couldn't qualify for Medicaid in a million years."

"You'd be surprised," said Mary Ellen. "Mine will."

"And so will mine," said Cynthia.

Susan remembered her parents' conversation during the Florida trip, the one she had overheard. The boys had rushed off to go swimming with her husband, leaving the three of them at lunch. Susan had gone to the bathroom and as she returned she heard her father say, "Bev, stop worrying about it. We're young, we've got plenty of time. And there are some things I want to think about."

"What's to think about?" her mother asked. "We leave everything to the kids, right?"

"There are other issues. I'm just not ready yet. Look, tell the attorney we'll call him back in six months to set up an appointment." This last he said in the same polite but firmly noncommittal tone he usually reserved for salespeople calling at dinner time.

Her parents had in typical fashion changed the subject when Susan retook her seat, and she hadn't pressed the issue. She felt self-conscious talking to them about their wills, concerned they would think she was money grubbing and not wanting to risk spoiling the vacation.

The women's conversation stopped abruptly as an enthusiastic voice announced over the loudspeaker that refreshments for the birthday party were being served in one of the enclosed rooms to the side. "And remember," the voice continued, "Birthday parties are always fantastic at Sunset Zone, the only indoor playground of its kind, geared for people in their Sunset years."

Cynthia said, "Well, excuse me, I guess it's time for pizza and cake."

"I sure hope my mother doesn't get pizza sauce all over her new Grandma Dior cardigan," said Frances.

Both women got up from the table. "Now where do you get that Decapitator?" Susan heard Frances ask Cynthia as they walked away.

"No need to worry, Susan," said Mary Ellen as she too rose. "With your and Derek's credentials and connections and the schools you went to, your parents will have their choice of institutions."

Susan barely heard her. She knew how much the schools and connections had helped her get another job ten years out. She clenched her teeth and pulled out her calendar. Instead of going to the museum with her parents tomorrow, perhaps she would make a few phone calls. She wondered when the next RCAT testing session would take place.

O, Georgia!

Stalag 3.14159
by Jeff S. Akins

The compartment was so utterly lacking in the luxurious appointments to which he was accustomed when travelling by rail that it took him several minutes after coming to consciousness to conclude that he was, in fact, riding through the night on a train. But what sort of railway passenger car was this?

His aching joints coveted the feel of a softly upholstered sofa, the antithesis of his present seating accommodations: a cold, hard, metal floor littered with coarse straw. When the urge to relieve his bladder became unbearable, he discovered the reason for the acrid smell of urine and feces assaulting his nostrils—the restroom facilities consisted of nothing more than wooden buckets, many of which had been knocked over, their contents spilled on those huddled around them. Struggling to find something pleasant in the midst of this filth, he imagined the beauty of moonlit hamlets, forests and streams passing by outside, scenes that he could capture with watercolors of pale yellow and midnight blue; but he was denied the pleasure of viewing them by the rough-hewn boards crisscrossed with barbed wire that substituted for a picture window. From his position on the floor, he could see only thin slivers of night sky through the narrow spaces between the boards—spaces which, despite their stinginess toward vision, were quite generous in admitting the frigid wind that whistled through the car's interior.

The wind made him glad he was not alone. As best he could tell—from the smothering press of sweaty flesh, from the voices that moaned and murmured in the darkness, from the snapshots of tangled human forms that burst forth intermittently in flashes of track-side artificial light—there were over a hundred others sharing this confined space with him. Over a hundred of them packed into this unfurnished boxcar like so many cattle or swine being shipped to market. Ordinarily he would have considered such close physical contact an intolerable invasion of his privacy; at the moment, however, he was grateful for the shielding warmth he found in this blanket of writhing bodies.

As to how he had arrived at this moment, he had no idea. He had no recollection of having boarded this train, no knowledge of its point of origin or destination. He didn't know who these other people were or why he was with them, or why he was being forced to travel under such squalid conditions.

"Where are they taking us?" cried out a man over the train's rumbling. "Why don't they tell us anything?"

"Didn't you listen to the soldiers?" responded another. "They are resettling us. They said this is part of the resettlement."

"Resettlement?" interjected a third, his voice heavy with sarcasm. "Do you honestly believe that?"

"It's what they told us."

"There is no resettlement, unless you count resettling us to our graves. That's where we're going."

"No! They promised us a new land, a chance to rebuild our lives . . ."

"They are liars of the first order. Have you not heard about the corpse cellars? That's where they are taking us. To our deaths."

As the men continued to argue, a baby's wail punctuated their discourse; an older child complained of hunger and asked her mother when they might get something to eat. "Soon now, very soon," comforted the mother in a voice pregnant with sadness.

It would not be soon enough. They had been travelling non-stop for hours, possibly days, without food or water. Many had already collapsed under the weight of such grueling conditions; several, he suspected, had died. His own throat was parched, his gastric juices gnawing at the lining of his stomach in a vain search for digestible food.

Suddenly he was unable to breathe—the stench of human decay and waste was overpowering, suffocating. He grasped at those around him, trying to climb on their backs to reach a crack in the boards through which he could inhale fresh air. As he did so the train lurched to a halt and he went tumbling across a mattress of bodies and fell to the floor, his head thudding against the metal. He lay stunned until he was revived by a blast of bitterly cold air that threatened to convert the boxcar into a freezer unit.

The doors had been thrown open, revealing an icy platform edged with snow. Several guards in nondescript brown uniforms loitered about, two of whom approached the boxcar with rifles thrust forward, ordering those inside to come out.

"*Raus! Los! Los! Schneller!*"

Those who were physically able needed no further encouragement; eager to escape the rolling cesspool in which they had been imprisoned, they stampeded out onto the platform and stood blinking uncertainly in the blinding glare of spotlights. Those left behind, too weak from hunger and disease to move fast enough for the guards, received vicious kicks and blows with rifle butts that propelled them toward the opening. When the guards had finished their evacuation work, only corpses remained on the floor of the boxcar; these would be removed by other prisoners and carried directly to the crematories. Those still alive were made to form a line facing away from the railroad tracks.

As he stood shivering on the platform, he noticed that one of the guards seemed to be selecting certain people for some unknown purpose. The guard walked down the line with hands clasped behind his back, pausing to examine each man, woman, and child, pointing to indicate those who were to step forward and segregate themselves from the group. No children and very few women were selected; of the men, only those who appeared the most robust were cut loose from the line. He himself was passed by, so that he remained standing with the majority when the chosen few were led off the left side of the platform and disappeared into the night.

The rest of them were ordered to march to the right; but he discovered, when he tried to move, that the soles of his bare feet had bonded to the ice. One of the guards shoved him forward, and he cried out in pain as his skin ripped away. Stumbling down the platform steps into a snowdrift, he overheard another guard, in answer to a question about where they were being taken, say, "You are dirty and infested. You must be given a delousing shower."

Once beyond the obliterating brightness of the lighted platform, he could see that they were moving toward a compound of some sort roughly one hundred meters from the disembarking point. Row upon row of drab, hastily constructed barracks dissected a field of moonlit snow; a cluster of concrete buildings, several with smoking chimneys, occupied a lonely corner—as if set aside for some unique purpose. All of this was enclosed by a barbed-wire fence taller than the train they had just left behind.

He became concerned about the painful condition of his feet; turning a purplish-blue, they burned from the coldness of the snow. All except the toes. He was beginning to lose feeling in the toes—a sign, he was convinced, of encroaching frostbite. Several times he had been on the verge of asking a guard if he might be provided with some shoes, only to realize that such a request would not be favorably received. He had observed that those who complained or who were unable to keep pace—the old, the sick, small children—were maltreated by the guards. So he continued trudging silently through the snow, trying his best not to limp or stumble, hoping that the promised shower would provide enough warm water to thaw his feet.

After being ushered through a gate into the compound's interior, they were joined by several other guards with leashed german shepherds and directed toward the concrete buildings, which were still a good distance away. His eyes fastened on the chimneys—black smoke swirling up through artificial light, spilling ink across the moon. As they kept walking and his breathing became more labored, he noticed a sickly sweet odor permeating the air.

"Oh, look, the Red Cross is here," said a woman, indicating a white ambulance with a red cross on its side parked next to one of the buildings. "We don't have anything to worry about. They'll take care of us."

He did not share the woman's conviction. He couldn't put his finger on the precise reason, but a vague uneasiness was running through his brain, a kernel of inchoate panic had lodged in his gut.

The guards ordered them to halt when they reached the vicinity of the concrete buildings. It was explained that they must enter one of the buildings, undress completely in preparation for disinfection, then run naked through the snow for about twenty meters to an adjacent building for the delousing shower. A chorus of feeble protests were met with harsh orders from the guards to move forward and disrobe; those who resisted were struck with rifles or fists and pushed roughly.

He stood in line with the others because it seemed he had little choice to do anything else. But as he neared the door to the building the kernel of panic in his stomach leavened, and, without any calculated decision, but acting on raw instinct, he broke ranks and bolted back toward the gate. The guards behind him shouted at him to halt; several rifle shots rang out, the bullets producing puffs of powder in the snow around his feet. The barking of the dogs increased the cacophony jangling his ears.

He was confused, disoriented. Where was the gate? He looked for the railroad car as a reference point; this helped him spot the gate, but he might as well have remained ignorant of its location. It had been closed tight, sealing the gap in the jagged barricade, and several guards at the front of the compound were running toward him at an angle that would have effectively foreclosed him from reaching the gate even if it had been open. His only option was to go left, toward a wooded area on the other side of the fence that might provide some cover—assuming he could negotiate the web of barbed wire.

He veered to the left and ran harder, his now completely numb feet churning up snow. Bullets kept zinging around him as the guards continued to shout and fire; they were either poor marksmen or, more likely, discharging their weapons in an effort to intimidate him into stopping. But he would not be denied. He would find a way through the fence, he would reach the safe haven of the woods. They would have to shoot him down to keep him from trying.

He was almost there now. He made for one of the wooden fence posts, thinking it would provide more support for climbing than the sagging wire between the posts. But as he reached for it something hit him in the leg and caused him to fall flailing into the barbed wire. Looking down, he saw one of the dogs latched onto his calf, its teeth penetrating skin and sinking into flesh. Two others were fast approaching. He hadn't heard them coming; once released, they were trained to chase their prey with silent savagery, giving no audible warning of the impending attack.

He screamed from both pain and terror. He had to find a way to disengage this beast before the others reached him. If not he would be at their mercy—food for their blood-lust until and unless their masters called them off. Forming his right hand into a fist, he swung his arm down with all his might, sledgehammering the dog's mouth with the side of his fist. It let out a muffled yelp but refused to let go, digging its teeth more firmly into his leg. He landed a second blow and this time the animal's jaw slackened and it staggered back. He took advantage of its dazed condition to deliver a swift kick into its throat with one of his ruined feet. The dog howled in pain, leaping around in circles and pawing wildly at phantom enemies, disabled for a moment—a moment which was all he had before the other dogs would be on top of him.

He plunged into the barbed wire without any thought of its deterrent qualities, scrambling up as if he were climbing a rope ladder. He was halfway to the top when his progress was suddenly halted. Another dog—its body vertically extended—had clamped its jaws around one of his deadened feet. He hung onto a strand of wire with fiercely curled fingers and kicked frantically at the dog with his other foot; but his awkward position rendered the kicks ineffective. As a last desperate hope, he channeled all his remaining strength into his arms and unencumbered leg and launched himself upward, hoping his foot would somehow slip from between the dog's teeth. Suddenly he was moving again, straining to reach the top strand of barbed wire, on the verge of accomplishing a miracle—then the bullet struck.

It grazed his skull and robbed his momentum. For an instant he was perfectly still; then he fell backwards, his legs entangled in the barbed wire, and hung upside down with his brain reeling. He saw the dogs only a short distance away, but they had momentarily lost interest in him. Their attention had been diverted by something on the ground, something that looked like a reddish chunk of meat over which they were scrapping. What finally sent him swooning into unconsciousness was the realization that it was his foot.

14

He was unaware of the guards taking him down off the fence and dragging him through the snow, but they must have done so. Glancing back in a state of twilight revival, he could see the trail of blood from the mangled stump of what had been his left foot, a trail that led to where they now held him before a closed steel door to one of the low-roofed concrete buildings. It was near the spot from which he had fled earlier, but all the other people were gone.

"Wait a moment, Fritz!" called out one of the guards. "We have another subject for the . . . delousing shower."

Fritz, who was on the roof holding a metal can, leaned over the side and shouted, "Well hurry up then! We can't take all night with this!"

One guard jerked open the steel door and two others shoved him forward into a morass of naked bodies. The door was slammed shut and locked, leaving them in total darkness except for a small square hole of moonlight in the roof. A shadow moved over the light, the can rattled as Fritz emptied his tin of Zyklon-B pellets into the chamber, and the hole of light was extinguished as Fritz closed the metal door to the roof grill. Then the chamber's pitch-black interior became a hysterical mass of screaming, gouging, writhing humanity as the pellets produced a deadly acid gas.

His own screams ceased when the gas had seared his lungs beyond their capacity to expel air. But he kept clawing at those around him, the instinct for survival refusing to die even after he had taken his last breath . . .

A rumbling in the darkness woke him. He sat up with a start, surprised at the vibration of the metal floor beneath him. He was able to breathe, to smell. The place stank like an outhouse. He felt around him. Straw. Warm, living bodies. He saw the night sky between boards laced with barbed wire. *Mein Gott!* He was back on the train. *Nein! Nein!* This was impossible!

He began crawling desperately over others, searching for a way out, seized with the irrational desire to leap from the speeding train. Then the train stopped. He watched, filled with dread, as the doors slid open on the icy, snow-trimmed platform. The guards in brown uniforms were there, the same ones as before, approaching the boxcar with their rifles. He could not go through this again!

He raced forward, shoving people aside, and burst out onto the platform. He ran away from the guards, ignoring their shouts, struggling to keep his footing on the slippery surface. He was sure he would make it this time. But he failed to anticipate the guard rushing toward him up the steps, whose rifle butt crashed into his temple just as he reached the platform's edge.

When he regained consciousness he was lying spread-eagled on a metal table, completely naked, his wrists and ankles held down by leather straps. To his amazement, his left foot was attached and functional, just as if it had never been severed. His body bore no marks from the previous struggle with the barbed-wire fence. He did notice, however, an uncomfortable pressure against his scrotum, the cause of which he could not determine.

He glanced around the room. It was small, sparsely furnished with a couple of chairs and a wooden table in addition to the metal table on which he lay. He tested the leather straps and found them resistant, but at least he was warm. Too warm, actually. The air was stifling, almost as if he were lying directly beneath a heat lamp. He lay back and closed his eyes, trying to recall his last moments before the onset of this insanity, hoping this would somehow transport him back to a state of normalcy—though he was no longer certain that he had any sense of what normalcy was supposed to be like.

He had difficulty remembering, but at last an image began to form in his mind: the image of an underground bunker. He had been there. But where was it? It was in . . . Berlin . . . beneath the Reichschancellery. Yes, he remembered now.

Eva had been with him, against his wishes. But he had granted her longtime desire and consented to marry her in the bunker. They had both declared themselves to be of pure Aryan descent and free from any hereditary disease, then taken the vows as husband and wife. After receiving congratulations and enjoying their wedding breakfast, he had retired to another room with Frau Junge to dictate his Will and Political Testament, in which he had urged his people to uphold the race laws and resist mercilessly the poisoner of all nations, international Jewry.

The rage began to rise in him as he recalled expelling Göring and Himmler from the party. He had given them positions of power and responsibility, and they had betrayed him by secretly negotiating with the enemy and attempting to seize control of the State. He had rightfully denounced them as traitors and stripped them of all titles and authority. He would have had them shot if the means had been available. But with the cursed Russians overrunning Berlin, he had been limited to executing Göring and Himmler with words, saving the bullet for himself.

Yes, he and Eva had taken the honorable course of action, avoiding the shame and spectacle of capture by his enemies. The last thing he remembered was sticking the barrel of a Walther P-38 in his mouth and pulling the trigger as his new bride bit down on a cyanide capsule. But if he had indeed shot himself, why was he not dead? Had the bullet misfired? Had he fallen into the hands of his enemies despite his best efforts to thwart them?

He turned his head at the sound of a door opening. Polished black boots stepped across the threshold, the precursor to a black-uniformed SS officer wearing an armband with a swastika, the emblem of the glorious Third Reich.

"*Willkommen, mein Führer*," said the officer. "We've been expecting you."

Relief flooded through him. "Release me at once," he commanded. "And get me some clothes and food."

The SS officer did not move. He stood staring blankly at the table.

"Did you not hear what I said? Release me at once, or I shall have you shot!"

A thin, cold smile rearranged the SS officer's lips as he said, "On the contrary, *mein Führer*, it is I who may have you shot. Or boiled in oil, or trampled by a horse, or injected with seawater, or torn apart by wild dogs, or burned alive. So many delicious possibilities. But do not concern yourself. We have quite a long time—you might even say an eternity—to explore them all, and more. Right now, however, Dr. Mengele wishes to experiment with the effect of electric shocks on monorchism."

For the first time he noticed the switch on the wall, and the wire running from the switch to a point between his legs, where the uncomfortable pressure on his scrotum persisted.

The SS officer's hand moved to the switch, and as he pulled it down he raised his other arm in a skewed Nazi salute and shouted, "*Heil Hitler!*"

The Führer screamed as the electricity jolted his genitals and surged throughout his body. And he kept screaming as this terrifying truth finally penetrated his blackened soul: *Der Führer's* was a scream that would last forever.

U-Haul
by Virginia M. McGuffey

Margaret Oakley had convinced herself that the books had started it. She and Tim had gotten through both Timmie's leaving for college and her going back to work. These events seemed anti-climactic after Timmie's teenage years, the girl who wasn't pregnant after all, three car accidents that weren't Timmie's fault, and a speeding ticket that was. Margaret was stunned that a marriage strong enough to bear all that could crumple because of a few books.

"Would you keep my place for me?" a small, elderly woman in front of Margaret asked. "I've got to go."

"Go?"

"You know." She pointed to the restrooms at the back of the store.

"Oh. Sure."

The U-Haul center was on the town's main road, in the hap-hazard sprawl beyond the city limits but before the town melted into rural farmland. Margaret had passed the old folks home, the hospital and the funeral home, in an odd, useful sequence that seemed beyond coincidence. Then there was the U-Haul place, and the nonsequitur, a doughnut shop.

It was crowded for a Saturday. A long line of people wound toward the front counter through head-high piles of flattened boxes. Tim hovered by displays of tape and bubble wrap, utility quilts and hand trucks. He studied each as though evaluating its proper place in the universe. Margaret stood in line and watched him when she thought he wouldn't notice.

The couple behind her were lovers, maybe newlyweds, gig-gly and young, touching and bumping each other, and sharing a mutual personal space as they stood in the boring line. She envied their carefree laughter and silly glances.

Tim picked up a brochure on boxes, the sizes and shapes and uses laid out logically, the way Tim would have laid them out himself had that been his project. He headed toward Margaret and she averted her eyes so he wouldn't know she had been watching.

He handed her the brochure.

19

"Make a list of what you'll need," he said.

Before she could say anything he was back at the edge of the room studying a large display describing truck sizes and how to choose. She looked at the brochure and wondered how many boxes it would take to carry her life away.

The old lady came back tucking her limp white blouse into red stretch pants that bulged over her gently rounded middle. Her olive cardigan sweater bore beige and red flowers and parted to reveal a thick silver chain that hung almost to her waist. The bluing in her gray hair was too blue, but it brought out the color in the lively eyes behind her glasses.

"Thanks. I'm Ollie Benton," she said.

She offered a damp hand. Margaret clutched her brochure and purse to her chest and merely nodded.

Ollie turned to the two men in front of her. One was middle age, the other late teens. They both had freckles and dark brown hair, tiny noses and class rings.

"You moving?" Margaret heard her ask the men.

"James Junior is," said the father.

"Where to?"

"First apartment. He'll learn to live on his own, to cook and clean," James Senior explained. James Junior rolled his eyes and looked away.

Margaret mulled over the past two days, reshaping memories of events which drifted in the haze that had settled over her thoughts.

Thursday Tim had come home tired. He and his partner had worked late closing swimming pools that people had left open too long and then wanted closed in a rush when the first freeze threatened. His jeans and sweatshirt were dirty but it was late and he didn't change. He rubbed his stubby, calloused fingers across his eyes and bushy brows. The gray in his thick black hair had become more prominent.

"How was your day?" Margaret asked as they settled at the

kitchen table for dinner.

"Fine," he said.

He stirred the brownish-red sauce with a stainless spoon and poked at lumps of boneless chicken breasts lying in a white Corningware dish. At the end of the table a tiny television offered a miniaturized summary of global events.

"Any dark meat?" he asked during a segment on British royalty.

Did he want to know or was it a complaint?

"They were out of boneless thighs," she half explained. "And anyway, the white meat has less fat."

The screen flipped to flood waters in south Georgia, a kid on a roof, a dog swimming in the water below, barking. Tim took two breasts and scooped extra sauce onto his plate.

"I'm up a notch on the abs machine at the spa," she announced. "You can work out too, if you want. It's free for spouses of employees."

He frowned. Had she hurt his feelings? She didn't think he was all that fat.

"Pass the salt," he said. His eyes never left the small flickering screen as he shook white specks onto the meat.

She presented the apple pie just after sports. The football season was proceeding properly and he seemed relaxed.

"Great pie," he said. The weather was next. Weather affected his pool business.

"New apples," he mumbled through a large bite. Compliment or criticism? The canned apples were almost as good as the fresh Granny Smiths, weren't they?

He picked at the crust and shoved the curled edge aside without comment. The frozen crust was a convenience. Before she had gone back to work she had always made them from scratch.

"Freezing rain with a chance of sleet by the weekend," the weatherman announced.

"Good dinner, thanks," Tim said when the five-day forecast concluded.

Always the same intonation, the same words. He took his

21

plate to the counter and opened the trash compactor to toss in his napkin. It was full. He tucked the wadded napkin into a space at the edge and turned the dial, but the machine did not respond.

"The repairman never came," she said. "I waited all day. Flu."

"Oh. When will he come?" Tim asked. He rinsed his plate and put it in the dishwasher.

"They put me on the schedule for a week from Friday. That's the next time I'm off when they have an opening."

Tim reached for a vitamin from the plastic container on the window sill above the sink.

"We can smush it down by hand and take it out more often until then," she said.

He swallowed the vitamin dry, picked up his clipboard and headed down the hall.

"What would we do if it was something major?" he mused.

She almost choked. "Well, I'd just have to . . . well, maybe you. . . ." her voice trailed off not quite catching him as he went into Timmie's bedroom, which was now the office.

"So you like having him off at college?" Ollie Benton was asking. For a moment Margaret thought she was talking to her.

"It's good for him," James Senior said. "And he's the third so we're used to the idea. First boy, though."

"I never had any kids," Ollie said in her please-ask-me-about-my-life voice.

He turned to his son and ignored her. Ollie tried Margaret again.

"So where're you moving to?"

Margaret looked at her and shook her head.

"Out. Just out."

"Oh. Not a good move for you, huh?" Ollie moved in close and Margaret drew back, bumping the couple behind her.

At first Tim hadn't noticed the boxed books in the den. He settled in with his clipboard of notes from calls and schedules and work. Sometimes Margaret thought she might as well be living in an apartment across town. She studied his slouched profile in the desk chair she got for him at a garage sale. He startled when she entered the room.

"I need help lifting some boxes," she said. "If you could put them in my trunk for tomorrow."

"Boxes?"

"Yeah. I packed up some old books for the Friends of the Library sale while I was waiting for the repairman. They called and asked if we could donate."

"What books?" Tim asked. He got up and followed her to the boxes.

"You know. Some of the older ones. For example, we have three copies of *Tom Sawyer*. I put two in. That sort of thing."

"Not the *Tom Sawyer* I had in grade school?"

"Well. That was one," she said. "It had crayon marks all over it."

Surely he wouldn't be sentimental about that. Well, maybe he was.

He dug through the boxes and rescued a number of volumes, mumbling to himself. After a bit he stood and faced her, books in each hand.

"Here I am at my busy time of year and you're rearranging my life!" Why was he so angry?

Piles of his books were now outside the boxes, leaving her volumes inside. She realized that she had included more of his than of her own. Somehow, they had seemed more valuable.

"What size truck did you rent?" asked Tim.

Ollie stared at him and then back at Margaret, her face oscillating on its thin neck like a floor fan on a hot day.

"Sixteen feet, the smallest," Margaret said. "It should be enough."

Ollie nodded.

"You could have used my company truck" said Tim.

Ollie raised her eyebrows at this.

"I hated to bother you," Margaret said.

Tim left again to inspect the vending machines. They had been waiting for almost an hour already and the line had barely moved.

"What's taking so long?" Ollie Benton asked Margaret.

Didn't she ever shut up?

"Why'd you use these boxes?" Tim had asked there in the middle of the den that evening when all Margaret wanted was to get them into the car and take a bath.

He grabbed the first box in his arms and it folded into itself as did the second. Advertising on the sides described a variety of sources and she could tell that the boxes were too big and flimsy for books.

"It was cheaper than buying them . . . " She stopped. He'd think she was complaining about money again. That's what made Dorothy's husband move out.

"Well, go get the kind of boxes you need!" he said. Did he sound exasperated with her? Lately she had begun to wonder if she could tell. "We can certainly afford a few boxes. To put *your* books in."

She tugged at another oversized box until she realized he had stopped.

He went on. "U-Haul has lots of boxes—book boxes, wardrobe boxes, in fact they have specialized boxes for every piece of property you might have—even a lamp shade box, if you can imagine that."

She had gotten a new lamp for her birthday a couple of weeks earlier. Was he suggesting. . . ?

There was the barest of pauses. "So go get what you need

this weekend!" A firm, but authoritative command.

And that's when she decided she knew. He wants me to move all my stuff, she thought, but "Oh" was all she said. He went back to his bookkeeping.

The next day she reserved a U-Haul truck and arranged for a furnished apartment. She inventoried those things she would want, her clothes, rocker, recliner, the new lamp, and of course, her books. The smallest truck should do.

"Do you need boxes?" the lady on the other end of the line inquired.

"Well, certainly," she said. "But I'll get them when I get the truck."

"Yes, ma'am. But we wouldn't want to be short when you come."

"You won't be."

"Actually, I never stayed married more than a couple of years. Tried several times," Ollie was saying. "Men aren't fit to live with. Too bad. At least it was someone to talk to."

Really too bad, thought Margaret. Maybe you'd be bothering someone else.

"But honey, I can't stand that sofa," the new bride was saying. She had on heels and wool slacks, a silk blouse and strong perfume. Her blonde hair was full and shiny with wispy bangs that she peeked out through.

"We've got to use it. It's a sleeper and yours isn't," said the groom.

"But it's so ugly," she whined, tears threatening.

Ollie leaned around Margaret to watch the couple's conversation.

"No it's not. You're being too particular."

"But I thought you said . . . "

"We never talked about the sofas. Never." He was quite firm.

Ollie studied the groom's face through squinted eyes then turned to see the bride's response.

"But then the chairs. My chairs don't match your sofa," she said.

"They're close enough. Or we can use mine," he suggested.

"No! Then the whole place will look like your stupid apartment. No way." She crossed her arms.

Ollie crossed her arms and tapped her foot. Margaret decided she had taken sides with the bride.

"Jack wouldn't have worried about having a sleeper sofa if it bothered me," Ollie confided to Margaret.

Margaret started to ask who Jack was but stopped.

"Your lamps go with my sofa and chairs. We can use your lamps." He was trying, Margaret could see. Ollie was wrong.

Tim had never tried, she had concluded. The more she had thought about it, the madder she got. And when she had announced her arrangements to Tim, all she got back was silence and a surprised, confused look in his eyes. He didn't ask her to stay or why she was leaving.

Then all those men at the spa on Friday kept trekking in and buying their wives gift certificates, massages and such. Tim had never bought her one. Some of the customers got the husband-and-wife special with the free champagne. Now that was romantic.

James Senior got fidgety.

"What's taking so long?" he asked aloud.

He peered around a stack of cardboard box flats to study the girl behind the counter. The girl could not have been more than twenty, probably still in her teens. She stood with her back to the counter, talking on the phone. Periodically she swept her long brown hair back with a chubby hand, her long red fingernails separating the strands.

Tim came up behind Margaret with a whispered revelation. "They don't have any trucks in."

"No? But I've got a reservation."

"So do all these other folks. The trucks they rented out yesterday aren't back yet. A whole group of them went to set up a Boy Scout camp in the mountains. Lots of new equipment to move."

"Yeah?"

26

"And they're having trouble with icy roads. The girl's calling other U-Hauls to borrow some trucks."

"Lordy me," Ollie butted in. "It's starting to rain out there. I hope it doesn't freeze."

An older man in the back heard her. "It don't never stick before December. Ground's too warm."

The bride panicked. "We have to be out of your apartment today so we can get the deposit back."

"Dad, I've got classes Monday. Do something," said the teen.

"But I've got reservations!" shouted a middle-aged woman at the end of the line.

"We all do, lady," Ollie shouted back.

"Anyone for pizza?" joked a man in the back. He was about fifty and wore khaki pants and a striped dress shirt. He stood reading annual reports that he pulled from a briefcase on the floor by his feet. An older couple sitting out of the line in a corner had spoken to him from time to time. Maybe they were his parents.

It was only 10:30 a.m. Margaret groaned. James Junior perked up.

"Yeah, let's call in an order." He headed for the pay phone. James Senior stopped him.

"I told you to eat breakfast. You'll have to wait."

"I would have let my kids eat pizza anytime they wanted. If I had had any kids," Ollie said with a finger in the man's face.

Margaret envisioned him biting it off, which of course he didn't do.

"Margaret, why don't you use one of my trucks. You may be here a while," Tim offered.

"No, you go on and go. I know you've got work to do. I'll wait and drive the U-Haul to the house."

"Do you know how to drive a stick?"

"Yeah, but I'm sure it'll be automatic. I'll be fine. Really."

"If you're sure. Be careful, now. Beep me if you need anything."

He was almost gentle. For a moment Margaret thought she should say something nice but then he was out the door. She pretended not to watch, in case he looked back, which he didn't.

"What's up with you two?" asked Ollie.

Margaret sighed. She pulled a paperback from her purse and held it in front of her face.

She and Tim had gotten sideways before but never this out of sync. Why did he want her to move out? And then that surprised look in his eyes. As if he didn't know.

The freezing rain had turned to large snow flakes that melted instantly on the pavement.

"Snow!" shouted a young boy. He ran to the window almost tripping over his baby sister in the car seat on the floor. Most of the customers looked past the falling snow for orange trucks.

"Charlie, you get back here right this instant!" shouted his mother.

She wanted to keep her place in line. Everyone did, though they had been there long enough that everyone knew where everyone else stood.

"You've got your book upside down," Ollie told Margaret.

She did. She returned it to her purse and studied the snow.

"Nice flakes, huh? I always like those big fluffy ones. 'Specially if they don't mess up the roads," Ollie said. "They were Jack's favorite, too."

The roads were dark and wet, and the white on the grasses and bushes along the road contrasted in an orderly way. Margaret wondered if she would have time to get the move finished before the snow took over the town's roadways. If she got a truck.

An orange and white truck drove up and the man at the front of the line smiled as the checkout girl began the paperwork.

"That the size you reserved?" asked James Senior.

"It's the size he reserved," the girl behind the counter assured him.

"I'll take any size you got. Put me down for anything," he said. "I don't care."

"When it's your turn, sir." She was trying to be polite.

The baby started crying. Margaret turned to see Charlie stuffing a pacifier back into her mouth.

28

"That's good of you, Charlie," said Ollie.

Ollie bent to inspect the baby.

"Cute baby," she said. She held out a gnarled finger for the baby to grasp.

The mother stared with a worried look.

"Can I hold her?" asked Ollie.

The mother hesitated, shaking her head in what might have been a tiny "no."

Charlie was clearer. "No! You might drop her. You're too old!" he shouted. He stepped between his sister and Ollie and held his arms out wide to the sides.

"I'd be careful," said Ollie, her voice soft.

"She's . . . sick. An ear infection. I wouldn't want you to get it," said the mother. "Otherwise it'd be fine." She smiled apologetically.

"Oh, sure," said Ollie.

"Charlie's been like that since his father . . . left," said the mother.

"Don't worry, honey. It happens," said Ollie.

"You're a good big brother," Ollie said to Charlie. He tried not to smile.

"My first husband, Jack, he would have been a good father," said Ollie to no one in particular. She pulled a tissue from her purse and wiped her glasses in a slow circular motion.

"Want to see my truck?" Charlie said after awhile. He held out a miniature U-Haul truck for Ollie to inspect.

Margaret turned toward the couple in the corner. The older man was talking to the man with the briefcase. Ollie stepped out of line to see. The piles of boxes dwarfed her small frame and she peered around one of them like a hunter in the forest.

"Son, Momma needs to take her medicine. I'm going to walk over and get her some juice," he said. He pointed toward the Krispy Kreme donut place next door. The hot donuts sign had just come on.

"I'll go for you, Dad," the middle-aged son offered.

"No, I'd like the walk."

"Would you bring back some donuts?" Ollie asked him. "Four dozen or so? My treat." She handed him a twenty. She had left her place in line but Margaret knew she would be right back.

The man returned in a few minutes peering around a stack of green boxes that filled his arms. He backed through the door, one hand jutting out at the base of the stack with a small carton of juice. Ollie scurried to help him. She handed the juice to the wife and took the donuts. She opened the boxes one by one and walked down the line dispensing the warm sugary circles. Everyone ate some except Margaret.

"You need one worse'n anybody," said Ollie.

Margaret stared at the shiny brown donuts and smelled the warm fresh fried yeast odor.

"No, thank you," she said finally. She did not want to feel good on a day like today.

In a few minutes all but one of the flat green boxes were empty and the last bore a single remaining donut surrounded by gelled circles of icing.

"Last one," offered Ollie.

Margaret stared into the box and almost reached for the donut, but she shook her head.

"No, I can't," she said.

"I'll take it," said Charlie, and it was gone.

The elderly man who had gone for the donuts was licking his fingers. He said to the middle-aged son, "I'm going to take Momma home. She's getting tired."

"Sure Dad. She shouldn't have come."

"She wanted to get out. You know her."

"I know. Thanks." He patted his dad on the shoulder.

"She's still worried about the nursing home."

"I know. But she'll make new friends."

"No, she won't," Ollie whispered behind a cupped hand she held toward Margaret. "They dope them all up and there's no one to talk to."

"It'll be different," the older man was saying.

"For you too," the son acknowledged.

"We'll be fine."

"Bye, Dad. I'll be there as soon as I get a truck."

"Bye."

The older man helped his wife into a large outdated Chevrolet with a rusted hood and eased the vehicle into the street. Two cars swerved to avoid them as they inched along the highway.

"You know, honey," Ollie was saying to Margaret. "You ought to open up. You got a lot buried inside."

Margaret shook her head and said nothing.

"You separating from that man that was here?"

"Yeah."

"He loves you."

"And how does someone like you know that?" Margaret could have bitten her tongue.

"I've known a lot of men," said Ollie.

"And you're still single," Margaret retorted. What made her say these things?

"There are always other men to marry, but there aren't that many Jacks," Ollie said.

"Leave me alone." Margaret wanted to pound the defenseless old lady. Then guilt replaced the feeling. It wasn't Ollie's fault.

"So what started this fight you've had. You're real upset, sweetie."

"Lady . . . "

"Ollie. Call me Ollie."

"Ollie, you have no clue! You couldn't even hang on to this Jack guy you keep talking about!" This last slipped out with an angry intensity. Margaret didn't intend to be so mean.

"Well, you see," said Ollie. "That one died. Poor Jack."

Ollie turned her back to Margaret and stared at the front.

"I didn't mean to . . . what I meant was. . . ." Margaret couldn't make herself say it.

"I know, dear. It's hard, isn't it? I remember the first couple of times I moved out. I've always wondered which one of the men I should have kept. After Jack it wasn't the same."

Before Margaret could respond, she heard customers in the

back cheering. Four U-Haul trucks waited at the traffic light a block away. More orange could be seen through the snowy fog in the distance.

Margaret's blood pounded at the back of her throat. She hadn't realized until that moment what an awful thing she was doing. She had halfway hoped she wouldn't get a truck. It hadn't been her idea, after all. A Tim and Dave Pool Company truck drove unnoticed into the parking lot before the traffic light turned green. Margaret was still looking at the group of orange trucks.

Tim parked and came in. "Dave is finishing the last pool. You can use my truck if you want."

His voice was wistful, gentle.

"See," said Ollie.

Margaret ignored her.

"You don't mind? I think the U-Haul trucks are here now."

"Whatever suits you."

"Go home," said Ollie to Margaret.

Tim looked at Ollie and back at Margaret.

"I sorted the books so it will be easy for you," he said.

"Not going to be easy at all!" Ollie inserted.

"I'll wait in the truck so you can think about it," Tim said.

The girl behind the counter was giving out trucks and explaining the fuel policy and confirming all the things she was supposed to confirm and getting all the paperwork right, person by person.

Ollie was next.

"Hello, Ms. Benton. I suppose you don't have your driver's license?"

Ollie dug in her purse.

"I don't seem to see it in here," Ollie said finally.

"No?"

Ollie thrust her hands into her pants pockets and patted the sides of the olive green sweater.

"No, I'm afraid not."

"Then you know I can't rent you a truck."

"Oh, I know," she said.

After all that time, thought Margaret.

"I can help, if you've only got a few things to move. . . ." Margaret said. Why was she volunteering for this? Of all things.

"No, no, that's fine. I don't need a truck, you see," Ollie said. "Well, it's been a lovely morning."

"Shall I call your sister?" the girl behind the counter was offering.

"Yeah. Tell her I'll start back in just a bit."

"I'll wait until you're walking out."

"You know me too well."

The girl chuckled. "I guess. Anyway, they'll come over and get you if they think it takes you too long to walk back."

Margaret watched the girl prepare the next form.

Ollie stood to the side and pulled at Margaret's elbow.

"Go get in his truck," she said.

"What?"

"Go get in the man's truck and go home."

"Leave her alone, Ollie," the U-Haul employee said quietly. "She's got to live her own life, you know."

"I suppose you're right. Oh well," Ollie sighed. "Such nice people to talk to."

"See you next Saturday?"

"I'll be here, God willing and the creek don't rise," Ollie said. And then she grabbed Margaret's hand and asked, "You going to use his truck? Or go home?"

Margaret smiled and shrugged, and then she turned to the girl behind the counter. "I won't be needing a rental truck," she said.

O, Georgia!

At The Camp on Lake Chatuge
for Weezer

by Robert Black

You are the presence we feel just beyond
The edge of thought, outside the compass of words.
The patois of wild geese, wind gust, moonrise,
Leaf fall, and opening bud are become
Your languages. Here your memories well
Like clear water, pool in the lake, and spill
Down your rivers—Ocoee, Tellico,
Broad, Hiawassee, Nantahala and
Four sections of the Chattooga, down
To two seas, to rise in vapors, and fall
Alike on Delta mud and Kenyan plain.
You are gone forever, but remain

ours.

Dr. Mary Louise "Weezer" Martin died in the ter-
rorist bombing of the American embassy in Nairobi,
Kenya on August 7th, 1998. Before moving to Nairobi
with her husband Doug Klaucke and their three chil-
dren, she lived in Atlanta. Home, however, was on
Lake Chatuge a stone's throw across on the North
Carolina/Georgia line. "The Camp" was a base for
their passion: whitewater paddling.

O, Georgia!

Oxymoron Soup
by Helen Freeman

Silent Word
Sound Unheard
Quiet Scream
Ghetto Dream
Placid Fervor
Screaming Murmur
Living Death
Stifled Breath
One Accord
Humble Lord
Lost Direction
Missed Connection
False Correction
Tepid Insurrection
Gentle Strength
Short Length
Silent Fury
Pensive Hurry
Clenching Loosely
Prickling Smoothly
Missing Link
Dry Drink
Hateful Smile
Forever A While
Benign Doubt
Muted Shout
Tentative Goodbye
Yes, Why?

O, Georgia!

To Promise A Soldier
by Catherine Hunter Wise

Kennesaw Mountain, June 1864

I stared over the earthworks. Lines of Union infantry rushed up the hill toward us, their colors waving. Our Lieutenant drew his sword.

"Fix bayonets boys," he shouted. "Powder or no powder, we must hold this hill!"

I slammed my bayonet onto the end of my rifle, then reached down and grabbed a rock. Glancing over at Cassey, I saw that she had done the same. A grim smile played about the corners of her sensuous lips. She had fought hand to hand before and had somehow held her own. I could not help her now.

At twenty feet we threw our missiles, some of us scoring hits. Then they were upon us, and it was each man for himself. Outnumbered nearly four to one, we stood not the slightest chance, but we fought. With bayonet, with rifle butt, with our bare hands, we fought.

Cassey took a blow to the head, and fell hard. "God damn Yankee!" I screamed and stabbed at the uniform before me. Blood sprayed. I swung and smashed a bearded face. A rifle butt hit my chin. Blinding pain ripped my head apart and I crashed to the ground. Muddy boots and tattered blue swarmed over me. I glanced to my right. Cassey!

She lay face down in the dirt, her cap was gone, and her golden tresses were red with blood. I crawled over and lifted her head. "Cassey!" I accidentally cried out, instead of Casey, the boy's, name she used now. Then whispered, "Cassandra, please answer me."

She stirred and opened silver - blue eyes. "Jake?" She whispered. "Where are we?"

"You're alive," I breathed and clutched her dear form close. "You're alive," I kept repeating.

Suddenly a hot musket barrel was jammed in my back and

a harsh voice rasped out. "Jes' move real slow now Secesh, an' I reckon he'll stay livin'."

I slowly glanced behind me and then nodded. The man had me dead to rights. I wasn't going anywhere. I turned back to Cassey. "Can you stand?"

She nodded and I rose slowly, pulling her up with me. She swayed a bit, but otherwise stood fine.

The Yankee motioned us forward and we marched down the hill along with several others from our company. We stopped near the edge of the road, and a guard was posted. I flopped down from exhaustion and looked around to see who was there. Our Lieutenant was with us, though badly wounded, and my friend John Winters sat nearby.

I leaned over to examine Cassey's wound. I was relieved to see she seemed more stunned than hurt, and the wound didn't look too bad.

Presently we were given water and a little hardtack, then left to find what sleep we could, but I could not rest. Far away I could hear the sounds of bugles and knew that both sides were caring for wounded and burying the dead. I wondered how our troops had faired, and idly hoped we prisoners might be rescued.

Close by were the sounds of my comrades settling into exhausted sleep. I thought of Cassey. What would happen to her?

Again I asked myself what I was thinking when I had agreed to let her accompany me. At first I had thought it novel, a great joke - her dressed as a boy; golden tresses cut short, her sensuous curves bound tightly. Cassey had always been a spirited young woman, and she refused to sit at home while I marched off to war.

"If you go Jake Williams, then I go," she had declared. "I'll not be one of those wives sitting at home fretting over what could be happening to the man she loves."

"But Cassey!" I had protested. "You could be killed!"

"So could you. And if you die, well I don't believe I'd care to live."

In the end I had given in. I never could deny her anything she truly had her heart set on. Besides I, like so many, thought the war would be over in a few months. That was three years ago. Three bloody, bitter, soul-testing years. I never would have believed a woman could endure so much.

I cannot say how many times I begged Cassey to give it up and go home, where she would at least be safe and warm.

In spite of my pleading, she insisted she was a soldier, and sworn to do her duty; and do her duty she did, admirably well. When I threatened to turn her in, she swore she would simply join some other unit. Fearing she would make good her threat, I kept my peace, allowing her to stay where I could look after her.

The others in the company thought that she was my younger brother. How they could mistake that beautiful young woman for a boy, I'll never know. She was tall, and broad shouldered. With her honey gold tresses cut short, she did make a pretty young boy, bereft of beard or deep voice. Simply another youth in the ranks of the hard pressed Confederacy.

Since I am also tall and broad, though my hair is darker, the lie of brothers was not too far fetched. Besides, I mused, no man would be willing to admit that a woman could shoot like she did.

My thoughts returned to the recent battle, and the Yankees around us. Our situation now was far from a joke or a spirited girl's lark. We were prisoners of war, and likely to be taken north to who knew what hardships. Cassey was no longer safe amongst the ranks of comrades, and I no longer had the power to protect her.

I reached out and gently touched her shoulder. "Cassey," I whispered. She turned over and faced me. I had been right, she was no more able to sleep than I. "How's your head?"

"It's sore but I think I'll live."

She gently touched my battered chin, and my heart leaped at the feel of her. After all we had been through, I still ached for her touch. My throat closed, and it was hard to get the next words out. "Cassey. We may wind up in a prison camp, love."

She nodded slightly. "I know." Her voice didn't waver.

"It could be dangerous."

She laughed softly. "More dangerous than being shot at?" In the dark she risked a quick hug. "I always loved your sense of humor, Jake."

I held her briefly in that quick embrace, aching for more.

41

It had been very hard on us, being so close, and having to hide our love. I could never touch her in the daylight, and the only times we had for loving were in permanent camps or if we could slip off for a few stolen moments alone.

Grimly I pulled away, the muffled sounds of our comrades reminding me there were other eyes to see. "Cassey I'm serious. The prisons are rumored to be hell holes of death and sickness. I can't see you suffer such. Tell them the truth tomorrow. Perhaps they will take pity on a woman and set you free."

She gazed harshly at me, her blue eyes blazing. "And what if they don't Jake? The Yankees outnumber us three to one. I took out a whole battery today and fought on the field as a soldier. I doubt they will view me as a shrinking, southern, genteel woman."

She shook her head. "No I'm far safer remaining a soldier in the ranks. Then I'll not get any unwanted attention. Besides, I've proven I can take whatever the rest of the company can."

"I know you have grit enough for two men, Cassey.　But a prison camp is different. It's not going to be marching and fighting. It's going to be surviving. Surviving with no shelter and very little food. They say sickness and hunger take more lives in the prisons than bullets take upon the field."

"How is that different from what we've been through the last several months?" She replied. "If it weren't for that dead Yankee at Shiloh, I'd have been barefoot ever since. You know that soldier was awful small and pretty. Do you suppose it was a woman doing what I've done?"

I shook my head, knowing she was purposely changing the subject. However, she did have a point. We had been through some pretty tough marches and bloody battles. "I don't think there's another woman who's crazy enough to pull this caper."

She made a face and squirmed against me to get more comfortable. I swallowed down the riot of emotions spinning inside and listened to her breathing.

Out of the quiet her voice floated softly up to me. "Promise you won't tell, Jake, for my sake."

I hugged her close, just for a moment. "I promise, my love.

42

I promise." I felt like I was promising my soul to the tortures of hell.

The next morning our guards woke us at dawn. We were given a little water, but no food and started on the road north.We marched two days to a railhead, and were loaded like cattle into boxcars. There were no blankets or even straw, so we sat or lay on the hard floors and spent our time speculating on our possible fate. The trip lasted several days, though it seemed like weeks. There was very little food, and often we would go more than a day without water.

The train stopped somewhere in Maryland, and several more Confederates were added to the crowded cars. Many of the men pushed into our car were barefooted and thin. When they learned our company's designation they reacted with admiration. "Hey you're the boys who held that hill at Kennesaw! You know Sherman finally gave up and quit! Turned the other way!"

The news lifted our spirits and made the going a little easier. We hoped that Atlanta would be spared, as many of us had homes and families there. We chafed at no longer being in the fight, for we were all men of action and would have preferred to partake in the defense of our homes.

Finally the seemingly endless ride was over. We left the train in a town whose signs read "Elmira, New York." Some of the townsfolk gathered to stare at our ragged dirty march through the streets to the gates of our new home.

The prison was a large compound, fenced by high brick walls. About ten feet inside the walls was another wooden fence, not very high or strong. I later learned this was called the 'dead man line.' Anyone who stepped beyond this mark was shot down immediately by the guards who constantly patrolled the walls.

The stench of thousands of unwashed diseased bodies nearly knocked me down. The men looked like thin scarecrows in tattered gray. Some huddled beneath ragged blankets pegged out like shelter halves, while others sat or lay on the bare ground. Thin smoke from a few meager fires completed the dreary surroundings. My God! I thought, we have been hungry in the field, but these men are starving!

My heart tightened with dread. I turned to Cassey, determined to talk her into confessing her identity. I simply could not have her living like this. She must have read my mind for she raised her stubborn little chin and slightly shook her head.

I sighed and turned back to the occupants of the compound. Most of the men sat or lay upon the ground simply staring at the new arrivals. After a few minutes, a man in a ragged officers coat stepped forward. "Welcome to hell, boys." He grinned from a thin, hollow face which had once been handsome. "Pick yourself a bit of ground. There ain't much else to call one's own."

The next several months were a nightmare. We battled heat, flies, lice, spoiled food and filthy conditions. Then it turned cold. The flies were gone, but there was no wood for fires. The few tattered blankets did little to combat the approaching New York winter.

Like the rest of us, Cassey's hair had grown, and I feared that she might begin to draw undue attention. Then, looking again at the gaunt form and hollow eyes, I realized there was little left of the vivacious beauty who had first captured my heart.

I watched as she crossed the compound, shoulders hunched against the cold rain. She flopped down next to me and held out two potatoes. "I traded the last of the tobacco for them." She looked hopefully at me. "Anything?"

I pulled two soggy biscuits from beneath my worn coat. "The soup ran out early today, but they gave us some hardtack."

She grinned. "Just as well. They've been straining those beans all week. Not much left in them."

My heart leaped. Where did she get the strength to smile? I wanted to kiss her right then and there, but there were other eyes, so I settled for smiling back at her and watching her eyes glow.

Suddenly she pressed her hands to her head. "Ahh." she moaned. Her eyes watered with pain.

"Headache again, love?"

She nodded. I reached out and put my arm around her, trying to cover her a little with my frayed jacket. I sighed in frustration. Her headaches were coming more frequently and lasting longer. The doctor said her wound had never healed properly. Since he was also a prisoner, with no supplies, there was not much he could do.

Sometime in late September, another wave of prisoners arrived in the already overcrowded camp. We were disheartened to learn they were from Atlanta. "We blew up the munitions and stores so the damn Yankees couldn't get at them, but much of the city burned," one gaunt barefooted sergeant said. He stared at us from haunted eyes. "I remember seeing the women and children fleeing; mothers with babes in their arms and the city burning down around them." He shook his head and shuffled away.

Cassey stared after him. "Jake." Her voice was tight with worry. "Mother and Aunt Evelyn went to Atlanta. Grandpa thought they would be safer there."

I stood next to her, not even able to put my arms around her for comfort. "I know, Cassey. We can only pray they made it out."

She nodded, but I knew our thoughts were the same. We had sacrificed so much at Kennesaw to protect our homes and families, and it was all for naught. The enemy had gotten through. Disheartened, we turned back to our piece of ground and our empty stomachs.

Winter had set in. The dreaded New York cold sapped the strength of even the hardiest of men and each morning left new corpses, stripped bare, for the guards to collect. We tried to find relief from the bitter winds by digging underground shelters with our hands, but soon the ground had froze. Those of us who had managed a little shelter tried to share, but there was not enough room for all.

Cassey's headaches were almost constant now. They left her weak and drained. I begged her to tell the guards who and what she was. "Cassey, please love. I can not bear to see you suffer like this. Surely they would release a woman, maybe even send you home. Anything would be better than starvation. Cassey you could die!"

She was beyond words, just staring at me with wild eyes.

John Winters crawled into our meager hovel. "How is he?"

I shook my head. "Not well. No longer talking."

"I asked the guard. Hospital's full. They're turning them away."

I frowned and glanced over at Cassey who sat numbly pressed up against the frozen earth wall of our shelter.

45

John touched my arm. "It's nice out. No wind, and the sun is warm. It would do him good."

I nodded and picked Cassey's frail form up in my arms. It was a good thing she was thin, for in my own weakened state, I doubt I could have carried her, and she certainly couldn't walk.

We came out into blessed sunlight and I set Cassey down. She coughed twice and wiped blood with her frayed sleeve. My heart ached. She had been coughing blood for a couple of days now and I knew those that started coughing blood never lived for long. I have never in my life felt so helpless. How could I have allowed the woman I love to come to such a state?

John touched my arm and pointed toward a commotion by the gates. "Something's happening. Come, let's see."

I glanced down at Cassey, her eyes were still empty. Sighing, I followed John to the gathering crowd of prisoners. Through the cracks in the fence we could see two wagons drawn up, loaded with what appeared to be clothing and barrels of flour and meal.

The people on the wagons were talking with the guards, but we couldn't hear what was being said. Soon the prison commander was brought, and a heated discussion ensued. One large man on the front wagon shouted, "Those men are starving!"

The commander shouted something back and with that, the big man on the wagon began defiantly grabbing bundles from the wagons and tossing them inside the compound. Several prisoners rushed forward to grab at the packages, only to be shot down.

The wagons turned away, and starved eyes watched as they rolled slowly back up the street. Rumors began flying through our ranks. "Town's people, taking pity on us. Trying to do the Christian thing." "Why'nt the SOB let us have those supplies, can't the pig see we're starvin'?"

"Probably afraid of a prison break. Like any o' us'n have the strength to make a run fer it," came a disgruntled reply.

John and I made our way back to our shelter and Cassey. She still sat silently gazing with empty eyes. I squatted down beside her and stared at her emaciated form. What was I to do? Why hadn't the prison Commander let us have those supplies? It wasn't much, but it may have made the difference for many.

I wondered how much longer the war would last. How long before we would see rescue — or would any of us survive to see home again? I knew that if by some miracle Cassey lived, she would never be the same again. The vivacious beauty with whom I had fallen in love was gone forever. The Yankee prison had done what no amount of fighting and death could have done. It had broken her. I even began to wonder if it might be better if she passed on. It would at least mean an end to her suffering.

Keeping such morbid thoughts buried inside, I handed Cassey the last bite of moldy hardtack I had been saving from earlier that week. She stared for a moment, then took the bite and chewed slowly. It precipitated another fit of coughing and there was more blood.

Three days later Cassey lay in the dark earthen shelter. She had not been able to keep even the bites of biscuit down since the other day and had accepted no water since last night. She was dying.

Although I knew death would end her pain, my heart cried out in bitter loneliness. It wasn't supposed to be this way. We were supposed to have had children and grown old together, not watch each other suffer and die in some Yankee hell hole far from our own country.

Cassey wheezed and choked. I realized she was trying to speak. It was the first time she had spoken in over a week and I pressed close to hear the last words of my beloved wife.

"Jake... love... you," she whispered. Then coughed again. She looked me in the eyes and some of the old spirit and fire returned to her for just a moment.

I touched her thin scarecrow cheek. "I love you too, Cassandra. More than you'll ever know. I'm so very sorry it's come to this. I never meant for this to happen."

"I was never sorry, Jake. Not for a moment." She gave me a shadow of her old devil-may-care grin. "We gave ... ... Yankees hell, didn't we?"

My heart lurched. "We sure did, love. We sure did."

47

"Promise me ..., Jake."

I nodded. "Anything."

She roused slightly, her voice becoming stronger. "Live, Jake. Live and tell my story." Her voice weakened again, and I had trouble following her words. "You never knew..., ...other women like me." "...one at Shiloh, ... Gettysburg." She rallied once more. "Live, Jake, for me. Tell the world that a woman fought for Dixie."

I nodded, my heart too full to speak. I leaned closer. She sighed softly, then there was nothing more. Cassey was gone.

I do not know how long I sat staring. I could not cry, there were no tears left. After a long time John came in and began to remove her clothing.

I panicked! He would know! He would find out she was a woman! Then I laughed out loud. It didn't matter now.

John looked sideways at me, no doubt fearing my reason was slipping. "Jake..."

I shook my head. "No John. Do not take the clothes."

"But Jake, you need the boots and your jacket is nearly gone."

"I know, but it's not important."

John attempted to be kind. "Jake, the boy's not going to be cold anymore. He'd want you to have them."

"That's just it, John. Casey's not a boy. I never had a brother, but I had a wife until now."

John paused, his mind denying the meaning of my words. "What...?"

I nodded. "You heard right. Casey--Cassey-- was my wife."

John's eyes held disbelief. "My God, man! You let your wife go through this hell!"

I bowed my head. All the doubts and guilt washing through me again. John must have seen my pain, for he placed a hand on my shoulder. "I don't know how she did it, but she was one hell of a soldier. We'll bury her in here. We can collapse the shelter over her and none will know." I looked up gratefully and nodded agreement.

In silence we set to work. John's words, 'one hell of a soldier' were Cassey's only epitaph. Somehow I think she would have approved.

A week has passed since we buried Cassey. With her gone the days have little meaning. I no longer feel the cold or the hunger; I merely concentrate on surviving each day.

By gambling with the other prisoners, I won enough tobacco to trade a guard for a book of blank pages and a stub of a pencil. I'll now open the book and begin to write. I must keep my promise.

O, Georgia!

Like Mother
by Vicki Husby

The chill of wintry air seeped under the window sill as little five-year old Vicki dreamt. "Daddy! Please let my daddy go!" She sobbed in her sleep, screaming for the snow monster to release her father, whom he held captive on his icy, snow-capped mountain. She cried herself awake and went running to see that her daddy was okay. As she tiptoed into her parents' room, she saw Yancey in his crib, also awake. As she approached her parents' bed, she saw only her mother. Daddy must be at work.

Yancey was hungry, he always was in the morning. Now that he knew someone was awake, he wanted out of the crib. He began crying, the only verbal communication he had mastered. Vicki gently shook mama. "Mama, Yancey's up. Will you make us some breakfast? ...Mama..." She kept shaking ever so gently, drawing out the word with her soft southern accent, " Maamaa....Mama, will you wake up and make us some breakfast?" Mama's eyes shifted a bit under the lids, and Vicki ceased the shaking. A tinge of pride erupted in the girl's body, breakfast always took away some of the morning chill. Yancey was now standing at attention by the bed railing. He surely needed breakfast, and some clothes—he only had on his diaper. For the moment he had stopped crying.

Sister began to softly caress Mama's arm, then slid underneath the bed coverings. Oh, Mama was so warm! Maybe breakfast could wait a little while. Yancey watched. He apparently did not agree, and used his one form of communication, crying. Vicki tried again to wake Mama. "Mama, Yancey is cold. Can you make us some breakfast?"

Groggily, she replied, "Go ask Peggy to."

Peggy, Daddy's sister, lived across the street. She worked midnights, and came home in time to wake her boys for school. She always fed them and saw them off to the bus before getting her own rest. Vicki climbed up the side of the crib. Yancey latched onto the neck of his rescuer. His body was freezing. The bottom of the diaper felt heavy, he was dirty. The two clung to one another as they descended the wooden lattice work, Vicki in fear of dropping her fragile load, Yancey in joy of the delicious warmth from his sister's body.

The two clambered into the frosty living room, passed the chilly draft of the front door, and headed to the unheated kitchen. Cereal was easy to make and Yancey could eat that, too. Vicki would feed him. Where was the cereal? The box wasn't underneath the cabinet. That's where it always was. Suddenly a clanging of cans echoed through the kitchen. Yancey had pulled all of the garbage from the can. Mama was going to be mad. But, he had found the cereal box.

There was nothing else to do except go to Peggy's. The prickly cold of the cement porch bit at the children's bare feet. The winter wind offered no reprieve, blowing underneath the girl's thin gown, crystallizing the urine in the boy's diaper. With the freezing temperature chilling their extremities, the toughened feet had no defense against the sharp gravel of the driveway. If only they could get across it to the pavement a little more quickly. Peggy's front stoop had grass.

Finally they were knocking at Peggy's door. She must be asleep because she did not come. They knocked again, shaking in winter's grip. If only they could bang loud enough on the wooden screen door, but the frigid hands ached more with each pounding. Hopelessness began to creep over Vicki. Peggy could not hear them. Ashamed that she had failed to feed him, Vicki protectively took her brother by the hand. Maybe he would know she was sorry if she loved on him. As they descended the steps, they could hear the trinkets on Peggy's shelves, just inside the window, begin to tinkle. Someone must be awake.

"What are y'all doin' out here? You're gonna freeze to death." The disgust this gentle woman felt was not betrayed by her smooth, concerned voice. She knew why the children were there, this wasn't the first early morning visit.

"Mama's asleep and we're hungry."

"Go tell your mama to make you some breakfast."

"We did. She said to come ask you." Soon enough Vicki had white bread buttered and on the worn and blackened toasting pan, while Peggy scrambled the last few eggs she had in the house.

The simple meal was delicious and warming, enough to take at least the edge off the chill resting on their flesh.

Twenty years later Vicki clung desperately to that one time when she could remember loving Yancey so completely, without the confusions of adolescence, self-preservation or tough love. God knows she understood the darkness in which he lived, suicide had been a consuming thought for most of her adult life. Afraid to make a full-fledged attempt and possibly fail, an accident was the only way to prevent dealing with the family. Besides, maybe God would consider it an accident, too. Or, maybe something bad enough would happen and she could deep six without anyone blaming her. Fortunately, when her suffering was the worst, she had had the children to think about. Their father was a travelling businessman, their mother lived in another state. Jessica had told her, "You're the closest thing to a mom I've got." That nanny position had been the only barrier to a carefully planned accident.

Acutely aware of Yancey's pain, Vicki had tried to feed him all the conclusions she'd reached. She understood he fought with waning energy to not just end it all. Daddy wasn't happy and Mama had long been at a distance in their lives, trying to fight her own demons since the divorce, and keep peace with the one she just married. Getting out of Granny's immediate reach had helped her mother some, but it left Vicki and Yancey feeling abandoned. Holding Yancey close, Vicki had chosen to assure herself that this too would be alright, if only she loved him enough. Besides, they had faced the pitfalls which normally trap "at-risk" kids, and had scraped by without drug addictions, pregnancies or juvenile hall. Certainly his depression would subside in time.

The call came in the middle of the night. He had hung himself. The paramedics had resuscitated him, but he was in a coma. When Vicki arrived, a tear rolled down his motionless cheek. Soon after, he slipped away. Holding his hand, she understood he had found his big enough reason. Circumstances threw him in a jail cell, and he had sworn he would never spend a night in one.

With Mama and Daddy distraught, Vicki had to take care of the funeral plans. This would be the last time she could do something for Yancey anyway, and everything had to be the way he would want it. The most fashionable, but casual clothes were selected. Wild flowers were in the family blanket, a reminder of his gentle, free spirit. His organs were donated, honoring an old childhood request, and two mothers were given a second chance to raise their children.

The plans were made, Mama and Daddy were with their families. Vicki sobbed uncontrollably, remembering a time when taking care of Yancey, and loving him enough, was her only concern in life. And Mama—she had to deal with Mama's immediate snap to reality. How could she be loyal to Yancey's pain and help Mama walk through a crystal clear realization of all she hadn't done? Daddy was headed toward the deep end, and blamed himself for not "being there." He wasn't even able to take care of his own problems, much less Yancey's.

Vicki contemplated how to take care of her parents. A visit to Mama down in Florida was a must, just to let her know she was willing to stay in the house with "the demon" so they could visit together. Stealing off to the sewing room, the two ladies sat on the floor, pouring contemplatively over childhood pictures. Silence punctuated with sighs betrayed emotions each tried to restrain.

"Vicki, what made you know I loved you?" Struggling to respond positively, to not expose her soul-wrenching need to feel loved, she replied.

"You always made a big deal out of my birthday. When you drove fourteen hours to Virginia just to be there on the day, then turned around and drove home, I knew you loved me."

Mama's appreciation that her daughter could think of something drew a small smile. Her troubled brow hinted she felt she had not done enough.

"I know I've been a lousy mother..." Often these kinds of comments had been fishing expeditions, manipulations perfected by her own mother. This time, Vicki could tell she believed it, felt it.

"Look at what all Granny did to you. You improved a far cry over that. That is all anybody can ask." The young woman remembered living with her grandmother for a while after her parents' divorce. It had always been best to approach Granny cautiously. It was alright to watch her fool with the numerous pairs of hi-heeled shoes, but conversation was rarely invited. Quiet admiration would be noted by the elder woman and yield the fewest onslaughts. Otherwise, a wicked slap across the face could be expected. The older woman's death had occurred shortly before Yancey's, and Mama, for the first time, stopped to take a look at where her life was going rather than running from where she had been.

Vicki honestly believed that her mother had tried to some degree, but her own pain kept her from complete forgiveness. She tried to remind herself of all her mother had survived.

"Mama, your brother had to raise you. And, at least you never shoved my head in the toilet or hit me. You didn't get drunk in front of us. When I tell you I love you, you say it back." Mama's head hung as she relived the painful memories—she was inescapably hurt by her own mother. Vicki had an irresistible urge to wrap Mama in her arms and rock her.

"Mama, you can start all over. Do what makes you happy. You can have jump ropes and dolls and tea parties, whatever you missed. You don't have to answer to anybody."

The truth of it blossomed in the woman. She looked reflectively at her daughter, proud of what she had become, wondering how much of it may be because of her. Vicki was so strong, and had handled everything when everyone else was falling apart. It was strange because the kids were so close. Mama recognized a defining moment, the chance to start over. "Baby, is there anything you want to know?"

Into the late hours, they talked. No excuses or "pitiful me" stories, just the simple truth. Everything fit. With the cache of questions exhausted, torrents of tears rolled down Vicki's cheeks, her body convulsed, throwing up and out the abandonment, hurt and anger of twenty-five long years.

"Mama, if I had known all of this....I have been hurt... and mad... for so many years! It is all gone, like someone has flushed out all the pain." The bond between mother and daughter was forged indelibly with tears of release, of understanding, and renewed commitment. " I can't stop crying...Mama, it feels so good to strangle those bad feelings inside me!" It also felt good to have Mama loving on her, sliding a reassuring hand up and down her back.

As she bathed in the love of her mother, Vicki couldn't help but think of Yancey. She had the distinct feeling he was there. She had felt him several times since he died, and it always wrapped her in comfort, with an overwhelming peace. His love alone was enough! What had not already been released came bursting forth in body rattling, invigorating, thunderous rounds of laughter. The shackles of guilt and inadequacy broken away, it was a spiritual celebration, their souls were freed.

That night mother and daughter snuggled together in bed. Wonder of a new beginning lulled them into the visions that sleepy eyes and relaxing minds find just before surrendering to slumber's embrace. Mama's breath was already slow and cadenced, but she uttered the last words of the night with a gentle whisper, "What do you want for breakfast tomorrow?"

Devil Leg
by William O. Dekle

"She's gonna sue us and it's your fault."

"What?! Who's gonna sue us? We haven't...hey! Who's *we*?!" Dossie Shanks knew she was getting half a story.

"Wait a minute, Big White," Dossie said, cradling the phone on her shoulder and trying to sound calm as she sat in her kitchen in Peach County, twenty-five miles from Big White, who spoke from his end of the phone at the usually uninhabited Collins family farmhouse, in neighboring Finn County. Nowadays, the farmhouse was only used for family gatherings such as the one they were preparing for today.

Dossie tried to comb a kink out of her hair and almost dropped the phone. She jammed the receiver more firmly between her jaw and shoulder and said, "You ain't making sense. I'm trying to fix deviled eggs and broccoli casserole and I don't have time for this. What're you talking about?"

Big White Quick and Dossie were cousins, Dossie being the elder by ten years. In high school, Coach Kicklighter had given Big White his nickname because, the coach said, "He's big and he's white." Big White stood six foot three. Not only was his skin pale but his blond hair appeared on first glance to be the color of a bed sheet. It hung over his ears and in bangs across his forehead. Social Grove had taken to the name, so Donald Turner Quick became Big White Quick.

"It's Juliette Rockmart." Big White sounded steamed and bewildered. "And she's gonna sue us," he said, " 'cause you put that stupid burglar alarm in this old farmhouse that don't nobody live in no more. That's why I'm calling you."

Dossie could picture long white lashes flapping wildly over round gray eyes. "She come out to investigate the break-in that didn't happen, but that was before she fell through the porch."

"Who the heck is Juliette Rockmart, and...? What break-in?" Dossie wondered if anybody would notice that she had forgot to buy sweet pickles and was mixing sour dills in with the vinegar, mustard and mayonnaise. "Don't go gettin' mad at me, Big White!"

A stern Dossie knew Big White tended to be excitable when he didn't understand something, which was most of the time; so she forced him to explain. "Just settle back and start at the beginning."

Dossie, graying black hair that tended to kink, forty-five, and pretty in a plumpish way, knew it wasn't on her diet, but since family reunions were special occasions, she tasted the deviled-egg mix again, just to be sure — as Big White spoke.

"Well, you know me and Grandma and Grandpa Collins come out here to the house to spend the night last night so we'd be ready to set stuff up this morning for the family reunion. You're coming, ain't you, Dossie?"

"I done told you I'm bringing deviled eggs and broccoli casserole. We'll get there 'fore noon. Now, go on."

He continued. "It's nearly ten o'clock now. I got up at nine. I usually get up at six; but I got up at nine because I got up at five. Is any of this making sense?"

Dossie knew Big White, so she said nothing, and instead tested the deviled-egg mix again. She added a dash of hot paprika. "I see her out there now—she's limpin around and taking instant pictures of my car tracks. Your stupid burglar alarm went off at five," he continued, "And if you've never heard one of those things, don't. When it rang, a bunch of stuff happened at once. Grandpa woke up long enough to decide he didn't care and he went back to sleep. The Russians coulda landed and he wouldn't worry. Grandma was shook up. She tried to turn off the alarm and fumbled with it, then hollered it must be broke because it wouldn't turn off. By then, I was deaf, but I reached the kitchen from the back sleeping-porch and got the racket stopped. Then I went back and got my shotgun and a flashlight and started to check things out. That's when the phone rang. It was the alarm company in Savannah. The lady said they never had got an alarm from this house before, which didn't make a lot of sense to me then and still don't 'cause there's always a first time. She asked should she call the Sheriff's office; and I said, 'Sure, call the Sheriff; we don't know what we're dealing with here.' I hung up and they musta called the Sheriff, but I don't know how long it took 'em."

"I don't quite understand," Dossie said, "but hang on a minute, Big White." She ran and woke Prentiss and told him to wake the boys, grabbed a comb, and ran back to the phone. "Go ahead; I'm back."

"By then it was light," Big White went on. "I walked around the house and everything looked normal: same old gray house, same old porch chairs; same plastic pots between the two front doors. Grandma's trying to grow cana lilies in 'em this year using store-bought potting soil. Anyway, no sheriff showed up, so I went back to bed and didn't wake up till Miss Juliette knocked on the door. By then I'd done forgot all about the alarm; so it was kinda shocking to be half asleep and open the front door and see a three hundred pound, red-headed woman with a gun and a stick, and in a brown and tan uniform that was too tight, telling me she was here to investigate the crime. I said *what crime*, and she started to get mad before I could remember."

"Then I remembered and told her the alarm had gone off at five and now it was after nine and where was she all that time. She said, 'I got the call at eight-thirty, and I live way on the other side of Fifteen Mile Creek, and it's Sunday, and I got a husband and three kids to get up and dressed for church, so be glad I showed up at all.' So I shut up and told her to do her stuff."

"Did she?" asked Dossie, giving her hair one more useless attempt at unkinking, then putting down the comb and re-re-testing the deviled-egg mix she'd adjusted with some sugar, this time by eating half an egg in one gulp.

"Yeah, and she's gonna sue us, and I don't think I like her."

Dossie spoke around the quarter egg that didn't want to go down. "Just tell me what happened, Big White," she mumbled. The sugar helped.

"Miss Juliette come in," Big White continued, "and looked in the dining room and saw the table already set for a full house and asked what kinda trick I was playing, having a full-set table and all, and I liked to a-got mad, but she's got me by a good hundred and twenty pounds; so I didn't; and I told her about the family reunion and how usually there's nobody in the old house, and she calculated that's why somebody decided to hit *this* house, even though there wasn't nothing in here worth stealing. Like I said, I don't like her, but at least she was starting to sound like a cop."

"I told Miss Juliette that since the alarm blasted, it probably scared 'em off, so I didn't figure anybody got inside the house and maybe she oughta take a look around the yard, but she already had her little black cop bag with her so she took some fingerprints."

"Big White, if nobody got inside, what did she take fingerprints of?"

"She said fingerprints were best on glass, so she found some glass and took 'em. She strowed dust all over the big piece of glass that sits on the old sideboard in the dining room. Then she took some prints off the plastic plates, even though they aren't glass, and she took one off a window pane that I betcha was put there by Great-great-granddaddy Collins."

"When she said she was done, she hadn't checked outside yet, so I suggested again that might be a good idea. As she was headed through the screened door, I went into the kitchen to put on some water to boil for coffee and that's when I heard the crash and felt the jolt."

"What jolt?"

"The house shook. I looked outside over the bar and she didn't have but one leg."

"Well, I'd sue you, too," said Dossie, finally starting to get interested.

When Dossie didn't speak, Big White said, "It looked to me like when she left through the front door, her right foot lined up straight on just one porch board, and the wood was solid, but there was a knot right beside the joist, and when all three hundred pounds clustered on that one spot, the poor old board just couldn't take it and that's what caused the wreck and made the crash. It sounded like when Kirkland's cement truck popped into reverse last year and backed through Ramsey's stockyard fence on goat day. Remember that?

"Well, naturally, I ran to the screened door that her half-acre haunch had jammed against the front of the house. She had one leg on the porch and one leg hid and she was flopped over forward screaming lawsuit and scrambling with her hands in front of her like she was about to do a pushup but couldn't hoist three hundred pounds."

"How tall is this gal?" interrupted Dossie.

"Right then about two feet," said Big White, "but she's maybe five eight standing up. Anyway, I was worried it was broke, her leg I mean; and if it was, how was I gonna get that big fat female outta such a fix without breaking it worse. Her face looked like a tomato you've kept one day too long, and she screamed all kinda language I won't repeat and I'm glad Grandma can't hear without her hearing aid turned up. I'm telling you, it wasn't a spot you want to find yourself in."

"What'd you do?"

"I run and told Grandpa."

"What'd he say?"

"He said he couldn't hear me for some nut screaming on the front porch. Grandma told me to offer her some coffee and Grandma was sure she must be a nice girl, what with working so hard on a Sunday morning and all. So I went back, but I didn't make coffee, cause when I looked out the door, she was kinda shimmying around, if you can call it that, knocking the screen door back and to against the wall and wiggling her right leg — that was the one sunk under the porch. She'd got it out up to about her thigh, so I figured: She's making progress, I'll leave her alone. Then she hollered to help her and I was really in a fix 'cause I wasn't sure where to grab. You can't grab ahold of a three hundred pound woman nowadays without breaking some kinda law."

"She's just hurt, and mad; that's all," Dossie said. "She ain't gonna sue nobody."

Big White ignored Dossie's interruption and went on. "Instead of grabbing ahold, I just kinda made grabbing-ahold noises and told her to roll right and roll left and don't hurt yourself and stuff like that and in a minute she had that leg out of there all by herself."

"Was it broke?"

"Heck, yeah, that porch is a mess!"

Big White took an audible deep breath. "Broke rocker, busted screen, black potting soil all over...."

"I mean the leg."

"Well....Right now she looks like she's dancing."

"What?!" Dossie almost choked on another test egg.

"Now she's quit dancing. I think she was jes' smoothing the tire tracks. She's walking around in the road toting the full load, so I don't reckon her leg's broke. But she don't look good. I can see blood on her knee and...."

"Ask her if she likes deviled-eggs."

"Huh?"

"Ask her if she likes deviled-eggs."

In a minute Big White was back. "She likes deviled-eggs."

"Okay, invite her to eat with us. And be nice."

Big White did as he was told and returned to the phone. "She's gonna stay."

"Good. How's she looking now?"

"Well, her face ain't so red, but you can tell she's still mad."

Dossie started filling boiled egg halves with the final deviled-egg mix and smiled. "Don't worry, Big White. Porches don't come cheap."

Big White stared at nothing, bewildered. "Huh?" he asked.

Dossie pictured the porch. "If she gets outta hand we'll sue *her*."

Ice Cream Supper
by Enoch Brown

My great aunt loved the rosin smell,
pussle-gut laughter, the bright letch,
trueborn, twisting in the droopy eye,
the do-si-do, the expert grope,
the twangy jew's-harp impromptu,
dim lamplight on the puncheon boards,
quips to egg on the born-again:
Lordy, you're deader'n Georgah
'an anywhere else til kingdom come.

And loved bandana for a bib,
the backslap, stagger and guffaw,
the rosy smell of brilliantine,
paradiddle on a tea glass
with clinks of two clean chicken bones.
My great aunt loved the whittled pine,
the bumpy glide, the galavant,
the hoot and hoopla, carrying on,
the chocolate stomp of the peg leg man.

O, Georgia!

Bad Luck Bird

by Farrar M. Atkinson

Watery eyes peered out from the shadows of the front porch.

"That you, Josh?" called a faint quavering voice.

"Yes'm" I replied.

Granny wheezed and began rocking slowly in her ladder-back chair. "Well, boy, I hate to tell you this, but somebody in this house is gonna' soon die." Her sad eyes blinked behind grimy spectacles.

I tossed my school books onto the porch swing and bent to kiss her moist cheek. Despite the cool October weather, Granny's wrinkled forehead was beaded with sweat and her usual neat appearance was frazzled.

"What makes you say that, Granny? Are you sick?"

"No, no. Just go in yo' house. You'll see. Shoo him out if you can. Tired myself plumb down tryin' to git that bird outta there." she stopped rocking and bent to spit into her Bruton snuff can. I opened the screen door and out flew a black bird. "Guess he was just waiting for me," I said.

"Well, Lawdy! I tried to git him outta there for an hour. Ya know when a bird flies inside a house, that's a sure sign of death. Doubt it'll be you that'll die, though."

"Sure hope not, Granny, nor you or Mama or Daddy either."

"Hush up, Josh. Don't go callin' off no names. Don't jinx nobody by sayin' who lives in this house."

I smiled and patted her blue-veined hand. "I'd better go in and start on my homework, Granny. Don't you worry about that old bird any more."

After getting a glass of water, I sat down at the kitchen table and thought about Granny's warning. Uncle Punk was the only one I hadn't named of the people in our household. Mama's youngest brother still lived with us—thirty-five years old and the blacksheep of the family. He's called "Punk, the drunk" by most who know him.

My folks have lived on the Pardue farm since my grandfather Jack built our white frame house in 1935. He died when
they were blasting the well. I was six at the time and remember
seeing my father drag him around the corner of the porch and lay
him under the pecan tree. When the dynamite hadn't gone off,
Gramps had stuck his head in the hole to see why—about the
time it exploded. Most of his face was blown away. They had a
closed coffin at the funeral.

That was eleven years ago, but I remember it well as
Mama and Granny had carried on so. Granny claimed he'd died
because he was always walking under ladders and breaking
mirrors. She said you couldn't tempt fate like that and get away
with it forever. Bad luck was bound to catch up with you sooner
or later.

Maybe that was why she hovered over us like a setting
hen, and was always fussing about things we did that would bring
on bad luck. The one thing that worried me most when I was little
was what she'd said about me 'taking after my grandaddy'. I was
tall and gangly like him. My eyebrows were getting dark and
bushy like his, and even my nose was getting more of a hook to
it, kind of a Pardue family trait. If I haven't inherited his bad
luck, I won't mind the rest, though.

Even Mama said Granny was the most superstitious
person she'd ever known. We wondered if anybody had a book
with all the southern superstitions in it. If not, we figured Granny
could write one, as she came up with a new one every time we
turned around. Like if your nose itched, somebody was coming.
And if you dropped a spoon, someone was coming soon. If your
hand itched, you'd shake hands with a stranger or receive some
money—depending on which hand. Oh, yeah, that stranger might
appear if ever a spider dropped down in front of your face. For
sure, Granny would never sweep the floor under our feet. She
said you'd never get married if she did.

Speaking of feet, if your foot itched, you were gonna'
travel. If you stubbed your toe, you should kiss your thumb, so
you'd 'see your true love before bedtime come'. She told me and

66

Thomas that when we washed our hands, we shouldn't dry them on the same towel together, or we'd fight forever. A lot of the sayings rhymed like that. We sometimes wondered if Granny just made them up to suit herself.

I remember once, when I was about nine years old, warts came all over my knees and right thumb. She picked them with a needle and made them bleed on some corn kernels which she fed to a rooster. That was supposed to make the warts go away. Mama didn't believe such and took me to a doctor. He laughed when I told him what Granny had said and done.

"I hope she sterilized that needle. Well, I can take care of your warts better with this," he said and touched them with an electric needle. The sizzling sound and the smell of burning flesh made me sick at my stomach. I preferred Granny's treatment.

Later that day, my cousin Thomas and I were out after dark chasing fireflies and toad frogs when Granny hollered from the porch. "Josh, y'all cut that out. You and Tommie are gonna' have warts all over your hands from catching them frogs. Thought you'd learned your lesson by now."

I'd had my fill or warts, so I quit and washed my hands with lye soap. Thomas said he didn't believe frogs caused warts or he'd have them all over his "you know what."

"You mean you put frogs on your <u>thing</u>?" I asked, shocked my twelve year-old cousin would do such a thing.

"Not 'zactly. I just put one in my pants till I could sneak up behind Martha Sue. Then, I yanked it out and stuck it down her blouse."

"Lordy, Thomas! Now she'll have warts on her tits, too," I fussed,

My cousins were lucky though. Neither of them ever got warts. I got lucky, too, for mine went away about a week or so later. Of course, Granny took credit for them disappearing.

Another time, she vowed she could shut up an old hoot owl. One night I couldn't sleep for its noise, she told me to tie knots in three corners of my bed sheet—said we only wanted to hush him up, not choke him to death. When he quit "whooing," I figured it worked.

Once, when Thomas had a nosebleed, which he was likely to have if we ran a lot and got too hot, Granny caught some of the blood in a little bottle and tied it to a tree limb. That was supposed to stop the bleeding. I don't recall it ever happening again after that.

She claimed she could even talk the "fire out" of a burn. Last year when Daddy accidentally burned his hand while placing wood in the fireplace, Granny spit on her finger and rubbed it over the red place. Her lips moved as she muttered the special Bible verses that would take away the burning. Daddy claimed his pain eased after that. The notion occurred to me that she would've been called a witch back in the old days. Maybe not, since she'd used Bible verses to heal him.

Granny watched us like a hawk. If you spilled salt on the table, you had to throw some over your left shoulder or you'd have bad luck. Lord help you if you broke a mirror, 'cause that brought on a seven-year curse. If you stepped on a grave, or tossed your hat on a bed, she blessed you out. No one dared hum or sing at the dinner table; it wasn't just bad manners, it brought on bad luck.

When you left the house, you had to come back in the same door, or if you started somewhere and forgot something, you'd better not return for it, as that would bring bad luck, too. Of course, everyone knew it was bad luck to open an umbrella in the house or to walk under a ladder. Granny never would let us tell a bad dream before breakfast, for it was sure to come to pass if we did. Even Christmas had a superstition. If the tree was still up on New Year's day, there would be a death in the family before that year was out. And just for good measure, Granny always knocked on wood when she said things. I think that was to ward off evil spirits.

Sometimes, there were ways to counter bad luck. If a black cat crossed your path, you could spit in your hat and wear it backwards or make an "x" in spit on your car windshield. Just to be on the safe side, I always carried my lucky buckeye and a rabbit's foot to protect me. When we were little, Thomas and I were always looking for lucky four-leaf clovers. Of course, we always crossed our fingers when wishing for things to come true.

Now, just when I thought I'd heard all of poor Granny's superstitions, she'd come up with this bird-in-the-house thing. Later at supper, it was all she could talk about. Mama tried to calm her down, but it did no good. We'd never seen her so upset since Gramps died. She remembered when she was a child and her baby sister had gotten pneumonia. She'd died a week after a bird had flown down the chimney. Granny would not rest, she said, until Punk came home.

By eleven o'clock, we figured something might be wrong. Punk seldom missed supper unless he went by the bar on his way home from the sawmill, so Dad and I rode over to Mooney's Tavern. I rubbed the buck-eye in my pocket while Dad went inside the roadhouse. He soon came out shaking his head.

"He was here but he left several hours ago, drunk as usual."

We drove more slowly back down the road, then decided to pass by the railroad tracks. We were almost to the trestle when the car lights flashed across a pile near the rails.

"Stop, Dad! Back up. I saw something over there!"

He aimed the headlights where my flashlight pointed. We got out and I crossed my fingers as I ran about four yards to the heap. I recognized Punk's clothes and smelled the booze. A bottle lay nearby. His cap was between the rails on the crossties.

"Oh, Lord," I croaked. "It's Uncle Punk, but where is his head?"

For at least half an hour, we searched up and down the tracks but couldn't find so much as an ear. Daddy finally said, "This is gonna' kill your Mama and Granny. Guess it'll have to be another closed-coffin funeral like your grandaddy's. The cow catcher on the front of that train musta' cut off Punk's head and carried it away."

He took a handkerchief out of his pocket and blew his nose. "Poor Punk Never had much 'a nothin', but he always dreamed that one day he'd take off to see the world. I doubt this was what he had in mind." He bent and picked up Punk's ball cap.

A squawk sounded in back of me. I jumped as if I'd been shot when a black bird swooped down over my head and flew into the darkness.

"That looked like Granny's bad luck bird," I choked, grabbing the rabbit's foot in my jacket pocket.

"Aw, you don't believe that stuff, do you?" Daddy scoffed, as he spat in Punk's hat and put it on backwards.

"Dad, I think that's supposed to work against bad luck brought on by a black cat crossing your path, not a bird."

"Now, Josh, I'm only wearing his old cap backwards so I can see better," he said as we loaded Uncle Punk's body into the car trunk.

I started to tell Dad I'd heard Granny say it was bad luck to wear a dead man's belongings but thought better of it, seeing as how he didn't believe in that stuff anyway.

You Get What You Need
by Devaun Kite

From the top of the hill McGuire saw the empty slip where her father's john boat usually stayed. Fishing. He was lucky to have that to keep him sane. She made her way down the hill. Without a sound, the leaves and grass and pine needles gave way under her footsteps. Ahead of her, across Lake Sante Fe, the sun threw a brilliant display of gold, orange and purple along the horizon.

Further down the hill, the smell of the lake grew stronger. A familiar smell, the swampiness, the decay, the new growth. The water lapped gently on the sand, then returned to its murky, mystical home.

She reached her chair. Her very own chair. She fell onto the carved wooden slats. This chair had weathered everything: her birth, her brothers' births. Her mother's death, and now this. This aching, disgusting, useless shell of who she used to be. Above McGuire's head, the wind whispered through the pines, playing the needles like soft, tuneless strings.

The sound of wood hitting metal echoed off the neighbors' boat houses. "*Daddy. It's got to be you.*" She looked for him. Harder to see now, the air had a smokiness to it, like the air at dusk in the Blue Ridge mountains. But she spotted him, through the haze. He dipped his oar into the still water, in a rhythm, with a sureness that filled McGuire with hope.

"Daddy." It came out like a croak. Like a pitiful, hopeless blob. No way had he heard her. She jumped from the chair and flew to the dock. She pounded past the cypress trees, each step hammering louder than the last into the aged wood of the dock.

"JoJo." She heard the pleasure in his voice, the surprise.

"Daddy." At the end of the dock she turned her back to the setting sun and climbed down the ladder. At the fifth rung the water seeped into her shoes. At the sixth, her pants grew heavy with the muddy water.

Her father said nothing about the assault on her clothes. He threw her the rope. She grabbed it and climbed back up the ladder. Slogged to the post where she secured the boat.

At the top of the ladder he stopped and looked at her. Even from the post his eyes looked older than she remembered. "My long lost daughter."

"A lot's been going on, dad. I would've come sooner, but—."

He came up to her, wrapped his arms around her and cradled her, like she was six years old again. "It's okay, I knew you'd come when you were ready."

Disgust filled McGuire. She pushed back, looked him in the eye. "What do you know?"

"Everything."

Anger flooded her head. Doug. How dare he? "How?"

"Doug's mom."

McGuire choked out a laugh. Hard to be mad at Mom McGuire.

"She was worried about you. I told her you'd find your way to help when you were ready. Been doing it that way since you were knee high to a duck." He held out his hand. She took it. He pulled her to the bench which looked out over the lake.

McGuire squeezed his hand. Felt the wrinkles, the calluses, she'd known forever. A knot grew in her throat, threatened to suffocate her. She squeezed harder.

"What is it pumpkin?"

"Nothing, it's just good to see you." Tears stung her eyes. Her father didn't notice, he continued to study the lake. She followed his gaze. The sun had set, checking out of Melrose, but light still came from beyond the horizon.

Pain drilled through the front of McGuire's left calf, moving like a hot worm picked up by an unfortunate traveler in a Third World country. Lucky woman she was, it was just pain. She wasn't crippled, or peeing all over herself. Lucky, lucky, JoJo McGuire.

She leaned over and removed her shoes and socks. Emptied the water in her shoes on the dock. She squeezed at least a cup of water out of her socks.

"When I heard..." Her father cleared his throat. "That you had, Multiple Sclerosis..." He enunciated each syllable of the disease, like it was a foreign language. "It broke my heart." He unclasped her hand, pulled a handkerchief from his pocket, and blew his nose. "To think that this had happened to my little pumpkin. That there wasn't anything I could do about it." His voice caught in his throat. He quieted.

Her poor father. Guilt filled her chest. How could she have done this to him? He'd had more than his share, screaming his grief into bunched up towels so that no one in the adjoining hospital rooms would hear, while his wife lay comatose.

"I'm sorry Daddy." Two sea gulls landed at the foot of the dock. Eyed McGuire and her father with expectation.

Her father stomped his foot. The birds jumped backwards, into the air. Flew on, in search of better deals. "Scavengers. They smell my fish."

"What'd you catch?"

He turned to face her, eyes filled with suspicion. He didn't answer.

"It's my fault." She looked down at her feet. Her "sausage toes" as Doug called them, warmed against the dock, which still retained some of the day's summer sun.

"What are you talking about, JoJo?" His tired voice ached into her.

"I've been so driven. Working all the time, wouldn't rest until I'd become a Sergeant. Work, work, work." She looked away from him, down at her hands working each other. "I gave it to my-self. Gave it—like it was a gift."

His hand covered hers. "I've read about this disease. It's genetic. You didn't cause it."

Wetness flowed hard down her cheeks. She pulled her hands away and wiped the tears. Sniffed.

He patted her knee. Slow, simple pats.

"I'm tired of acting like things are okay. Like it's nothing when my arms burn. Or when needles and nails I can't see, attack my legs. Like there's nothing scary...." She didn't say what she wanted because she still didn't cuss in front of her father. "About my own body turning on me."

73

"I know."

"I don't like being flawed. I can't work like I used to. I fall asleep every afternoon. I can't compete, I can't produce."

He leaned his head into his palms. The wrinkles on the back of his neck folded over each other.

Panic shot through McGuire. What would she do when he was gone? How did he get to be so old?

"It's not all about competing and producing."

A flash of anger exploded in her head. This from the man who gave her the idea in the first place. "I can't believe *you* are saying that."

"When your mother — ."

"It's because I became a cop. You wanted me to work on the train, like you."

"No. Would you let me finish?"

"I'm not stopping you."

"I know what I taught you when you were little. It's hard out there for women — ."

Like she needed him to tell her that.

"I saw too many give their lives to husbands and children. Then twenty five years later, the husbands left and the women had nothing. I didn't want that happening to you."

"It worked dad."

"I just wanted to protect you."

McGuire bit the inside of her mouth. But now what? Until this, she had continued to rise in her profession. Now, in spite of her father's training program, she would be just like the divorced women. She'd have nothing. Even less. She would never have children.

"What I was trying to tell you before," said her father. "Was that when your mother got sick…"

McGuire closed her eyes. She didn't want to be sixteen again, see her mother's thighs, covered with reactions to the chemo injections.

"After she died, I realized that *accomplishing* wasn't everything. It hadn't protected me from losing the most important thing

74

in my life."

McGuire opened her eyes and looked at the sky, now purple with a rising moon.

"I'm not just fishing out there every day. I've been figuring things out. I guess it just took something horrible like what's happened to you, to make me understand what I've learned."

McGuire swallowed hard. "And what exactly is that, Daddy?" She heard the adolescent sarcasm eke out of her. He deserved it though. Completely changing his philosophy, her philosophy, when she was thirty-five years old.

Her father snorted—a laugh with only the sound of air blowing through his nose. "It's good news, honey. A lot like what your partner is always shooting his mouth off about. We are not what we do, what we produce...we're not better people if we have more external rewards than our neighbors. We just are."

Jesus H. Christ. Not him now, too. "We just are, huh?"

"Don't get me wrong. *Doing* gives most everyone satisfaction. Like all the years I ran the Silver Meteor... "

He wouldn't say Amtrak. Still hated that they'd taken over.

"And all the years you've been a crackerjack cop. You're good at what you do, and it's made you happy."

Made was the operative word. McGuire catapulted off of the bench. Plopped down at the edge of the dock, next to an old cypress, her feet dangling toward the turgid water. As a child, she never hung her legs off the dock at night. Too many monsters lived down there. She pulled her feet up and crossed her legs.

"Now you're confronted with a change. It won't serve you anymore to find your identity in your job."

When had her father become a psychiatrist? Her partner, the fledgling Buddhist, had to have something to do with this. They probably met once a week for discussions. She wanted to shout across the lake. Watch her outrage disappear into the darkness. She leaned her head against the cypress. The bark dug into her temple. Somehow, the pain, when it came from the outside, comforted her. "I don't want to find my identity somewhere else." Even as she said it, she saw Mick Jagger plant those fat lips on the microphone. Heard him scream, "You can't always get what you want."

"I know," said her father.

She rose. Back on the bench, she nestled into the crook of her father's arm. "Can I spend the night here, Daddy?"

"Of course. Be sure to call Doug."

"I will." Across the lake, away from the lights of Melrose, the stars twinkled. A breeze caressed her cheek, warm, with the smell of salt and fresh cut grass. She smiled a thank you to her father, and to Mick, who roared, "If you try sometimes, you get what you need."

City Streets
by Maxine Hamm

All races
Tired faces

Some hurting
Not working

Need feeding
And leading

Wrong placing
Time wasting

All needing
Some bleeding

Just turning
Not learning

Where going
Not knowing

Just meeting
No greeting

Illusions
Intrusions

Full lanes
Daring games

Silent blade
Life delayed

O, Georgia!

Awaiting The Muse
by P. Hoover Denson

How often through the years I sat
Gazing out at star lit sky,
Praying that the Muse would come
And rest upon my inner eye.
And then I'd write.
Plumes of light
Carnation scent
Gentle breeze
Creation bent.

I would squeeze my soul into a pen
To pour it out in flows and spurts.
But then the Muse would take her leave
As Whimsey with his mistress flirts.
And then I'd sit.
Mists of gray
Droning bees
Chilling frost
Murky seas.

In time I learned to drop the chase
Made Discipline my only lord.
The Muse still has a pretty face
But turns away as if she's bored.
And still I write.
Free bird
Heart dance
Budding worlds
New chance.

O, Georgia!

Gardens of Grey
by Monica W. Munn

Salt on a slug
I caught a tear on my tongue
How do I solve this lick?
Revolving me, I turn so wise:
Man on an axis—meat on a stick.

Death hangs, thinly-veiled, over the intensive care unit, the same vapors masking the Frankfurt skyline, so that only the occasional lights in skyscrapers, the flashing red of the radio tower, blinks through - in step, in a lock step, with the flicker of the EKG. This I only suppose; it sits above me and behind, an unimposing machine with different-colored lines, the same zig-zags that children assign in passed notes, in textbooks, to confused or grimacing smiley faces.

They won't let me sit up or write here, but I do it between the shifts, during the off times, the light of these devices moving faintly across my tablet, mottling the words in a dance of head injury logic. But unlike the consistency of the machines, the carefully-planned hospital routines, it doesn't flow onto the paper like in the past; surrounded by the nothingness of this sterile white womb, I am gripped only by one-liners, realizations that sneak through the shadows and find their way in. I thinly record these, thoughts to a theme, and they dribble out weaker than the hospital soup, little more than a contemplative narrative, a self-analysis. Escape from this purgatory?

A nurse comes in to draw blood, misses the vein, and the blue runs five inches long on the softest part of me. I sleep again, vaguely hearing rustles and moans from the beds on the other side of the white divider. A man speaks slurred German in his sleep, incomprehensible. I awaken to see two ancient feet meet the tile floor beneath the separator to my left. I know he's on his last leg and not supposed to be out of bed; I buzz the nurse, point silently to the other side of the white barrier when she arrives, and hear her, a flurry of white robes, the slight squeak of Birkenstocks, scoldingly guide the old man back into his lair of sheets. As soon as she leaves, the voice from the other side of the room wails out again: *"Sag 'was!!* One word young lady... anything....*bitte,* one word!" And he fades again into a series of groans as I wonder how he knows who is there and when he saw me and how does he know that I am awake? I don't answer - it frightens me to communicate with the dying.

The passing of time is different in the hospital: this daylight, night always outside, the waxing and waning imprecise, inevitable but somehow irresolute. Each morning is the same as the others—gentle light from overcast skies, shrouded skyscrapers, the sun sending an occasional blurred ray onto the white tiles, walls, sheets. Even with this skyline view, it's all like a movie, a zoo—me (shelf/half-life unknown), the eternal subject behind the glass, always looking outwards and up and wondering if the decomposition has begun to set in like that of those around me. When I step back and try to look at it all, the overview, the self-assessment, is unclear: a choppy, yet consistent time lapse—*how do you feel today, how do you do? Is the pain better or worse and yes you could die at any time, but why do you ask and why is it exactly that you want another tranquilizer?* I wonder if the nurses have ever broken themselves, if they have ever broken anything besides half-baked relationships: they all smile so.

Angry at their obliviousness and impervious to my own, I dream myself elsewhere: I am once again in a rose garden, one year past, sitting on the grass beside the lazy, dirty Main River. It is the first time that Love has shaken me to the roots, so that I am melancholy, speechless, thoughts incomprehensible, obsessed, hell-bent on self-destruction, unable to hope, carried away, lost in the tangle of petals and thorns. I sit for hours in the sun. I sweat and watch strangers, from time to time bend furiously over a notebook of poems. I damn myself for my lack of expression, praise myself for still being able to hurt and be helpless, for dying inside, curse myself again for daring to diminish the intensity of it all with words on paper. I was alive (then). But now I see there had been too many roses in that patch, the sickly vapors hanging like a gas, as heavy as the fog and pollution clinging to the buildings outside the windows of my prison.

I regard the flowers by the hospital bed once again—no thorns, just a creamy coral hue. The nurse turns them over periodically, the cleaning woman hurries in to mop up the puddle. They do not seem to want to die -- like me, suddenly. I have gotten too close and now I am straining for the other direction, a broken, ghostlike semblance of the non-dead. To keep my hopes up, I conjure foggy scenes of home: Louisiana bayous, the Gulf Coast highway, the Georgia sun in Autumn, the reaches of the Outer Banks, train yards with my grandfather at the age of five. I almost don't see the nurse come in, wince when I feel the needle enter my belly, return her sadistic smile and wonder what in the hell I am doing here.

The specters of gravity, of concrete drift in. The lampposts move slowly by and someone hops off the train and onto the platform. The muddle of my coma-sleep, the clacking of the wheels, a figure gaining its balance on the cement. The thoughts flash through like half-dreams before an exhausted sleep. It moves by more quickly, starts to whiz above the groaning of the tracks—metal on metal in the fog-chill of the early hours—and I know I have to decide. En route to depot, last station. A slow-motion leap (I watch it from above) and then nothing... and the beeping of the machines brings me back to the numbness and the haze. The room spins like a faceless satellite around my head, skull cracked open like the frailest of Fabergé eggs. The blip, the drone, the nurses: padded shoes sound like Death itself sneaking up from behind. Thoughts running through this jumble are four horses kicking in unison.

The nurse comes again the next morning, no warning, and awakens me with another needle in the stomach. I weakly let her know I perceive this to be an attack; I tell her she's not to touch me again, fantasize about decapitating her, wish that I could also invoke this upon myself. The doctors come, ask me how I am, and I cannot explain my fear of the sudden absence of the separation I have always believed in: the flesh from the bone, the ideas from the meat. Things have come together now and I don't know how they work; the thoughts have fallen in battle to the leaking container that creates them. I dream of Asian nuns clogging on my skull.

I am moved out of the ICU unexpectedly, am warned not to cough or sneeze, am told every day by the doctors that I could fade at any time. The room spins less maniacally and so I still refuse their laxatives, devour the painkillers which do not work, sneer at the bedpan. They harass me about this, try to scare me again with predictions of an untimely demise. I tell them to leave a probably-dead patient alone and to let me handle the most basic of my functions on my own. They shake their heads, neither as weak nor as stoic as I, as I guide myself from the bed to the wall to the bathroom. They leave me, their last warnings hanging behind them like the chemical smell of the antibiotics before I open my mouth and swallow.

I cannot believe in this present tense, convinced that the treatment should be as extreme as the situation they tell me I am in. But they simply make their rounds, moving in a group, clipboards held high, scribbling madly while forbidding me, still, to do the same. Another handful of pills, the usual slab of greyish meat and water-soup for lunch; dinner, bread with cheese and butter. They gawk, ask me the same vague questions, do not impress me as the saviors that I hope them to be, and walk away, still a gaggle, drifting in formation. The doors close quietly behind them, leaving me, as I have been since I hit the concrete, without having gathered any hope from the healing of a wound that I can see, without visuals whatsoever. I stare out the window in disbelief, wishing the throbbing would wane so that I might be strong enough to find some words, something solid to which I can hold.

The shadowy lump of sheets in the next bed moves for the first time since they rolled me in and I resent it for being able to sleep. "It" is a "she" and her form sits up awkwardly, yawns, and tries to focus. I turn over, synchronized now to being alone in my calamity, and close my eyes to shut out the new situation, which is all too fast for the truth of my moment. I find myself trying to make out her face in the middle of the night, the lights of Frankfurt casting a pallor over our two beds, stiff and parallel in rank.

She, who has somehow witnessed the first hours of my minuscule uprising, the rejection of the bedpan, the ceremonial pushing away of food trays, smiles at me from the opposite bed when they rouse us for shots and coffee, and throws me the channel changer. I stare at the television, unseeing, the noise louder than the trains, and absorb none of what it projects at me. Talk shows, people with relationship problems, the evening news, soap operas; all of it passes me in a blur that I cannot comprehend. My world consists of the grey, the meat, the noise, the needles, the padding of feet. I no longer understand how things outside go by so quickly, can roar like they do.

Countless nights of the same and I wait until the halls are quiet, until she is snoring. I pad dizzily through the corridor, reel my way down the stairs, grasping the handrails for support like the old woman I have come to be, grope past the chapel doors along the wall and cross the threshold into the gardens. They are small and frozen and I cannot see - the silhouette of the hospital blacks out the streetlights, but I catch the growth and fall of the shadows with each passing car. I watch the traffic lights turn through the ivy-covered fence, feel the shocking cold of the air in my lungs, and sit, shivering but back outside, on an old metal bench near the wall. I climb swimmingly into my bed an hour later, triumphant for the first time in weeks, as if I finally know something that the doctors cannot. I feel, all of a sudden, that they do not want me to get air again, want to keep me from that world, want to indirectly deprive me of what I have known. I am awakened as usual, with the pin-prick, the coffee, the bread, and the clamor. I decide there is no reason not to talk to her, especially since I perceive, for the first time in my life, that I am dying.

But she does not have her hearing aid with her. Conversation consists of screaming, and the strain of hearing and speaking at her volume makes me believe my head will implode. I request another room, the din of it all not allowing me to sleep or know any peace. But everything is full and I only get accusing looks for asking. I continue: the pressure in my brain, the light always the same, the routine unchanging. I feel myself becoming dull—healthier, but numb—and when I ask the doctors what's to become of me, they shake their heads and tell me it is all different, that everyone charts his own course.

Lilly has a badly-broken arm and a terminal case of loneliness. She continues to scream at me from the other side of the room, confides about her longing for something of duration, her lack of faith that anything about her condition will improve. Her arm swells inside the cast, she develops an allergy to her morphine, and she tells me, in detail, about things that can blindside, that can change everything. I wonder if I will talk differently, walk differently, have a tic after I get out of the hospital. The horror sets in, the paranoia, the realization that the most I can do is think about it, wonder, and even the doctors do not have a clear picture. I lose faith in their knowledge: everyone charts his own course. I don't know what is happening in my own head, the temple walls crumbling, the central computer down, the capital of my flesh-bound nation overthrown, the uprising violent. But I know for the first time ever where the soul has its seat: in the middle of what I have shattered. I am alone in Germany, alone on this earth; my bleeding brain, my caretakers' lack of control makes this painfully clear.

Still shrieking, her grey hair a shock, Lilly tells me about the dance hall days of the 1920s, about meeting her true love, life before Hitler, her Jewish mother. She cries about her loneliness, for all the good times with her husband and her isolation after his death. She wonders about the rest of her family, now so-far-away in America. She laments for my mother, an ocean apart, who must be worried about me, tells me that, when this is all over, I should go *home*. She recounts the knocks on the door and her brothers disappearing to Auschwitz because of their mixed blood, a political concept. I try to imagine her, as she tells me it was, working in the department store and surviving because she was not betrayed by her coworkers. Her parents, she says, *Gott sei Dank*, both had heart attacks and died before the troops could come for them. She is still grateful for being spared, the rest of her life ripped out from beneath her.

Lilly scars me in ways more extreme than the bone shards pressing into my brain. I consider her situation as if it had happened to me personally, weigh her circumstances against mine, against the limits I have known. I begin to realize that these thoughts are still based on my perceptions from the other side of the ocean and the horror is too much to imagine, the situation too real to take a solid form in my American skull; it sounds like a movie to me, a screenplay, a TV special, and all at once I know that my life has been too safe, too clean, too sheltered to be able to ever truly relate to hers. My head throbs, still a time bomb, and becomes unexpectedly relative. The self pity wanes, but the self-hate, the fear sits on my shoulder like a scorpion, poised. I revere her for living through it, for carrying this fact with her: I can still only wonder what the reality of my tragedy is. I look at her with wonder now, not being able to imagine that the tears in her eyes could have ever stopped falling.

They discharge me much later than I would have liked, still without hope or information. I go back to the gardens by the Main, but it is a barren season and there is only trash stuck between the stalks of the rose bushes. An intense, cold wind blows up from the river and I watch the freighters trudge by at the sluggish pace of the current, the couples, bundled up and hand in hand, and I think of my lost love, my cracked consciousness, wonder what all of it was for, and feed the ducks on the Mainschaukai, hardly believing that I am supposed to resume normal activities and go on as before. Shake the pillars of the temple and the spiritualists all go mad. It makes no more sense to me now than a few days ago, but what else to do but try and sink back into the routine, the safety of the mundane—to seek, once again, the separation that incompletes me? I sleep. I bathe. I listen to old records, suddenly unfamiliar, soundtracks to a period that has long since passed. I call friends and my words fall short of the reality.

Months pass. Days go by. Hours. I sit in my office in the Adlerwerke, once a machine factory, used, as was every other, for munitions manufacture during the wars. And as a Konzentrazionslager: yes, a camp. In the first weeks of my return, a plaque appears on the front of it heralding the victims of the Third Reich who died there because of the forced labor, the torture, the starvation, the cold. Now the heat burns warmly and shields its suit-and-tied computer drones from the Siberian air masses that pull their way through with the winter grey. I think of Lilly, now sitting at home with her crutches and memories and pictures of the dead. I have cake with her sometimes in the cafe by the gardens, the roses frail and shrunken. I retch and I reach and still I do not know. The days as dark as the storms in my head, I write again, spilling the words out like tears, thinking every moment to be my last.

The Crochet Piece
by Genie S. Bernstein

Bent and frail, the wizened old woman waltzed across the yard with surprising agility, her little spotty dog frisking at her side. Her skirt and petticoat brushed the tops of tennis shoes that had never seen a court but were able to crunch through grass glazed with frost without sliding out from under her. Cotton hose, the ones she'd always rolled over garters knotted above her knees, would no longer stay up on her thin legs, so she'd taken to wearing the anklets her great niece Mattie handed down, neatly folding them to show off a row of store bought lace on the cuffs. Not that it mattered to anybody but her. She'd long since moved on from ignored to invisible. Her progress was briefly interrupted by a bright Bantam rooster shifting his harem of hens out of the path. Pausing, she watched her breath float out in front of her face in cottony puffs.

"Might know, here comes Aunt Tildy," Selma complained, wiping mist off the inside of the kitchen window. "Set your clock by her." She sighed wearily and turned her harried face from the sink to set the kettle on the stove.

"She probably saw me drive up," said her daughter Mattie, slumped in a kitchen chair.

With a wry smile, Selma shook her head and said, "Near ninety and she don't miss nothing. Your Daddy swears she can spy a tick on a dog all the way out to the road."

"Earl says she makes his skin crawl, way she sits crocheting, not saying nothing. Can't ever tell what she's thinking."

"I don't 'spect she thinks much at all, Mattie. She ain't never had a whole lot of sense."

"That why Grandma Lou always looked after her?"

"Yeah, she ain't never been on her own."

"But she was married."

"Your Grandma said that Mr. Feagan just took her to raise his kids after his wife died. She weren't nothing but a girl herself." Selma folded the dishtowel and draped it over the spigot. "I wish your boys would stop putting their tongues down in their bottom lips and calling her 'Snuffy' like they do."

89

"I know it. I get on them about it, but they see their Daddy doing it. Earl always low rates Aunt Tildy. I don't know why, she don't do no harm." The young woman made a face and pursed her lips in thought. "Maybe it's me being named after her."

His hateful words hung in her head: 'She ain't worth shooting, Matilda. That old hag is gonna outlive us all, still be turning out these ugly pieces of crap after we're dead and gone.' That's when he threw the new set of antimacassars she'd made for their anniversary in the trash.

Aunt Tildy's crochet riled him as much as it fascinated Mattie. The way she could sit for hours on end, transforming one long smooth thread, coming from nothing and going to nowhere, into beautiful intricate works of art, each finished project as much of an individual as any person ever thought about being.

The door scraped open enough to admit the spotted dog to the kitchen's warmth. He was closely followed by his diminutive mistress. The thin skin on her cheeks was pinked with cold and the exertion of her short walk.

"Morning, Aunt Tildy," came her niece's exasperated sigh.

"Morning, Auntie," greeted her great niece.

Petting Mattie lightly on the head, she made her way to the stove and dipped steaming grits into her cracked pottery bowl. Selma plopped a pat of butter in the middle, a lot bigger portion than that tiny bit of grits deserved.

She could make her own grits, of course, in her cozy trailer out back, but they didn't think so. There'd been a big fight about that.

"Hell, Selma," her niece's husband Clarence had bellowed at the top of his lungs. "Your Aunt Tildy is gonna burn herself up, you can't let her keep on cooking."

Selma might've thought he was right, but she'd said, "She's underfoot too much as it is, you want her to be up here all the time?"

But then came a day when Aunt Tildy stepped outside for a minute to feed the cat, and stopped to gather a little mint along the

90

way. It was long enough for the hem of the curtain to catch on the burner under a simmering pot of soup. Just the barest edge singed, but as soon as Clarence got wind of it, a little more'n a month after it happened, he'd had a hissy.

Aunt Tildy creamed the butter into the grits and set about mixing herself a good cup of coffeemilk, two heaping tablespoons of sugar, just like she'd always made for Mattie when she was growing up.

The old woman's mind strayed into the past, to all the time she'd spent with her golden-haired namesake, the sweet young voice chirping like a bird in spring, "Tell it again, Aunt Tildy, tell it again."

"Which'n?" she'd ask, her nimble fingers laying the crochet down in her lap so she could stroke the girl's shiny braids.

"You know." The child's blue eyes would fairly dance with anticipation. "The one about the dolls."

"Well, let's see," she'd cast her mind back. "It was near seventy year ago," she'd say, pulling forth details as clear as the morning light, clearer. "Me and my sisters, your Aunt Zode and Grandma Lou, we made us some pretty dolls out'n rags we found in our Ma's quilt bin. We took a brushbroom and cleared us a playhouse under the scuppernong arbor. After a time Zode and Lou got fancy and went to putting on airs.

"Lou says, real bossy-like, 'Tildy, me and Zode is going to the store, you watch our babies while'st we's gone.'

"Zode said, 'And don't you do nothing to 'em, neither, just watch 'em.'

"They prissed on off and I waited a right long spell before it come to me they'd gone off to play by theirselves. I took myself to the chicken yard and got me some fresh droppings.

"When they come on back, Zode says, real sassy, says she, 'Are our babies all right?'

"'Shore,' I says, 'they's fine.'

"They picked them dolls up and Lou says, 'Did they cry?'

"'No,'" I says, "'but they messed.'"

She cackled every time she told it, and Mattie rolled around on the porch screeching like she ain't heard it a hundred times.

One time the girl got a right serious look on her face and asked her, "How come you do that, Aunt Tildy?"

"I ain't got no use for meanness, Child, no use at all."

"What's Earl done now," asked Selma, lighting up a Salem.

"Nothing special."

"Something's the matter." She laid her cigarette on the side of the sink and stooped over to crumble a biscuit into the dog's dish. Scratching behind his ears, she said, "There you go, Tiny."

Aunt Tildy washed out her empty bowl and packed a good size pinch of snuff in her bottom lip. She dropped the little tin of Tops back down in the deep pocket on the left-hand side of her apron and started fishing around in the one on the right-hand side. She came up with a fist sized ball of yarn carefully anchored, as always, with a crochet hook. She resumed her seat at the table and worked at unskewering it. Getting the hook free from the ball, she breathed a contented sigh, situated the thread in a permanent groove across the top of her index finger and began her count, ...thread over...draw through...

"I can't stay with him, Mama," Mattie said, almost in a whisper.

...thread over...insert hook ...

Selma leaned back against the counter, took a sustaining drag of nicotine, and settled her eyes on her daughter's swollen face.

...thread over...draw through two...

"He's awful to me, and to the boys. Never has a thing but a cussword for any of us." The girl shifted under her mother's gaze and toyed with the ruffled edge of a crocheted doily under the bowl of fruit in the middle of the table. The memory of rescuing it from the trash flitted through her mind. She could still hear Earl yelling at her, 'Don't you bring another piece of that crap in my house! Do you hear me? Your damned old aunt is crazy as a bat.'

"What about the new baby?" asked Selma, her worn face

falling into a familiar pattern of pleats.

Mattie smoothed her hand lightly over her rounded belly and said softly, "It's because of him. I'm not going to sit by and watch Earl bully another child. A baby deserves better, I deserve better, hell Mama, we all do." She slid a loop of the doily over her ring finger and plucked at a loose thread.

...thread over...draw through two...thread over...

Smoke wreathed Selma's short brittle hair and the worry in her eyes deepened. "How you gonna get along?"

"They'll put me back on at the café after the baby, and Earl's always got the sawmill."

"You 'spect he'll help?"

"He'll have to, the law'll make him, besides it'll look bad if he don't."

...chain three...slip stitch...thread over...

Selma stopped smoking for a moment and considered her son-in-law. "He does care a right smart what folks think."

"Yeah, acts like a different person at church and in town."

"Is that right?" Selma narrowed her eyes slightly. "Does he ever hit you?"

Mattie tugged at the end of the loose thread and watched absently as several stitches unraveled. "Not much."

"How about the boys?"

"Some. I spend most my time trying to keep them out of his way." Mattie's bottom lip trembled as she yanked the doily out from under the fruit bowl and worried the unraveling thread. "I just ain't got no use for meanness, Mama, no use at all."

...insert hook...thread over three...draw through two...

Making her way ponderously across the room, her mother sank into a chair and ground her cigarette into the ash tray. She took a deep breath and squared her shoulders. "Your Daddy can clean out the back room for the boys. We'll put a bassinet up in the front room with you for the baby."

A tear dropped off Mattie's chin and soaked into the fabric in her hands. Using the lace to stem the flow of others, she said, "Aunt Tildy, I've gone and put a hole in this piece."

O, Georgia!

The old woman looked up from her work and held her great niece's gaze. Her reedy little voice rang out clear and true. "Don't you pay that no mind, Honey. I done started a stronger one. You gone be real proud of this'n."

Dubious History
(an excerpt)
by P. Hoover Denson

Prologue

HISTORIAN LIES CLOSE TO DEATH,
VICTIM OF HIT AND RUN

That was one headline I could have lived without, one press release that could have gone unread. But there was no denying the facts, and except for one glaring error in the article which was quickly corrected in the next edition, the facts were basically right. The victim in question was already history before the newspapers even hit the stands.

I turned the page of the scrapbook and forced my mind back to the point in time where my tidy little life began to take on overtones of a Grade B movie.

PULITZER NOMINEE DIES IN TRAGIC ACCIDENT
LOCAL MAN FALLS PREY TO HIT AND RUN DRIVER
IN PHILADELPHIA
FUNERAL FOR GEORGE FAIRFAX
AN INTERNATIONAL AFFAIR

And so they went. I had articles clipped from newspapers located all across America. Correction, America, Canada and even a few countries in Europe.

As the victim's nephew, I didn't really relish reliving the horror that I had experienced several years earlier, but my publisher felt the time was right. My last book, The Great Debate, a bestselling novel about intrigue at the First Continental Congress, had made me a hot commodity. And that book was, after all, inspired by the bizarre scenario surrounding my uncle's death.

The truth, sometimes, is at least as strange as fiction.

Relentless. The only description for the weather that summer. The heat had topped ninety degrees for three straight weeks without a hint of rain. For late June and early July in south central Ohio, this was the stuff that records were made of. Riding down country roads was a pilgrimage of sheer depression. Corn was severely stunted, dust flew freely, animals languished in whatever shade was available.

Only a good rain, a cool front, or much-needed air conditioning could boost morale, and none of these seemed to be imminent at that point in time. Air conditioning is something which you pine for here in late July or August when a ninety-degree high is common. But the dog days are usually relatively few and when late September hits all thoughts of central air blow out with the arrival of Indian summer and crisp cool air.

I remember that day so clearly. As I sat at my desk looking out the open window in my den the phrase "These are the times that try men's souls," ran through my mind. Sometimes such a potent phrase is coined at a key juncture in history but bears repeating through countless ages because, though hackneyed, there is no more apt nor succinct phrase.

Life seemed routine enough at the time. I was simply another middle-aged college history professor trying to look at well-known events from a new angle. One needs a fresh perspective when teaching a class of freshmen a required course or when authoring yet another article on something such as the founding of this great nation. And originality is hard enough when working with dry facts without the weather turning on you.

But the old line "publish or perish" was long ingrained in my mind and I knew that there were a hundred struggling would-be history professors waiting in the wings for my job. So there I wearily sat.

That afternoon I was working on an article for the history publication "America Remembers." With the 1996 elections looming on the horizon, I was supposed to be doing a series of short vignettes on the issues of the day surrounding certain key elections of the past one hundred years. I was thick into the throes of research into the election of 1896.

This was the first in the series and if I wanted to find my byline in subsequent issues, each article had to grab the editor's attention.

Behind me an old-fashioned, circular floor fan whirred on, a remnant of my childhood in the fifties. Daydreaming had a tendency at these times to creep up on whatever project I was working on, and drowsiness repeatedly threatened to overcome me as the afternoon wore down. At one point my head was actually beginning to loll until the dog started barking and snapped me back to reality.

All hostility about barking dogs in the dead of night goes out the window when you consider the positive aspect of the afternoon wake-up call. General Patton, a stout Scottie, could rouse an army and indeed had moved more than one mail carrier to pull out his trusty mace. Luckily, either Mariah, my bride of six months, or I had been able to intervene on his behalf before the situation had ever gotten out of hand.

Instinctively, I bolted out of my chair, tripping over the footstool as I ran toward the current commotion. Fortunately, I recovered in sufficient time to run outside before an arriving truck, the source of Patton's agitation, had rolled to a stop. I waylaid the General and put him on the screened-in porch just as two men jumped out of the cab.

"Zachary Honeychurch?"

"That would be me."

"Sign here, please, sir."

They unloaded one rather unwieldy box before moving on their way in the late afternoon heat. Their truck sent fresh dust clouds roiling as they made their way back down the long unpaved winding road that had brought them up to the century-old rambling farm house we called home.

Before I even had the presence of mind to search out the necessary tools to uncrate the item now lodged under my roof in a corner of the living room, the telephone rang, and the first disastrous note was sounded. The caller was a representative of the Hutchington, Virginia, police department calling to regretfully inform me that my uncle, George Fairfax, had been the victim of an apparent hit-and-run accident in downtown Philadelphia the previous evening, and had not lived through the night.

At that point, the crate was temporarily relegated to that ethereal file labeled "later" and I ran, much more agilely this time, to the barn to break the bad news to Mariah.

Mariah is tall, at least five nine. Willowy would be an apt description of her—she has an olive complexion, with large brown eyes fringed with incredible lashes, and long glossy black hair befitting her Native American heritage. She's a natural beauty whose charm has never been lost on any male that I ever saw her encounter, although she seems impervious, or perhaps jaded, to her effect on men.

On first meeting, she seems totally self-possessed, but everyone who has ever known her would agree that her personal demon has to be her need for intellectual approval, despite the fact that she is a Phi Beta Kappa with a Masters in English and a doctorate in process.

My uncle George, for his part, was a noted historian who, just shortly before his death, had been nominated for a Pulitzer. He was one of those rare individuals about whom it could be said that everything he chose to discuss became fascinating in the telling. He retained incredible bits of trivia that most people would never even have encountered, thereby making every conversation a learning experience.

George and Mariah had become fast friends within an hour of first meeting, as I knew would surely be the case. It wasn't just her obvious charms, though. She won George over with her interest in American antiques, one of my uncle's passions. Her knowledge of antiques was scant, but her interest was profuse. He, on the other hand, had great knowledge and an equally keen interest in antiques and they quickly fell into a student/teacher relationship. Before long, he had her collecting furniture. However, where she prefers the neglected castoff, something she can revive and make her own, he favored the well-polished antique.

That afternoon I found her among a heap of old furniture in different stages of refurbishment. She was busy working on a Queen Anne chair for an elderly neighbor. I went in quietly, waiting until she had a good stopping point, before interrupting.

She took the news about George better than I would have expected; or perhaps I should say, differently than I might have expected. It was almost as if she anticipated it. She sat down near the half-stripped chair she was working on and made a cryptic comment about something she had seen in the sky the night before which she knew did not bode well for someone near her. It was something about the type of moon. She was forever calling on strange bits of old Indian lore from some ancient memory she would not allow as her own. Then a single tear streamed down her cheek and I knew she was hurting.

The sun was beginning to fade as I made the final arrangements for our trip to Virginia. Had I known how my life would ultimately go spinning out of its orbit, I might never have left Springfield, Ohio.

Hutchington is a quiet town nestled in soybean country in King Albert County, Virginia. With a population of about 10,000 people it still boasts much of its colonial charm. Various city commissions through the years had passed mandates to retain the town's quaint historical appearance as much as possible in order to draw the tourist trade (as well, of course, to maintain their rich cultural heritage). Even the inevitable fast food franchises were subject to a building code within a three-square-mile radius of the heart of town.

The area had been settled in the spring of 1775, by two young brothers, Emmett and Isaiah Hutchington who, story had it, had come from New York with their new brides to begin life nearer to relatives already settled in Virginia.

Emmett, the elder, was twenty-six years old and a furniture maker. Isaiah, who was two years younger, had studied architecture and had worked as an apprentice for two years for a firm of architects in New York. The area, already home to a scattered handful of planters and farmers, welcomed the artisans to their fold. With their combined abilities, the brothers built their families beautiful, if somewhat modest, homes.

It was not long before commerce began to move out to them and Isaiah found himself the mayor of the newly chartered town of Hutchington. The year was 1797. Unfortunately, Emmett never got to see the town's charter. A mysterious fire a few years earlier had destroyed his home and claimed the lives of both he and his wife. Ironically, Isaiah was the only Hutchington ever to be mayor as his only children to live beyond the age of ten years were girls. Emmett's only child, Charles, had left Hutchington after the fire and had never been heard from again.

Most of these facts are well-documented on plaques interspersed throughout town. A handful of original buildings, predating the town's charter, including Isaiah Hutchington's homestead, had been preserved or rebuilt according to plans still intact in the courthouse. They are perched in the west section of downtown Hutchington which is dubbed "Olde Towne" (the "e," I suppose, was to impart the really old designation) where on any given day of the year, except holidays, one can observe life in colonial days reenacted in all its simplicity.

My mother's people, the Fairfaxes, had not settled in the Hutchington area until the early 1800's, and though they could not claim to be original settlers, they were well ensconced in the town's growth primarily in the fields of law and education.

The Fairfax family home is on the east side of town in an area which at the time it was built was considered to be the 'suburbs'. It seems a sudden influx of well-heeled citizens escaping city life from nearby Richmond had pushed out the town's borders between 1880 and 1910. The area, "New Town," no "e," was strictly residential and by 1985 many a home in that section, including ours, had been put on the National Historic Register. I would speculate that the New Town district, many of whose homes had been featured more than once in popular home and architecture magazines, has become almost as big a tourist attraction as Olde Towne.

The Fairfax house, a classic two-story, Victorian affair built in 1883, sits on the east side of Brandywine Street on three full acres. The front yard boasts a flawless Bermuda lawn bordered by red-tip photinias while the backyard is dotted with numerous active fruit trees and a circular wildflower garden which dates back to the time the house was built. A brick walkway surrounds the garden and cuts through it in an "X" pattern. At its heart is a huge cement fountain with seating all around it.

True to my uncle's nature, it was all meticulously maintained with the help of a yard man employed to take care of the "yard drudgery" as George was fond of calling it. That would be cutting the grass and trimming the hedges. The upkeep of the garden and fruit trees was strictly George"s domain. Gardening, you might say, was his avocation.

The backyard was also home to a garage large enough to house three cars with room to spare. A tool shed was attached to the rear of the garage. It had been built somewhere around the early 1920's to house the family automobiles. It now held a 1953 Jefferson Green and Corinthian Creme Hudson Hornet, my uncle's love, and his 1989 red Suburban. It was also, at that point in time, home to my blue Volvo.

George had taken advantage of a mild spring and dry summer that year to undertake a bevy of home improvements. Just prior to the time of his death, the exterior had undergone a facelift. It had been painted moss green with white trim. The overall effect, I thought, was to impart the feeling that the house had sprung up out of the earth just like its surrounding flora.

George was careful to assure that the interior of his home was equally well-maintained. The rooms, set off a broad central hallway, were full of beautiful antiques, some original to the house, but most period pieces added by George himself. The house had initially been fitted with gas light fixtures which were converted ten years later when electric lighting was installed, fixtures which remain in place even today.

George's love of history was only matched by his complete fascination with technology (sort of the yin and yang of historical perspective.) So, in the kitchen, juxtaposed next to the 'modern'

1917 stove, was a counter full of appliances ranging from a micro-wave to a Cuisinart food processor. In the living room, behind the closed doors of a chifforobe dating to 1908, was a 35- remote-con-trolled cable-ready color television. And in the library, an exquisite tapestry screen circa 1830, could be folded up to reveal a computer and color printer set-up, complete with a speedy modem and a fax machine.

Every room, in fact, housed evidence of the rapidly advanc-ing future. As George was fond of saying, "We are constantly creating and recreating history. Everything contributes to the story."

A few years earlier, he had put in central air conditioning but with twelve-foot ceilings and a temperate climate it got little use, until that fateful summer. Finally, in lieu of a dog, he had re-cently installed a state-of-the-art alarm system.

In the last couple of months prior to his death, my uncle had been retained by the city commission to write a book about the town's history for its approaching bicentennial. The idea for the book had supposedly been the brainchild of Mayor Reid Woodward, the first in the Hutchington bloodline to hold the town reins in sev-enty years.

Nevertheless, it had been unanimously endorsed by the city commission as a win-win endeavor in light of two facts: the town boasted two hundred years of history, and lodged within its borders was a world-renowned historian who had from time to time written articles on various aspects and personages of the town.

From my uncle's perspective the book held the allure of being work literally in his own backyard, and he was already well-acquainted with the town's history. Writing the book would be the most time-consuming aspect because so much of the research was done.

Upon his demise, and before I could depart the city limits, the town fathers appealed to me, a relatively unknown but nonethe-less published author/historian to continue where he left off. My primary edge over the multiple historians lined up on the town's borders was not my personal relationship to the deceased, but rather the fact that I had spent every summer from age four years to college in their fair town visiting my uncle.

My parents, being teaching archaeologists, took off during summer months to work in places ill-suited for a child, leaving me in the loving care of my mother's brother. His peregrinations, if he was involved in traveling at all during those times, took him to more civilized locales. I spent several accumulated years in Hutchington and ended up following in my uncle's footsteps rather than my parents. He was my friend, my mentor, my idol.

I even looked like my uncle - same blond hair and blue eyes, both about five feet, ten inches tall with muscular builds. People who did not know better mistakenly assumed we were father and son and often we just let them believe what they would. We did seem to have that unusual psychic link reserved for parents and their offspring.

After both my parents died while I was still a young adult, my uncle and I became even closer. I was, in fact, the benefactor of his estate as his wife, Charlie, had died when I was a boy of ten years and no children had been born to carry on his name.

So upon his death, I had a chapter in my life to close, an estate to settle, and suddenly, should I decide to accept the offer, a book to finish. Unfortunately, George's claim to fame lay in his ability to ferret out the stories behind the known history...what really made the textbook stories interesting, and much of those anecdotes, I feared, would have been in his head, and therefore died with him.

I, on the other hand, was not known for my interviewing ability. Indeed, I think I went into teaching because I was looking for a job which required me to speak _to_ people rather than _with_ people. I was okay among friends, but I was more than a little shy when it came to strangers.

I requested a short time to think it over and Mariah and I flew back to Ohio. At the least, I had loose ends to tie up, and at most a new wife I was reluctant to part from and, ah yes, the crate. We almost forgot to open it before I left town and literally had to go back into the house as I was leaving to do so. When opened it revealed a beautiful desk shaped like a kidney bean. Uncrated, the front of the desk faced the wall and in the interest of time we just left it there until we could decide where we wanted to put it.

We assumed that it was a late wedding present from George. He was the only one with the money or inclination to send such an expensive gift and, even more importantly, it appeared to be an antique. I say assumed because there was no note or card attached to reveal the sender.

We decided that I should go to Virginia and finish the book, if for no other reason than as a tribute to my uncle. Then too, if I was lucky, I might discover something about the desk while I was there. Mariah agreed to fly in and assist me with writing and editing as time allowed and I agreed to fly home occasionally to take care of anything that needed taking care of.

So with her blessing and the university's consent, I took a year's sabbatical and set out for Hutchington, somewhat reluctantly, for the long haul.

What Reminds Me Of Your Love

by Holly Barrios-Gayman

What reminds me of your love in this pale
Wintery garden whose silent magic sleeps
Beneath the angel's stony wings—she keeps
The garden spellbound with her whispery tale
Of eternal cycles reviving frail
And ancient blossoms when the gray sky weeps
Its liquid life again and fragrance leaps
From melting air in spite of winter's wail.
I see you kneel—matching stone-to-stone
A careful chinking as they gently touch
The angel's feet, these stones your heart's true key.
A timeless moment for you two alone
In quiet communion, your smile holds such
Promise—just as when you proposed to me.

O, Georgia!

Harbor
by Lisa Kurth

I catch myself
drifting toward you yet.
When I am tired,
hours seem to be lifting me
into an old harbor.
I forget
the tide is out now,
foam breaking on reefs,
on black water,
the hissing shelf
of the last wave shoreward.
Waking,
I catch myself.

O, Georgia!

Blackberries and the Bull

by Teresa Linderman Bueno

Even before my eyes opened, I somehow knew it would be a day I would remember forever. It seemed normal enough - just another hot, lazy summer morning. As I lay there in the bed I wondered what woke me up – the distant sound of a lawn mower, a truck rumbling past, or the roar of the katydids in the pin oak trees outside the window – or maybe it was that 'something-special-is-'bout-to-happen' feeling.

No matter! I jumped out of the bed with the enthusiasm and energy only available to me prior to puberty, like a jackrabbit. I never was quite sure what a "jack" rabbit was – or how it was different than the cottontails I saw from time to time, but according to Granny (who never saw one either) they were the fastest of all the rabbits.

I slept in the front room - Larry's old bedroom. Larry is my uncle, Granny's only son and "her baby boy." In the wintertime, Granny would trot into the bedroom, lower the shades and tightly close the curtains. Every night as she would go through the bedtime ritual, she would warn, "Could be a peeping Tom around somewhere – or an old tramp hitchhiking up or down 411. Why, you just can't be too careful these days." But it was summertime now and the hot north Georgia summers were different. The fear of tramps and peeping Toms paled in comparison to the torture of the heat—shades remained up and curtains were pulled all the way back to welcome any hint of a breeze. At night, in the front room, the streetlight would glare in and bounce off the waxed and buffed hardwood floors. Between the heat and the light and the noise from those big ole' trucks on the highway sleep didn't come easy in the front room, even for a worn out kid. And in the hot summer morning the sun blasted through the windows as it did this morning demanding that the sleep end and the day begin.

It hurt Granny bad when Larry eloped. Granny had wanted Larry to marry Casaundra Lesland; instead he ran away with Brenda Franklin—nothing but trash was Granny's incessant lament. That was the one thing I thought Granny was wrong about. Why, Brenda was the lead majorette! Maybe her folks didn't have a big fancy house like the Lesland's, but they weren't trash either. I always liked Brenda—still do.

I think to ease her pain and perhaps to retaliate Granny changed near 'bout everything in Larry's room. She painted the walls a lovely orchard color. (A color she loved, but which was despised by Larry as a teenager. Truth is he probably wouldn't like it today either.) To top it off, she hung soft, white, frilly Priscilla curtains. The bedroom suite; a double bed, nightstand, dresser and chest of drawers all made of a light maple wood, was bought with money that Granny made at the elementary school lunchroom. Although Granny liked having her own money, I think she resented having to work. To tell the truth Granny and Papaw seemed rich to me, and I never understood why she had to work especially since she didn't really want to.

But it was summer and school was out—for Granny and me. I had just turned eleven the month before and I was visiting Granny and Papaw without my brothers—a double treat. I was the first grandchild and proud to say Granny's favorite. Momma resented that. Truth is Momma resented a lot of things. For that matter so did Granny and most all the women folk in the family. I think it comes from being raised Southern. Back then women married early, had babies and stayed home. Seemed like women in my family wanted more, somehow, and just didn't know how to get it – so they just resented the hell out of everything.

In spite of it all, Granny and I always had a big time. Now I was visiting Granny, and there was something special in the air. That morning, as I came into the kitchen where Granny was washing green beans in the sink, she greeted me with her standard question,

" Mornin' Hun. How 'd you sleep?"

"Just fine," I answered, my standard response.

"I was thinking we could go blackberry picking in that pasture cross the road from Mable's," Granny said over her shoulder as she dried her hands.

"Really?! When?" I was jumping with excitement.

"Soon as you eat some breakfast," she answered off-handedly.

Man alive, I love blackberries. Blackberry cobbler, blackberry preserves, blackberry anything! I never had a blackberry dish I didn't like – but some are just better than others. And anything blackberry that Granny fixed was great!

"So, can we fix blackberry cobbler for dinner?" I begged.

"Well, we need to get on the ball if you want a pie for dinner," she responded.

I never understood why Granny called a cobbler a pie. Every time I asked her about it she would just answer, "Take me at what I mean, Hun, not what I say."

After a quick breakfast of scrambled eggs cooked in the little iron skillet, and left over biscuits from Papaw's breakfast, we started to get ready.

When fixin' to get ready to go blackberry picking, the first thing to do, of course, is to put on blue jeans and a long-sleeved shirt. I don't care how hot it is. Last winter's jeans can be really hard to get on when you're a hot and sweaty growing girl. To start with, the jeans were too tight and I had to work really hard, which made me sweat more and then they were even harder to pull up. Next thing I know, I'm on the floor kicking and pulling on my jeans and looking like some kind of rabid dog on his back panting and frothing at the mouth. Once the jeans were on, the shirt was a breeze. Next came the socks and shoes – I hadn't seen those since cold weather. In the wintertime you need shoes because it's cold – the summertime it's an entirely different matter. It's your armor against snakes! Granny says snakes just love blackberries. In all my blackberry picking days, I never once saw a snake. Guess Papaw was right. He would fuss at Granny saying, "Snakes are more afraid of you, Lucille, than you are of them." But that didn't keep us from preparing for one of her biggest fears—close encounters of the snake kind.

Now the worse part about picking blackberries—other than the snakes—is the chiggers. I hate chiggers. Chiggers are worse than anything. They are tiny, little red bugs that live in blackberry patches and lie in wait for some unsuspecting victim to show up. Then they jump on you when you aren't looking and crawl slyly, so you can't feel them, to the elastic in the waist and legs of your underwear. Once they get there they dig into the skin under the elastic like the Russians themselves were coming. Now I'm not sure how they know which direction your underwear is and I've often wondered if you didn't wear underwear would they still dig in? I suspect they would, cause nearly always a few of the little buggers seem to end up in your socks. I never really knew if these were just the confused ones or some kind of outcasts. I couldn't tell you this for sure, but I suspect that if you were to pick blackberries naked you could avoid them all together. One thing I *can* tell you for sure – if you picked blackberries naked in Chatsworth, Georgia you would never live it down. Heck, around Granny it was barely acceptable to bathe naked much less go blackberry picking.

Snakes may be a fear, but chiggers are a reality. So in those days before "Off " we used critically placed kerosene to ward off the little critters. After all the buckets were gathered up and put in the trunk of the car, Granny would head for the kerosene. She had a quaint little vat to hold her kerosene. It was made of galvanized metal, and with its spout and lid it looked more like a campfire coffeepot than anything else. It held about a gallon and a half and was perfect for Granny's special kerosene needs which included, among the many, chigger repellant.

"We'll just put some around our wrists and ankles," she would say while we squatted in the corner of the garage where the kerosene was kept. She would tip the coffeepot so that the kerosene would dribble out on to an old kerosene-soaked rag. The strong, but somehow pleasant odor, would fill the garage. After thoroughly rubbing our wrists and ankles, we were finally ready to go.

We headed to a pasture across from Mable's. Mable was Granny's older sister. She was surprisingly smart, had a kind heart, a sweet disposition and was over all just a little too easy going for her own good. Granny was always quick to point that out. Mable lived with her husband Floyd down Highway 411 south of town. Floyd was a good man, Granny said; he just had a small problem with selling moonshine. But there was no time for visiting today. We were going blackberry picking!

Mable knew the man who owned the pasture and had asked if we could come to the property from time to time to go blackberry picking. It was fine with him. "Just watch out for the bull," he advised.

We turned down a dirt road through the trees that led to the pasture fence.

"We'll park here in the shade," Granny said as she pulled over about 50 yards shy of the pasture. It was very important to park in the shade whenever possible. There was plenty of shade in the cool of those old oak trees. She just sat there for a moment.

"Why are we just sitting here?" I asked impatiently.

"Shhhh.... We don't want that ole' bull to know we're here," she whispered.

I followed her lead. We quietly got the buckets out of the trunk, and then tiptoed over to the fence to survey the situation.

We stood near the top of a knoll in the trees. The fence was made of four strands of barbed wire and it enclosed about ten acres. I held on to the next to the top strand as we looked out over the pasture. There it was - in the middle of the pasture stood the most magnificent blackberry patch I had ever seen. Even from our distant post, I could see the plump, beautiful, glistening blackberries hanging like thousands of little sweet volunteers crying out, "Take me, take me!" Ahhh black gold!

"Look! There they are, Granny! Let's go!" I said with excitement. She grabbed my arm and answered, "Just hold your horses. Where's that bull?"

Looking closely we could see that on the other side of the blackberry patch was a small herd of ten or twelve Hereford cows calmly grazing. Alongside them was their ever-vigilant guardian, the bull. He was big—I mean really big! His coat was mostly brick red; his feet and face were white, as was the tip of his tail. His eyes were demonic - small, beady and pinkish-red in color. Although it was hot summer, his coat was heavy and wooly. It curled up around the base of his mammoth horns which reached at least three feet

113

across and then curled toward the front of his massive head. Every so often he would lift his head, stop chewing, look around, snort, smell the air and then continue grazing.

"Man, Granny, he looks mean."

"Looks mean? Hon, he IS mean. Now here's the plan. We will slip in here. The important thing is to use the blackberry patch as a blind. As long as we stay on the other side of the blackberries from him, he can't see us and we'll be safe and sound." I just nodded.

Like a couple of super spies right out of James Bond we slipped through the strands of barbed wire with our buckets. We hunkered down and headed for the blackberry patch. If you have ever been around a cow pasture you know that cows don't graze near cow pies. And grass tends to grow in high patches around cow pies. So we carefully traversed around the cow pie islands of high grass. Once we reached the safety of the patch, we quietly and quickly began to pick. Granny kept looking out for the bull as we picked. Careful to keep the patch between us and the grazing cattle there was only one problem. Granny and I always seemed to have things to talk about when we were together – even when we should be quiet. It seemed like things that wanted to be said just floated around in the air unsaid until they found us – then they would disguise themselves as our thoughts so that they could escape into the world as words in our conversation. I guess in the middle of that pasture on that hot summer day we were easy targets for those little unsaid things. We started talking, quietly at first, nothing of real importance. Just the simple kind of conversation that makes a little girl feel like she is someone worth listening to. Time seemed to stand still as we talked and picked, and I'm not sure how long it was but after about a bucket and a half a piece, Granny looked up and yelled, "Good Lord have mercy! Run, Tessie! Follow me! Follow me!" She grabbed the two buckets full of blackberries and took off up the hill toward the car.

I whirled around to see what she had seen, and there he was – the bull! While we were talking and picking we had forgotten about the bull. Our voices must have attracted him and now that he had seen us he wasn't about to forget about us. He was trotting right toward me – head and ears forward, nostrils flaring. I turned back around to see that Granny was half way up the hill. Like the blackberries bouncing out of her buckets, any maternal instincts of protection she might have had were left behind. But that was what I loved about Granny – I felt big around her – like I was smart and pretty and knew how to take care of myself. Now was the time to take care of myself – for sure!

I grabbed the two buckets that she'd left behind with me and took off with the bull closing in. Now I had another problem – I couldn't stop laughing! I had never seen my Granny run like that! And in spite of the bull, it was the funniest thing I had ever seen in all my born days. As she ran up the hill she deftly hurdled each of the cow pie islands we had so carefully avoided on the way down the hill. I was amazed! And then, as if on cue, just as she hurdled one of the cow pie islands, a cottontail rabbit jumped out of the grass and lit out like Snyder's pup. Granny let out a yelp that you could have heard all the way back in town if you'd been listening – or maybe it wasn't a yelp – maybe it was a sonic boom. Because just when I thought that she was going faster than humanly possible for a Granny, she became a blur and with one final swoop she came to the fence, set the buckets down and went over like a high jumper, managing somehow to land on her feet. I was impressed.

She turned and with her eyes near popping out of her head yelled again, "Run, Tessie, run!" With my side splitting with a stitch from laughing and running, I managed to make it to the fence with the buckets of precious blackberries. I set them down and scooted under the fence just in the knick of time. Once we were safely on the other side of the fence the bull seemed to lose interest. He had done his job—he had ousted the intruders. He turned and went back to his harem. We went home and made a pie that to this day has never been rivaled.

Something I would never forget did happen that hot summer day. It was a spectacular event for me as a young girl and it will live at least as long as I do. My Granny is dead now; and there is a big new highway running through the middle of that pasture.

The lazy cows with their fiercesome bull are gone and probably forgotten by most others who knew them. What little of the fence that remains is grown over with a blanket of honeysuckle vines. And in the middle of the pasture there is no sign of the once magnificent blackberry patch that stood so proudly and gave so generously. Whenever I drive past that pasture, I slow down and remember that hot summer day long ago - and it all lives again. I know that for me, Granny, the bull and the blackberries will always be there. And if I close my eyes and look and listen real close I can see Granny running up that hill with a bucket in each hand—blackberries bouncing everywhere—hurdling those cow pie islands; yelling back to the young girl, "Follow me, Tessie, follow me!"

I try, Granny, I try.

Dollars On The Ceiling
by April S. Fields

Some nights I don't think I can do it, not even once more. I stare at the warped and dented back door of the Winchester Grill and Lounge. I want to turn around, get into my orange Hornet and drive until I get to my mother's house in Villa Rica. I'd get a real job and a nice clean little apartment where Libby and I could be together like it should be.

It seems this idea comes more often lately. I'm so tired. A weight like a heavy arm is draped around my shoulders. And there's no end to it. These Baby-Boomers, always at odds with the reality of their fading youth, want nothing but the old songs. Worst of all, though I never thought it could happen, I've just plain lost heart. I don't feel the music anymore. I know I sing like some kind of robot, the words programmed, uninspired.

"One more week and I'm out of here," I lie. The door groans, giving in unwillingly.

As I pass the kitchen, I hit a thick wall of the aroma of hot grease. Harry's voice calls out from behind me.

"Yo, Angel, could be a crowd tonight," he says, "Jack over at the Ramada called. Some convention in town. This could be your big break, girl." He winks and clicks his tongue. A cigarette, forever a fixture in the corner of his mouth, bobs up and down like a lever as he talks.

"You saying this is a convention of talent agents, or what, Harry?" I keep walking. I can feel the tight grip of a headache slowly moving up the back of my neck. I hate conventions. Obnoxious drunks.

"You never know, girl, you just never know."

"Right, Harry." I'm wondering if he was born with that cigarette or if it just grew there later. The absurd vision of a newborn with a cigarette nearly makes me smile.

In the doorway of the closet-sized room I ask myself how long I can keep doing this. I don't even remember the last time I let myself get excited about the possibility of being discovered. I dimly recall believing it would happen some day. I definitely used to have some imaginative daydreams. Even after my Jason era, and all the depression, I still had hope that someone would walk up and offer me a chance to prove I could sing as good as any of the hot-snot stars currently on the charts. All I ever needed was one little break, you know? I could have been so good. But instead, night after night, month after sorry month, I sing for these loud-mouthed, inebriated jerks in a rundown dive that looks like a saloon in a bad western. I could be singing in glitzy showrooms. So, where am I? In a smoke-choked, bug infested bar famous for its cold draft beer and dollar bills stapled to every square inch of the ceiling. Reality wins. I ought to be glad I'm working at all. It could be worse. No use dwelling on the thing. Life's meaner than a whore dog in heat, Jason used to say.

    I dress and touch up my makeup in the broken full-length mirror. I stare hard at the pale two-part girl fragmented by the long diagonal crack. I smile weakly at the irony of it. I squint, trying to will away the dark circles underneath my dull gray eyes. When that doesn't work I smooth on extra concealer, realizing performing in the near dark does have its advantages.
    Sometimes when I look in the glass, I see myself melting slowly away. It scares the hell out of me to realize how little time I've got left. I'm twenty-six years old, looking thirty and feeling forty. This I know — in this business, it's not enough to have the voice, you better have the looks, too. My days are numbered. Then what? I'm clueless — I don't even want to think about it.
    The thing is, from age ten I could never see myself doing anything else but singing. I never prepared myself for any contingencies. Sometimes knowing what I did to myself by dropping out of school, turns my gut to ice. I've been promising myself and whoever else might be listening, if I could get a break, I'd go back to school and get my life on track. If nothing else, I owe it to my kid. If I could break out of this dead-end life, at least I could keep her from going down the tubes. I stopped daydreaming about Hollywood and big money long ago. All I want now is to live a real life.

I just don't know how to get there from here. It's as if my prayers are nothing but promises.

Four serious years tagging after Jason with his rock band doing one night stands in sleazy joints was an education I wish I'd skipped. I must have been out of my mind. Where did I think it would take me?

Sure, it started out exciting. Then, after Libby was born, the constant traveling, all-nighters, and Jason's drugs became a nightmare. I kept hanging on believing it would change. I'll always have this two-inch scar on my chin as a little reminder of how it did. Though there's no way I'd ever forget. Even now when I close my eyes I can hear Libby crying, Jason's arm stretched up, fist hard, ready to swing down like a wrecking ball. I know it's no good to keep thinking about it. Anyway, all's well that finally ends, they say.

I shake it off, snatch a last disgusted look and smooth my black crepe dress over my hips. The sharp angles under my palms remind me I ought to eat more often. I straighten my shoulders, toss my hair back, pull the chain on the dangling bulb and head out to meet the long night.

Friday nights are always bad. People looking to wind down from the stress of the week. I work here every night except Wednesday. During the day I pick up extra bucks working as an aide in a nursing home, changing sheets and mopping up pee for minimum wage. But Wednesdays belong to Libby. I grab a couple of hours sleep then drive the hour to Mom's in time to have breakfast with my child, the only person who gives me a reason to stay here on this sick earth.

The room is empty except for Sam and Charley already warming up in the corner.

"Angel, let's open with forty-six tonight, that always gets them in a tipping mood." Sam's nimble fingers ripple up and down the keyboard coaxing unexpectedly large sounds from the small electric organ. "Man, I need some big tips tonight. Car payment due next week. Where did this month go?"

"The older we gets the faster it goes. That's what I knows."

Charley's grin peels back the lower half of his black face, revealing more teeth than seems possible. He thumbs along the thick bass string, a big ear tilted close to the fret.

"Harry says there's a convention coming in tonight," I tell them. "You'll make your car payment, no problem. As much as I hate those slobbering convention drunks I have to admit I'm a little short on rent money myself."

"You still in that dump downtown ?" Sam asks. "I don't know how you stand it. I told you I could get you a deal on a place in one of my brother's condos in Roswell."

"Your kind of a deal means two hundred dollars more a month to me, Sam. It takes everything I've got to pay Libby's day care. You just don't understand." I study a cigarette butt wedged in the broken corner of a dark linoleum tile, wondering how long it's been there. "Someday, when she's set, I'll move." A wave of grief for something lost washes over me, stinging my eyes. I swallow hard and change the subject. "Let's warm up."

Sam pulls his dense, "Brillo Pad" hair back into a thick rubber band. He adjusts knobs, flips switches and without even looking at Charley starts on beat. I always feel a great respect for these two musicians. Their music comes clean and easy. They never seem to mind this place. I admire their appreciation for the chance to work regularly. Most never make it this far in this crappy business.

The guys wind themselves up into the sound and the beat playing the same pieces a thousand times over, always appearing as though they love it each time. I wish I could feel that way. It would be easier. Every time I plan to quit I'm forced to face the truth. I've been singing since I can remember. Performing for a crowd fits me like a pair of five year old jeans. When I really want to, I can turn a good song into a spiritual experience. But now, the plug is pulled; whatever I had is about drained away.

By ten o'clock people fill up the handful of table seats and they're standing three deep at the bar. I watch them while we're resurrecting the dead — the old songs from the sixties and seventies. They laugh and talk over the music, whooping it up as usual. I wonder if they even hear us. It occurs to me I could probably make up words, delivering them with feeling and these clowns would never know the difference. What would it matter anyway. Once I tried to persuade the guys to learn a few new numbers, something current, which had turned out to be like trying to get my mom to give up her afternoon soaps. They like it the way it is; no rehearsals, no effort. And like Charley had said, "Them good ole' boys like to waller in yesterday, girl. Why you want to mess with a good thing?"

So, from nine until two, Sam, Charley and I pump out the best of yesterday. I work the audience, too, announcing birthdays and anniversaries, drawing them into my rehearsed charm. They slurp it up with their drinks. Someone always asks about the dollar bills on the ceiling. Every night is a rerun. I look up at those dollars, defaced with names and obscene messages, knowing up there in the dark those greenbacks are as untouchable as my dreams.

As the evening matures, the crowd regresses. Sam and Charley each play a solo to encourage extra tips. After each set, I slip back into the kitchen to get away from the smoke. No question I'm destined to die of lung cancer but no use hurrying it.

"Sounds mighty fine in there, Missy B," Old John says, his near toothless mouth stretches wide across his face as he looks up from the grill. He waves his drippy spatula in a salute, slinging brown drops of grease on the floor.

"Thanks, John, I wish I thought so." I open the big cooler and scrounge around until I find a shriveled apple.

"Lord, child, you got so much talent I don't even know how you ain't been grabbed up and carted off to Vegas." With a corner of his dirty apron, John stops a trickle of sweat meandering down his old carved cheeks.

I've been in this conversation before and I'm not in the mood. "Maybe someday, huh, John?" I smile patronizingly and step back into the dark unhealthy room. I find a lone stool at the bar, order a mineral water and take a bite of my apple.

"I enjoyed your last set," the deep voice comes from my right side. I don't turn to look.

"Thanks."

" Ever thought about recording?"

Great, I think, just what I need, another jerk. Why don't these guys ever come up with something a little more original? "No," I say, turning to get a look at this one, "But I guess you're a big talent agent just itching to have me sign a contract you happen to have back in your room."

I'm surprised at the tall, well-groomed guy and almost regret my sarcastic remark. He's not a bad looker. At least he's in a suit which gives him a few extra points over the other bums who hustle me.

"Well, no, nothing like that. But I can offer you a studio to do a demo and probably good exposure to some top names. But, whatever. Up to you. I can tell you I have a good track record," he says while he's handing me a card. "Call my office if you're interested."

He smiles, slips off the stool and disappears into the fog like the cliched ending of an old movie.

I blink at the card that reads: Louis Andrew Productions, Sound Studio, Agent.

My eyes slide back and forth from the card to the thick air trying to figure out exactly what his game could be. I shake my head. It's too easy.

I'm sitting here staring at nothing when Sam comes up and touches my shoulder. "Angel? You okay? It's time. Angel?"

I suck in air, look at Sam and say weakly, "Yeah," but think, no way.

I look around for a place to stash the card but can't bring myself to put it down. I motion to the guys and they start up again. But, for some reason, as the sound competes with the throbbing room, I feel a lifting up, like after an illness, a fever leaving. An old strength and power comes to my throat. I feel fresh air coming from somewhere, filling my chest until I think I might explode. I sing my heart out, riding the top edge of a perfect pitch.

At the end of the set the crowd goes crazy. They stomp, cheer and clap for most of five minutes. I look at Sam and Charley laughing and nodding their heads. I am inspired. It comes up from the pit of my stomach and spreads in a tingling vibration to my fingers and toes. I go with it. I grip the mike with both hands and start again, alone. This time I'm doing something I wrote years ago and I've never done for anyone before. I'm pouring it out on the crowd like syrup. I'm so into it, it's like I'm removed from this place. I can hear my voice plaintively — almost see it — sure and unaccompanied flow out across and around the room. I don't hear anything else. My lyrics press into the crowd, settling on them like the sobering realization of man's mortality.

...yesterday places and yesterday people how far away yet still remain /Deep inside my heart always in my dreams and still unchanged /But tell me where did I go wrong, and show me where do I belong /All those hopes and dreams left in yesterday with a better song /All those hopes and dreams left in yesterday.

When it's over, I open my eyes and face a subdued room. No one moves. No one lights a cigarette or orders a drink. No one clinks a glass or coughs. There is no sound. And then I know I really blew it this time . What a nerd I am. I was caught up in the moment and lost my head. I am so embarrassed. I turn to look back at Sam, to see what to do next, when it starts.

Cheers, whistles and stomping grow into a mounting pandemonium. Everyone begins standing, first individually and then in groups. The applause and clamor claims the small space. It seems as though it will never stop. Every time I try to say something the noise cranks up even louder. All I can do is stand here and take it. One thing's for sure, it's better than any daydream I ever had.

I can't believe it. I bow over and over. I turn my palms up in a gesture of complete exasperation and the card I've been gripping falls bent to the floor. I ease down, pick it up, and reading it once

O, Georgia!

more, throw my head back, laughing. All of a sudden those dollars on the ceiling look so close I think all I have to do is reach out to touch them. But the only thought racing in circles in my head is, I promise, I promise, I promise...

On Friendship
by Meryl Larsen Martin

In me lies all the wonder lost
The carousel music left unsung
The fireflies' uncensored dance
Through willow's lacy fingers hung.

If asked I am the child's caress
The bluest sky beyond the clouds
The tender cradle of twig and grass
Summoned high in netted boughs.

See in me a whispered kiss
A beam of gold dust in the dawn
Of sorrow's flight on sparrow's wings
Of friendship's never ending song.

O, Georgia!

In Winter's Cemetery A Redbud Tree

by Virginia (Jenny) Bishop Heaton

I travel through late winter's cemetery
    of tall wooden markers
    to life that was
    and ultimately will return.
It seems another cold forever
    in this perpetual, bitter season.

Suddenly, I glimpse a living ghost
    dressed in sheer, lavender-pink
    with yellow flowers dancing at her feet.
I gasp in disbelief,
    then catch myself and smile
    that I should doubt reality.

How eager is this newborn, who dares
    to gently lead
    the rebirth promenade!
Beneath a sky of low-flung gray
    opposing all foreboding gloom
    stands spring's promise.

As witness to this miracle, how can I doubt anything?

O, Georgia!

As We Forgive

(loosely based on John 8:I-II)

by Kathleen Gunter

The sun is finally setting. I thought this day would never end. Standing in the shadows, I hear the sound of angry voices. With my slender body pressed tightly against the stone wall I watch in stoic silence as the holy parade shuffles past. This shadowy nook is a perfect place for one to spy on these servants of God, though tonight even a blind man can see their jealousy and contempt. It is no surprise to me to see my husband Jacob trailing behind them.

As they pass by, their long robes leave snake-like trails in the dust. One by one, each priest jerks his long robes aside to descend the temple steps. Bringing up the rear is Jacob and the rest of their entourage of admirers. Their departure is slow. They start and stop at least a dozen times to argue over a fine point of law. Something has really upset them. I must remember to ask Jared what has caused such a commotion.

Though their dust has settled I continue to wait in the shadows. The coolness falls quickly after sunset and I pull my cloak close around me. Impatiently, I fidget with my bracelet as the minutes crawl by. I am getting tired of these secret meetings.

O Lord, why am I here? I'm getting too old for this. Why, I'm nearly old enough to be his mother! I don't know why I still agree to come, I don't love him. But here I stand in the night, waiting for him... again.

Still toying with my bracelet, my thoughts are interrupted by a bird-like whistle. Looking up I search for him across the way. Though barely discernable, I can make out the silhouette of his young muscular form. He too is hiding, waiting for the priests to fade from view of the outer court. It is safe now. I scurry across the court and reach him unnoticed. Impatiently he takes my elbow and maneuvers me silently into the night for another lover's rendezvous.

Hurrying through the street he whispers, "We've got to stop meeting like this. If your husband ever finds out. . ." He shudders as his mind conjures up the horrifying possibilities.

Anger boils up in me like bile and hot tears sting my eyes. *I have done nothing more or less than what he has done many times over*, I rationalize. Then speaking aloud, "Don't worry. He won't even notice that I'm gone."

I hate my husband more than I love Jared or any of the others before him. This unexpected surge of emotion fuels the angry flame inside me causing me to stiffen slightly and walk with defiant determination, but Jared doesn't notice as we pass from one street to another. All too soon, we reach our destination and slip quietly from sight.

The hours slip by and gratefully, darkness gives birth to early light. Anxious to return to our respective dwellings, our two cloaked figures exit hurriedly into the dim morning light only to collide with the plump form of a temple priest. The force knocks me to the ground.

"Watch where you're going!" growls the old priest, bending over to help me. He grunts as he strains to help me to my feet.

Jared panics when he realizes who we have run into. Before he can be recognized, he buries his face in his cloak and swiftly makes his escape. I am not so lucky. Back on my feet I try to slip away as well, but the old priest is still gripping my wrist. In all the confusion my cloak has slipped from my head and exposed my face. I turn away, trying to conceal my identity, but it is too late. The old priest looks at me and then in the direction of the young fugitive. Returning his gaze to me, a smile of both recognition and realization flash across his wrinkled old face.

"You . . . you are Jacob's wife . . . Miriam." He states slowly. His eyes narrow and with the next breath he hisses, "Adulteress!"

An evil grin spreads across his face as he rejoices in the possibilities my misfortune offers; a divine way to hurt Jacob. The old priest has always disliked my husband. I can sense his mouth watering in anticipation of the havoc he will bring down on him. Still holding my wrist, he starts walking hastily down the street, dragging me unceremoniously behind him.

"Ooh, you're hurting me!" I complain as I reluctantly follow, stumbling over the cobbled street. With my free hand I try to grasp the edge of my cloak to cover my head and face from those who are bound to look.

"A~dul~ter~ess!" He announces again to those who would hear. "You will pay the price required by the law! A~dul~ter~ess!"

I struggle against his grasp, but it's impossible to free myself. Shame washes over me as he drags me down the street. My mind is filled with excuses. I never thought I'd get caught. It's not as if I'm the only one who *"sins!"* Who cares anyway? I've tried to be discreet, but God has played me for a fool, again. What have I done?. Why did this have to happen to me? Why?

Like a punch in the gut I am hit hard with regret and shame. Breathlessly I stagger, overwhelmed with my circumstances. I hear my heart pounding, and I lower my face in shame. People are looking out their windows, around doors, and through half-opened shutters. I will bring disgrace to my family's name and to my husband's family as well. But it is too late to worry about that now. Tears of anger and frustration run freely, turning my eyes black and streaking my carefully powdered face. Through this flood of self-pity I see my life melt into a meaningless collage of faces, events and emotions.

It is over. No more secrets, no more hiding and no more lies. It is truly over and I don't care. Why do I feel such relief? I don't even care what happens to me. In fact, I believe I'm *glad* it's over. I call out, trying to get the old priest's attention, but he can't hear or doesn't want to hear. He just keeps marching down the road with me behind him. Oh, what does it matter anyway. I don't resist anymore because I know he is right. I have sinned and the penalty... is death by stoning.

Now it's me that shudders. My body aches just thinking about it. I hate myself and I hate life. Why, someone like me doesn't even deserve to live. I'm so lost in my misery that I don't realize that we have stopped walking or that the priest has released his grip on me. I stand docile, lost in thought while he talks to a member of the Sanhedrin. For a moment, I allow myself to wander through my childhood memories one last time.

I grew up an only child and very spoiled. As the apple of my father's eye, he gave me everything I ever wanted, like this gold bracelet. Touching my bracelet I remember fondly my father's wonderful face. Removing it, I look to see if I can still read the words engraved inside: *The Lord is my rock, my fortress and my deliverer.* (Psalms 18:2a) The Lord can't love the likes of me. The guilt is too much. I replace my treasured bracelet. I have now brought shame to my father's memory. I'm glad he's dead. He died suddenly while I was still a young girl. Mother and I did the best we could, living with her older brother. A few years later, I married Jacob, a Levite of reputation. I was in love and looked forward to a comfortable life and a family. I began my married life trying to be a good wife, but God played a cruel trick on me. I'm barren. My husband's disappointment turned to neglect, unfaithfulness and cruelty. Our marriage is filled with bitterness and hatred. So I gave up. All I ever wanted was to love and be loved.

I shake myself free of those memories to study the scene taking shape around me. I find that others have joined in the conversation. Our little group is fast becoming a mob, and they all seem angry, with everyone talking at the same time. The level of excitement rises along with the pitch of their voices. Then I hear the name of Jesus.

Jesus? That's the name Jared mentioned last night. He's the reason they were upset last night. He's the country preacher they all hate. I've heard Jacob talk of this Jesus, too. He said that he knows all things and that He is a miracle worker. He even said that Jesus can heal the sick, talk to demons, and feed the multitudes. He has even raised a child from the dead!

"It makes no sense," he once said. "He does nothing but good, yet they all hate him."

Jesus. Again I hear them spit out his name distastefully, accusing him of blasphemies and cursing him. Without warning, the old priest grabs my arm and the whole group starts walking toward the temple. Entering the outer court they spot a rather large crowd of people gathered nearby, listening to a man who appears to be teaching. It is obvious that this is Jesus.

The priest and his cronies approach the crowd, rudely interrupting his speech. The crowd of listeners drifts silently away to observe the coming spectacle from afar. Once again, I am roughly dragged forward then pushed toward the teacher, falling on my knees at his feet. Jesus reaches down and helps me to my feet. Before I can thank him for his kindness, the old priest questions him.

"Teacher, this woman was taken in the very act of adultery." The old priest pauses, and my accusers whisper among themselves. "Now, Moses in the law commanded us that she should be stoned. What do you say?"

There is a hush now. Like the fox who has the rabbit cornered, the holy men edge in closer, waiting to hear what Jesus will say. They are already licking their lips, tasting the blood from the kill. Dejected I stand beside Jesus; eyes downcast and unconcerned, waiting for the verdict. I already know what must happen, why are they asking him? I am surprised when instead of replying, Jesus stoops down beside me to write in the dirt, ignoring their request. I watch him out of the corner of my eye, and I'm astonished by what he writes. My accusers believe this is a ploy for time and complain loudly, impatient for his response. They are so anxious for his answer that few of them notice what he is writing in the dirt. But I have been watching him closely. I see clearly what he is writing. As each word takes form, my hand involuntarily reaches for my throat. How does he know? My eyes grow wide in disbelief. How can he know? Tears fill my eyes and a sob threatens to escape my lips. With both hands I cover my mouth to avoid making a sound, but inside I am screaming.

The rumblings from my accusers fast becomes a demanding chorus. "Well, what do you say?" repeats the old priest, his face flushed with excitement. "Answer us!" And the crowd agrees loudly.

"Yes, yes. Answer us!" they demand.

The sun clears the temple walls as Jesus stands up, shrouded

133

in its' light. Unaffected by their demands, he looks at me and then at my accusers. Calmly and evenly he replies. "He who is sinless, let *him* cast the first stone."

Their demands become murmurings filling the cool morning air. Questions swarm like buzzing bees as Jesus once again stoops to write in the dirt at his feet. I begin to shake until I think my knees will buckle beneath me. Already I can nearly feel the crushing pain of those punishing stones bruising and breaking my body, but still, I can't take my eyes from him. This time indignant, self-righteous eyes follow his finger in the sandy soil. The crowd squeezes around him to watch. They become increasingly silent as he writes.

My eyes are glued to his words. I am so intrigued with what he is writing that I fail to notice the impact his written words have had. I don't hear the random gasps or see the embarrassed looks. I am oblivious to the tears of regret nor do I hear the shuffle of retreating footsteps. The tension is so thick, I can scarcely breathe. I only have eyes for Jesus as He stops writing and stands.

He turns to me and I am too ashamed to look him in the face. "Woman? Where are thine accusers? Who condemns thee?"

Startled that he would speak to me, I swallow hard. Timidly, I raise my eyes to his, then hesitantly look around. To my astonishment I find that they have all departed. There is no one left but me and Jesus.

"Lord..." I hear myself say as I search amongst the bystanders who are slowly drifting back to the teacher. I cannot find even one of my accusers. "Lord, there are none...?" And my heart shouts back...there are none!

Afraid to believe my eyes I look back to this teacher, healer, and miracle worker. Gently he says, "Neither do I condemn thee. Go, and sin no more."

I am speechless. Bodies begin crowding in around us and soon he is busy teaching again. Nervously twisting my bracelet I look around at the curious eyes looking at me and then watching him.

"Thank you Lord." I whisper.

As the crowd closes in I slowly inch away. I am still shaking and can barely stand so I lean heavily against a cold stone wall until I can regain my composure. I am filled with relief. "I'm free!"

I've never felt like this before. I feel like a burden has been lifted. I feel ten years younger. I feel....happy. Strength seeps back into my bones. Stepping lightly into the sunlight I wait for my eyes to adjust. The temple grounds are alive with activity and I feel more alive than I have ever felt before.

"Miriam, MIRIAM!"

Surprised, I turn toward the familiar voice to see my husband running toward me, clumsily, trying to avoid bumping into people.

Reaching me, he shouts. "Thank God you're alive!"

My eyes fill with tears and I cannot look him in the face. "You know then?" I whisper.

"My brother ran to tell me what was happening! I thought I was too late, that you would be...dead. "

Taking me into his embrace he holds me so tight I can scarcely breathe. I push him away...

"Jacob, I can't breathe!" He releases, me and I back away. Now I can see that he has been crying.

"Jacob, why are you crying?"

"Because I thought...I thought I lost you..." He pulls me to him again. The revelation of forgiveness unfolds before my eyes and fills my heart.

"You did, but now I am found..."

135

O, Georgia!

Labor Day
by Edith Harper Pinson

"A hard day's work,
for an honest day's pay."
That's what my Papa,
used to say.
"Gotta get up early,
and jump out of bed;
Gotta work all year,
just to keep the family fed;
Gotta always try hard,
to do my very best;
But on Labor Day,
Gotta day to rest."

O, Georgia!

The Yard 'Fore It Rains

by Lisa Kurth

The yard 'fore it rains sits full and thick,
sweatin' in air moist as watermelon rind,
heavy, like you could slice it.
And Lord, it's hot!
So hot it'd curl a dead man's hair!
Too hot to eat.
Dark, soggy clouds hangin' low in the sky
lookin' like they weigh a ton,
like some ol' hefer needs milkin' real bad,
keep a comin' closer, bringin' with 'em a smell like an ocean,
makin' everythin' alive go stiff and still.
And we all know it's a comin'.
Mama's day lillies and the pink crepe myrtle 'side the house
stand wide awake with blossoms that know they's in for a beatin'.
Ain't no stoppin' southern rain—
'falls hard and fast, like bullets.
Last time it come a good rain
'nearly whupped us all t' death.
Ain't no wind t' welcome it,
nor breeze from the river to warn,
and nary a sound is heard
'cept for footsteps echoin'
on not-long-gonna-be-dry summer grass.
Then all of a sudden it gets real quiet...
like after a big crowd's just stopped clappin',
and you don't hear nothin' but the wait.
Then every fearless yard member looks up real slow-like
and breathes in one final, sweaty breath,
and Mama's yard undresses itself.
Ya'll hear it?

O, Georgia!

A Lesson For The Teacher

by Paula Woolf

"I know two-digit multiplication *looks* tricky, but it really isn't hard once you see the pattern. Watch." I reached for his pencil to work an example. He jerked his bony hand away.

"Don't want no help!" He spat the words at me. An icy stare from his dark brown eyes dropped a wall between us.

"But you've missed two whole weeks of school. We began this while you were out." Softening my voice, I added, "By the way, I should introduce myself. I'm Mrs. Woolf and I'll be your math teacher from now on." I extended my hand.

He didn't take it. Instead, he leaned back in his chair and crossed his arms. His eyes remained fixed on my every move.

I tried to mask my disappointment. "Well then, if you decide you need some help, just raise your hand." I forced a smile.

His glance fell to the blank paper on his desk and he shrugged his shoulders. As I walked away, I heard the crunch of paper being wadded up and a single, dull thud as the ball hit the tile floor.

That was my first encounter with Percy, destined to become the most memorable of my fifth grade math students in the inner-city school. The school year was already into its fourth week when I joined the faculty as a replacement for a black teacher in fifth grade math. A recent court order had mandated the black/white faculty ratio in public schools throughout the state.

As I stood in front of my all-black class of squirming fifth graders that first day I experienced something I had never experienced before. I was the minority here. I, who had never even been in class with a black student until college, now stood facing a sea of black faces, not a single one smiling at me. To the students I was a white teacher who had taken the place of a black teacher—their black teacher whom they had admired and respected...and with whom they shared a common bond. These children didn't understand discrimination laws or employment ratios. I wasn't sure I did either. Reassigning a competent, well-liked teacher solely on the basis of skin color didn't seem right.

141

Missing my first two weeks there, was one of my third period students, a boy named Percy. Frequent absences at this school were common, but seldom were students out for two straight weeks. Finally I overheard some of the students talking about Percy being in the hospital.

Surprised at this news, I consulted a co-worker, Miss Arrington, who taught one of the fifth grade language arts classes. She had many of my students, including Percy.

"So you haven't had the pleasure of meeting Percy?" She grinned as she leaned back in her chair and tapped a pencil on the desk. "Believe me, you'll know when Percy is around—he's a handful! Actually, that's an understatement."

"Really?" I bit my bottom lip. "I thought I was making a little progress, but it sounds like my biggest challenge lies ahead."

"Every day is a challenge around here. This isn't like teaching in the suburbs." Miss Arrington turned to look at the clock on the wall. "It's about that time. Oh…what was it you wanted to know? Oh yeah…Percy. I did hear something about him. He's been pretty sick. In fact, they tested him for spinal meningitis, but the tests came back negative. He'll probably return to school next week…and in rare form if I know him."

Each day as I wrote his name on the absentee slip, I wondered just how much of a "handful" my missing student would be. I wondered what he looked like. I'd never known a "Percy" before.

Finally the day came when I looked up and saw a body filling the once empty desk. Not at all the overgrown, intimidating figure I had imagined, he was a painfully skinny, frail-looking child with closely cropped hair. A perpetual motion machine, he jerked and twisted his body into more positions in his seat than I thought possible.

Even though Percy rejected my initial attempt to help him with his math, I remained as positive as I could. That often meant deliberately overlooking behaviors designed to frustrate me. I refused as much as possible to give him the negative attention that he sought.

Yet, there was something about this kid that made me lie

awake at night. He was bright—I was sure of that even though he had done nothing in class so far to prove it. If only there was a way to reach him...

Gradually I made progress with the students. Some actually greeted me with a smile when they entered the classroom; others seemed at least a little less resentful. Armed with a couple of classes in behavior modification, I instituted a point system whereby the students could earn special privileges for desirable behaviors. To my great relief, they were receptive to the idea and the system worked remarkably well—with everyone except Percy.

As the weeks passed, his behavior worsened. Despite his diminutive size and sickly appearance, he was a ringleader in the classroom. Miffed that my reward system was working, he made it his goal to distract the class whenever he could by jumping from his seat, dropping his book on the floor, or making loud, inappropriate noises right in the middle of my lessons. Academically, he put forth little effort, never bringing his homework to class and seldom starting, let alone finishing, the day's assignment.

Finally I resorted to calling his mother. As frustrated as I was with Percy's behavior, she gave the school her full support to use whatever measures we felt necessary to deal with him, including corporal punishment. Furthermore, she informed me that Percy had an aunt working in the school cafeteria. She suggested that I give the aunt a daily report on his behavior.

These measures and their accompanying threats forced a slight modification in Percy's actions, but not his attitude. He was a little less disruptive and he *occasionally* completed an assignment now, but the hatred directed toward me only intensified. I could feel it every time he looked my way.

On the Friday before Christmas vacation, I was excited. I had stayed up half the night filling sacks of candy and preparing holiday games. Parties weren't officially sanctioned at the intermediate school, but I couldn't imagine not doing something special for the kids. After all, it was Christmas.

When third period came, Percy walked into the classroom more subdued than usual. Always one to make his presence known, on this day I wouldn't have known he was there had I not glanced up just as he came through the door.

I eagerly distributed the bags of candy and began playing games. As the class period neared an end, I walked around the room to check that at least some of the candy wrappers had made it to the trash can. When I came to Percy's desk, I saw that his candy was untouched. He was sitting quietly, his head resting on one hand.

"What? You didn't eat your candy? Are you sick or something?" I asked the question in jest, but then I noticed he really didn't look well.

"Don't want no candy," he replied in a quiet voice. He was careful not to let his eyes meet mine.

"I'm sorry, Percy. You really don't feel well, do you?"

There was no reply. I started to place my hand on his forehead, but he jerked his head back.

"Maybe you should go see the nurse. I'll—

The bell rang. Percy stood up and began walking toward the door.

"Wait! You really should go see the nurse."

Percy never looked back.

I was scarcely aware of the other students as they filed out of the room, some even wishing me a "Merry Christmas" as they passed by. Absorbed in the fun of the games, I had not even noticed Percy—and for once he had not commanded my attention.

Later that afternoon the students filed into the auditorium for a school-wide, holiday program. I knew where Percy's language arts class was sitting, but as the rows filled, I saw he wasn't there. Percy had a history of health problems and there was a nasty flu virus going around. Why had I not insisted that he go to the nurse?

As we were shuffling our classes back down the hall after the assembly, I saw Miss Arrington. "Where was Percy? I didn't see him in the assembly," I called over the roar of the students' voices.

"Sent him to the nurse," she yelled back.

At home that night I could not stop thinking about the skinny black boy who worked so hard at making us both miserable. The one time he might have accepted my concern I had completely ignored him.

I glanced over at my tote bag where I had left it on the sofa. I had a student list in my grade book. One quick call and maybe I wouldn't feel so guilty.

I dialed his number and a young voice answered.

"Hello," I replied. "Is Percy there?"

"No. He be at da hospital." With no further explanation, the child, most likely one of Percy's four brothers, hung up.

Now I was really worried. At the *hospital*? And I had not even noticed that he was sick until class was over?

Saturday morning I phoned Percy's apartment again.

"Hello," a sleepy voice answered.

"Hello. May I please speak to your mother?"

"She be asleep." The voice sounded strangely familiar.

"Percy, is that you?"

"Who dis?" he asked suspiciously.

"Percy, it's me, Mrs. Woolf. How are you? I called last night and whoever answered said you were at the hospital and—"

"You calling my mama? What you want my mama for?" Percy's agitated voice interrupted my string of questions.

"Yes—er, I mean no. Well, I did ask for your mother, but I am really calling to check on you. I was sorry to hear you were sick. Are you—"

"I got da flu. You wanna talk to my mama. The words were an accusation, not a question.

Again, I tried to explain. " No, silly, I don't need to talk to your mama. You're not in trouble. I just wanted to see if you were okay. You didn't look so good in class, and then you weren't in the assembly. I was worried about you, Percy."

"I got me some medicine. I be okay. Are you sho' you not callin' my mama?" His voice sounded more perplexed than angry.

I laughed. I couldn't help myself. "I'm sure. I'm sure. Look, I'm really relieved to know you're okay. You drive me crazy sometimes, but I do care about you. I just wanted to check up on you." I sighed into the phone. "Well, have a Merry Christmas and I'll see you after the holidays."

A click on the other end broke the connection. I smiled, imagining the expression on his face as he hung up the phone. Was it so hard for him to believe that my only reason for calling was to check up on him and make sure he was fine? Silly kid!

The holidays passed quickly as holidays always do. On our first day back, the children were apparently exhausted from two weeks of late hours and T.V. It was an unusually peaceful morning.

Third period came. Percy walked—not ran—into the class-room and quietly took his seat. He put his book on his desk and pulled out paper and pencil from his tattered notebook. No jerks or body contortions or strange noises...nothing. I watched as he sat patiently waiting for class to begin. Then he looked over and caught me looking at him. I smiled—and he smiled back. For the first time in three and one half months, Percy smiled at me.

I would never have believed it had I not seen it myself. A metamorphosis had taken place. The Percy in my class now was not the same child I had constantly battled. This Percy was a model student. He listened to every word I said and he did all his work— almost perfectly. Instead of F's, he made A's and B's. (I *knew* he was bright!) There were no more distractions or weird noises. Even more amazing, if any of the other kids started to get out of line, it was Percy who corrected them. If there were errands to be run or chores to be done, Percy immediately volunteered.

I was baffled by this sudden change in Percy's behavior and attitude. I wasn't doing anything differently in class.

As I sat having a cup of coffee with Miss Arrington one day after school, I described the change in Percy. I was certain she had noticed it, too.

"Wait," she said as she placed her cup on the table. "Are we talking about the same Percy? Mine hasn't changed one bit. No, maybe that's not right. Actually he has calmed down a little for me, but he still has his moments." She rolled her eyes. "And he sure knows how to pick them."

I smiled and thought a moment. "This is so bizarre. I've never seen anyone do such an about face before. And why isn't he acting the same for you?"

At that moment, Mrs. Franklin walked into the room. An older woman, she had been teaching at the school longer than any other teacher on the faculty.

"You two look like you're having a discussion. Sorry, I didn't mean to interrupt, I'll—"

"No, please, sit down," I said. "Actually, maybe you can help us. Do you know Percy?"

Mrs. Franklin smiled. "Doesn't everyone know Percy?"

I went on to explain about the change in Percy's behavior—at least the change that I had seen. "I just wish I knew what clicked with him. Heaven knows, I'd like to try it with some students in my other classes."

Mrs. Franklin thought a moment and then she got a funny smile on her face—the kind you get when you've searched all over the house for your glasses only to find them perched on top of your head.

"Wait a minute. Percy's aunt mentioned something to me about your calling his house to check on him when he was sick."

"Yeah. He couldn't believe I was calling for a reason other than to get him into trouble."

"You don't get it, do you?"

"Get what?"

"What that meant to Percy."

"All I did was make a simple phone call."

Mrs. Franklin shook her head. "It was more than that. I grew up in a neighborhood like this one. Percy lives in a world where crime and violence are rampant, where the words "father—unknown" appear more frequently on the school registration cards than a man's name, where everything he owns has to be shared with a houseful of siblings. Through his own prejudice, he sees you as a member of the white society, a society far removed from his way of life. Whatever you said or did in the classroom was your job. You get paid to be nice or offer help. He expected that. When you picked up the phone and called to check on him, you showed concern for him as a person, not just one of your students. The call said you cared. Percy never expected that."

147

It seemed so simple...too simple. One phone call could change everything? Yet, the change in that young man continued. As luck would have it, I was assigned two sixth grade math classes the following year and Percy was once again in my class. The positive student/teacher relationship blossomed into a special friendship.

I left my teaching position in the spring to have my first baby, but every now and then over the years that followed I would get a phone call from Percy. "Just calling to check on you ," he'd say. "Just checking."

Wayward Spirit
by Thomas Lynn

The log house rested in a clearing hewn from the dense forest of the north woodlands. A stone fireplace and chinking of hard clay provided the only warmth on long cold wintry nights, when the wind whistled and snow painted a white portrait upon the land.

The seclusion satisfied Jonah's need for privacy and during all of his sixty years he was not dependent upon anyone for anything, neither friend nor companion. Although naturally shy and reticent, he never failed to extend a hospitable welcome to the infrequent travelers who chanced upon his cabin. On such occasions this modest and unassuming man would politely point them in the direction of Elkton, the nearest community. Or if the hour was late, reluctantly invite them for an overnight stay.

Unscheduled guests often remarked about the rustic comforts of the seemingly austere one-room cabin situated among the tall conifers and leafless deciduous trees. They also delighted in the tales recounted by their host while sharing the crackling intimacy of his hearth. A favorite story was his telling of "the letter."

Perhaps it was pride or a rare moment of nostalgia for fond childhood remembrances, but whenever his visitors became absorbed in the charm of their stay or silently meditative concerning the happenstance that found them far from their intended destination, Jonah took down the small leather packet from the mantel above the fireplace. He carefully removed the faded letter from within and his voice became at once solemn and tender as he interpreted the words which he had committed to memory.

He related how the letter was scripted by his mother as a very young lady. Her name was Saryna and she was hopelessly in love with handsome young Dominich. She had penned this letter with the intention of influencing him favorably toward marriage.

"Dominich was a most impressive catch," Jonah proudly explained. "He was the first-born son of a Magyar chieftain and therefore heir to a sizeable fortune. Unfortunately, he was also obliged to wed into the royal family. Poor Saryna was a commoner; worse, a gypsy soothsayer. Thus, there was little chance for marriage with her Dominich unless a magic spell was invoked."

At this point, Jonah would glance at each of his guests and whisper mysteriously. "According to the old legends, a maiden could win the man of her choice if she wrote him a letter on special paper made from pressed leaves of Calluna heather grown on Carpathian steppes, and written with a pen dipped in her own warm blood. Gypsies believed such a letter would persuade a man to believe his fondest dream would be attained by wedding the lady whose name appeared as signature."

Here, he would pause for the proper moment before continuing with the story. "It only remained," he said, "for the maiden to solicit her intended's vow never to speak aloud the words of the letter. For such was the social stigma of that time that proper ladies did not communicate with young gentlemen without formal invitation. It therefore seemed a normal and prudent request on the surface, but it was in reality an ancient magic invocation."

"But what would be the result," his guests often interjected, "if the intended bridegroom proved not to be a gentleman and dared to voice the words that were written in the letter?"

"Of course it seldom happened," was the hesitant reply. "But the ancient gypsy arts are not to be taken lightly and I am certain such a foolhardy man would have been dealt with quite appropriately." The guests were suitably amused, especially when they learned that Saryna and Dominich eventually did marry. The remainder of their visit was spent pleasurably in the company of this quaint old man.

It was a typical bitterly cold night that brought the stranger, Rufus Quigley, to seek shelter at the cabin. Like other travelers before him, he too chanced upon the forest clearing after losing his way amid the confusing panorama of trees and underbrush disguised under the colorless wintry camouflage. This man, however, was not an ordinary traveler. He was a fugitive, dangerous and in flight from certain execution if apprehended. His horse, stolen during the early stage of his escapade, had bolted leaving him afoot, stranded in the wilderness with only the clothes on his person.

Grateful for the extended invitation to share a bed and a modest meal, he listened as the tale of the gypsy letter was duly related by his host after supper. Unlike previous visitors, Quigley was not entertained by the reading and rather suspected something else of special value in the letter. He observed a radiant sparkle in his host's eyes and a reverence in the old man's voice when the letter was proudly displayed. Not for a moment did he accept all that gypsy nonsense but surmised instead that the letter probably contained other secrets. Didn't the old geezer make mention of a fortune? It followed then that there was possibly a lot of money hidden away somewhere, not necessarily within the cabin, but surely nearby.

Quigley observed how Jonah kept the letter in its leather pouch and refused to let his guest examine it for even a moment. Perhaps it was some kind of map showing the location where the old man had hidden whatever cash or valuables he possessed.

Rufus Quigley was determined to have it.

He listened to the serenade of the north wind and carefully observed Jonah select three small logs beside the fireplace which he placed at the front of the blackened grate. This served to bank the fire so it would burn slowly throughout the cold night and keep the chill away while the two of them slept. Jonah bade the stranger a good night, but instead of going directly to bed himself, he again took down the letter and read silently from it as he sat at the rough wooden table in the center of the room.

Quigley was now convinced of something worth possessing in that letter. The thought tormented him through the night until he could stand it no longer. Jonah's eyes closed in apparent sleep while he yet sat at the table holding the letter in his hands. Quigley slowly removed the rawhide belt from his trousers and held each end securely tight. He crawled slowly from the cot and inched his way across the floor until he stood behind the old man.

Too late, Jonah sensed his peril and started to rise to meet the threat but the younger man moved with a quickness born of desperation and practiced guile. He snaked the belt around his victim's throat and twisted at the nape of his neck. In spite of his age, Jonah was a strong man and he resisted with ferocious might but was unable to break the stranglehold. He began to lose consciousness and Quigley never eased the pressure until certain the old man was truly dead and not merely trying a subterfuge. Finally, he loosened the belt from around Jonah's neck and let the body slump forward onto the table.

"At last!" Quigley was triumphant. "Now the letter's mine."

He snatched it from Jonah's lifeless grasp and spread it out before him. For a long time he stared at it and in disbelief discovered that he was unable to read it because the words appeared in a foreign language. Angrily, he pounded the table with his fist and swept the letter into the air only to watch it hover momentarily before drifting to rest near the old man's outstretched hand. Quigley picked the letter up and when his temper subsided, examined it again, reciting each word aloud to see if they sounded familiar in English. It was no use. There was only one thing for him to do. He had to find someone to translate the letter for him. But where would he find such a person in this wilderness? Perhaps a college professor or at least a teacher of some sort.

The nearest school was in Elkton.

"That's it! I'll take the letter there in the morning." Further sleep was out of the question so he sat and awaited the first light of dawn . . . and Jonah waited with him. The passing of one man was of little consequence to the other. Shadows fluttered like swaying serpents from the lone candle at the table, casting grotesque patterns as the two men sat opposite each other.

Once more, Quigley read from the letter that was yellowed with age and brittle from much handling. Exasperated at his inability to decipher its message, he returned it to its thin leather pouch which he slid inside his own shirt pocket. Propped against the cabin wall was a photographic array of smiling faces staring in his direction. A woman, and a man standing with an arm around her, both looking directly at him. He tore his gaze away from them and glared at the dead man. Jonah remained motionless, his hands resting on the table and his own gray eyes accusingly peering at the man who unconcernedly had taken his life.

A perverted smile revealed jagged and decaying remnants of uneven teeth as Quigley hummed an irreverent bawdy ballad and gathered his few belongings. Jonah's sheepskin coat would insulate him from the cold wind and freezing snow. "Jonah, old pal," he addressed the dead man. "You won't be needing this where you're going." He laughed at his own joke and prepared to leave his late companion to the solitude of the cabin. Outside, the wind sang its own tune of death and the trees echoed a whispered eulogy.

Quigley opened the cabin door to see that a fresh blanket of snow had fallen during the night. He pulled the hood of his parka over his head and tied the great sheepskin coat about his waist to keep out the cold. The town of Elkton was ten miles to the northwest and he wasn't eager to spend another night in that cabin with a corpse. Without a backward glance or a second thought at the crime he had just committed, he stepped out into the budding storm.

The countryside was heavily wooded and a coverlet of white blanketed the surrounding forest to hide its minute details from view. Quigley remembered a small creek that wandered nearby in an indirect path toward the distant village of Elkton. It was about three hundred yards from the cabin and although its stream would now be frozen solid, the bed would yet guide him in the right direction. He was soon able to gain his bearings and gradually make his way to the rim of the clearing. From there he turned toward the creek and as he trudged along, his boot tracks filled with snow nearly as soon as he made new tracks. In a few moments, there was no sign of his passing.

The mounds of driven snow proved treacherous. More than once he was brought to his knees by a submerged rock or deceptive tree root. He was scarcely able to raise his eyes through the howling wind to confirm his course and for the most part was forced to walk with head bowed to avoid the pelting snow. Furious gusts transformed the gentle flakes into shards of ice that penetrated his protective face mask.

Quigley was a determined man but as the hours passed without sighting his temporary objective, the creek bed, he worried that he may have become confused in the heightened storm. He had no choice, however, except to continue moving onward, convinced that he would locate the creek before much longer. Afternoon surrendered to the inevitable dusk of evening and a feeling of gloom and depression settled over him while he labored blindly through the deathly pallid universe in which he had thrust himself. The only sound heard above the throbbing of his heart was the wailing cry of the wintry wind moving ominously through the topmost reaches of the denuded oaks to embrace the heavily laden arms of ponderosas. He dared not pause to rest lest his landmark elude him unnoticed in that vast sea of white.

Despite the clutching snow that retarded every footstep, he eventually recognized a steep declination of the terrain and knew that at last he was approaching the creek. He was elated and crossed the remaining distance with renewed vigor.

The small channel, its outline nearly indistinguishable from the steady overnight downfall of snow, rambled generally in a northerly direction. It was impossible to see beyond a few feet and the storm gave no hint of lessening. Quigley was barely able to recognize the changing contours of the ice-sculptured creek through the cheerless mist. Nevertheless, he plodded on with stubborn determination until his balance betrayed him and he sprawled incongruously in the snow, helpless to move. The wind meanwhile continued to yowl with the mournful cry of an abandoned banshee.

Rufus Quigley was a brawny man, strong and back-alley tough, but now for the first time in his life, his body labored wearily in a hopeless cause. His legs were exhausted from their futile efforts at slogging through deep drifts of clutching snow.

Daylight eventually dimmed and the soft white woodland robe cast spectral silhouettes upon ridges and valleys. The topmost branches of spruce and poplar whispered secretly among themselves about this lone intruder who now lay motionless and quiescent on his unsullied pallet, and the snow, as if to keep from waking him, finally ceased its downward flight. He knew he should rise to his feet but he was comfortable where he was and Elkton was so far away.

Perhaps someone was looking for him even now, but *No,* he

told himself, *nobody knows I spent last night at Jonah's cabin except Jonah, and he ain't talking!* He chuckled at the thought of the dead man complaining that he was slain and robbed while his killer simply walked away into the woods. *I will return some day, old man. Just as soon as this damned letter tells me where to find that fortune of yours.*

Quigley tried to reassure himself by patting his shirt pocket which held the letter but it was difficult to move his arm. Perhaps it was the frigid air that penetrated his clothing for he was painfully aware that his blood no longer circulated freely within his veins. He knew that he should not fall asleep. It was vital that he stand and shake off the lethargy now threatening his very life.

He had to keep moving!

With an effort born of the false courage of despair, he lurched to his feet and willed his frozen limbs to move forward one weary step at a time. He continued to push ahead with scant regard for the coming darkness or the pain accompanying each breath of arctic air. It was understandable that he failed to hear the shouted, "Hello!" Several moments elapsed before the voice called out once more."Ho there! Can you hear me?"

Quigley stopped and swayed unsteadily, first in one direction and then another as he sought to confirm what his disbelieving ears told him. He heard it again. Someone was calling to him. The shouts were louder and he peered intently in all directions until he glimpsed the dark outline of a figure waving his arms and making his way toward him.

"Over here," Quigley tried to yell but his voice was hoarse and muffled. "Here I am!" Now his own footsteps pressed forward and he realized that he'd made it! He had defeated both the blizzard and the old man, and Jonah's fortune would yet be his.

They were near enough to each other now that shouting was no longer necessary. "I saw you from my cabin window and thought you might be lost."

Quigley paused to catch his breath. "Lost? No, I'm not lost," he replied, "but I am tired. I was on my way to Elkton and the storm caught me."

155

"Guess you could use some rest and a nice hot fire to dry out. My place is over the next rise. You're welcome to stay for the night and start again when you're fresh in the morning."

He gladly accepted the invitation and together their boots crunched the snow underfoot until a cabin came into view. After removing their heavy clothing, the two men crouched before the blazing fireplace, smoking their cigarettes and letting the fire bathe them in a welcome intensity. Quigley felt the flow of blood once more warming his body, but he marked his rescuer as somewhat strange despite his welcome hospitality. A slight accent gave his speech a certain unfamiliar guttural sound and it was plain that the man was not from this part of the country.

Neither offered a name and each was seemingly content in silent appraisal of the other.

Quigley turned his gaze upon the furnishings decorating the cabin. He suspected his benefactor to be well educated, judging from the many books resting on the shelves lining one complete wall. Frilly lace curtains at the window and several hand-drawn pictures of a lady, obviously once dearly loved but now evidently departed, further told of a proud man who probably lived more for the past than the present. Was it possible that his new acquaintance would be able to interpret Jonah's letter? More importantly, could such a man be trusted to preserve the letter's secrecy, or would it be necessary to do away with him in order to retain the treasure for himself. The decision was easily reached. If this man could decipher the contents of the letter — he would simply have to die.

After a filling meal accompanied by several tumblers of wine, they began to relax in each other's company. Quigley hardly listened to the conversation of his companion for he was debating how to approach him. It was during a lull in their newborn camaraderie that he decided to take a chance. He therefore related his possession of the letter but omitted implicating himself in the sordid details of either robbery or murder, offering a suggestion instead that the letter was written in a gypsy language.

"As it happens," said the other man, "I do have some knowledge of the Finno-Ugric language of the Magyar people and would

156

be happy to translate the letter for you."

Quigley produced the thin leather pouch from which the letter was extracted and presented it for examination. The other man seemed pleased just to touch it but he made no move to unfold it.

"Well, how about it?" Quigley impatiently asked.

"Oh, I know about this letter." The voice was soft.

"What do you mean? How could you know about my letter?"

"I know it isn't your letter," was the surprising reply. "These words speak of an enduring love and were written by the beautiful Saryna to her young man." A peculiar tenderness was evident in his words. "Never was a love more eloquently expressed in its foretelling of a romantic treasure beyond imagination."

"But what does it say about the real treasure?"

"The real treasure was the lady's love. She married her young man and they came to this country when her new husband's royal family disinherited him. They were both quite happy and a son was soon born to them. His name was Jonas and you must have stolen the letter from him because you could not have obtained it otherwise. It was all he had of his mother and he would not have willingly parted with it."

"Jonas! You mean . . ."

"Yes," he was interrupted. "You knew him as Jonah."

"How do you know all this?" Quigley dared to ask but was frightened of the anticipated answer.

"I have seen this letter before, a long time ago. It was written to me. I am Dominich."

"Jonah's father? No! You can't be. Jonah's father is dead."

"That's very true, but you see . . . you and I . . . we are both dead!"

This was a startling statement and Quigley was completely astounded that the man who now stood before him, claiming to be Jonah's father, candidly pronounced each of them dead. Somehow this man was trying to deceive him.

"Look, uh, Dominich, or whatever your name really is, I'm willing to share the treasure with you but don't try any kind of scam with me because it won't work."

"I can see you are not yet convinced," Dominich said. "You are the victim of a gypsy curse and undoubtedly you must have spoken the words of the letter aloud, did you not?"

"I don't remember. Well, all right, what if I did?"

"The letter specifically warns against that, but of course since you are unfamiliar with the language, you would not have known the danger."

"What are you talking about?"

"I'm not certain what the curse intended," the other admitted. "Not being a gypsy myself, I can only imagine what Saryna prepared as a punishment for disregarding her warning and since you are indeed dead, killing you in some horrible gypsy fashion now seems quite unnecessary."

The calm discussion of his death was unnerving. "How can I believe what you say? Clearly I appear before you as proof that you're lying."

"Let me show you the evidence." Dominich led him back down the slope to the frozen creek bed. There, partially visible but preserved in a glacial tomb, was the unmistakable presence of Quigley's body half-buried in the snow. "It is certain," said Dominich, "that you are alive only in spirit and that you are destined to wander this woodland forever to atone for having killed the son of a gypsy sorcerer."

"No! It's not true!" shrieked Quigley. "It's the letter you want, isn't it? All right! Here, you can have it. Take it!" Frantically, he removed the letter from his coat pocket and tossed it away from him. "I don't want it!" But there was no denying the finality of his fate. He plainly saw himself lifeless in the snow and knew he would forever roam these woodlands without entity as foretold by the spirit of Dominich.

As perverse and vile as Quigley was in his pursuit of earthly pleasures, so was the sentence of his wayward spirit fulfilled eternally. And somewhere an ethereal contentment touched the aura of the gypsy enchantress, Saryna.

For such was the power of the Magyar.

158

Bone-Men

by Bonnie Brooks Fangmann

The prisoners come attended to the park
And move about without a sound,
on long, skinny legs,
white pants flapping
like loose skin.

They move across the grass,
delicately, as if on stilts,
a pantomime precise and serious.
And when they speak—
if they speak—
it is in tones as smooth and bare
as tree trunks stripped of bark.
Their words pass like puffs of smoke;
their footsteps leave no mark upon the
    ground.

Bone-legs, moving silently,
with disjointed grace,
cleaning up the debris
left without thought
for the bone-men,
on cold mornings
when the sky is white
and leaves are droppping like wet
    stones.

O, Georgia!

Would You?

by Katherine Ward

Would you, would you, do anything for me?
I mean anything I asked of you.
Would you show me that you love me?
Would you prove to me you're true?

Would you, would you, promise me;
Would you pledge to be my wife?
Would you promise to be mine forever?
Forever means for all your life.

Would you, would you, want to please me?
Would you show me how I'll know?
I need some proof that you love me.
Would you take an arrow to a bow?

Would you, would you, die for love?
You be Juliet; I'll be Shakespeare.
Would you always be faithful to me?
Would you give your life without a tear?

Will you, will you, test our love?
Will you take this gun and shoot me?
Then I'll pull the trigger once again.
As together, forever we'll be.

(In honor of teenage lovers' double suicides,
Carroll County, Georgia
January 1999)

O, Georgia!

Oh, To Write A Song For My Love
by Terry L. Hensel

The cup's heat brought little comfort to my bludgeoned "left-on-the-slab-to-turn-blue-with-neglect-as-life's-blood-drained-into-the-five-gallon-galvanized-bucket" soul. Its porcelain contours weighed a ton as I raised it to my lips to draw the last draught of warmth. My eyelids labored up as I searched for her behind the counter. Oh, wretched heart, lie still as I splay you upon this table and cleaver you into many pieces to feed the hounds. What value are you heart, since Tess no longer desires us? Where is your warmth to keep my soul alive?

She saw my empty cup and snatched up the pot on her way to my table. Her new-moon blonde hair was pulled back providing a clear view of her eyes, which sparkled with the vigor of her life and soul, but I knew she could communicate knife-sharp pity and rejection with those eyes. Bright red cheeks rode above jowls which undulated with her stride. They were pushed back by her open-house smile as she greeted a customer who had just entered. Her breasts, full and commanding, kept her uniform, and the rest of her body in proper formation. I was in love with her moon-pie naval, silhouetted on her brown frock by the dark water stain, which she got from washing the dishes between serving customers. How I longed to talk to it one more time while my head rested on the grand expanse of her waist. I worshiped her hips, royal elephants upon which the Queen rides, for their steadfastness and beauty. She, who once was my joy and comfort, had become my sorrow and misery.

"Tess," I pleaded.

"Now, Jack," she said, refilling the cup, "This is the way it has to be. Life is too short, with great passions to be enjoyed. I'd hoped you were the one, but you're not. Jack, you just don't have any heart. You know I need heart."

"Of course not, Tess. You've ripped my heart out."

"Now, Jack."

There was that pity again. I looked away in frustration. The wind blew a leaf across a puddle on the driveway outside the window. Soon another leaf joined the first. The wind had them skittering in one direction, coming together, pulling apart, and twirling in circles. They reminded me of that first night I met Tess.

The Blue Ridge Walkers played every Saturday night at the VFW, and I strummed bass. I had a bit of a dilemma, but a pleasant one. Jennie, blonde, blue-eyed, looking pretty in her sundress, and a lot like Ellie May Clampett, was flirting with me. Pat, dark eyes and hair, tanned from working her horses all day, slim legs in tight jeans, sat at a table not far from the band watching me steadily. A rueful smile plied my lips as I considered my decision.

Jennie came from Calhoun with her friends to listen to our group. Pat's aunt had come to town for a visit, so this Saturday night, she didn't have to sit with her Grandmother. Two women, one man. Musically, I knew that I couldn't play the bull fiddle and the chin fiddle at the same time, but, romantically, I had been pretty lucky playing two heart strings simultaneously.

Two women, one man. I didn't want to make a decision. I liked them both, but how was I going to persuade them to share me? Two more songs, the set is through, and then the break and the confrontation. I wasn't too successful solving my problem. I couldn't get my thoughts past, "Well, shoot!"

Shellie started Wynona Judd's, "No One Could Love Me Like You." Sam Walsch and his partner stepped onto the dance floor. Sam was my size, maybe a few pounds heavier than my one hundred fifty. The woman he led dwarfed him with her bulk, but the way she slid into his arms was like pulling chaps over jeans. They were coupled in an embrace of rhythm and intimacy that created its own gravity and the other dancers blundering around were lesser moons to the mother planet. We closed out the set with George Strait's light-hearted "Overnight Male," and Sam's date stepped out with an exuberance of life and dance that made "Overnight Male" a much better song. I couldn't take my eyes off her. The woman captured life and wore it with a passion I only dreamed of.

I don't remember too much of the rest of that night. My eyes never left Tess. My mumbled apology when I introduced Jennie and Pat at the break was lame, and I knew it, but I couldn't think and it didn't matter. I lost them both. Jennie pitched a fit; Pat shook her head and walked away.

Sam was at the hardware store, putting up stock the next day, when I asked him about Tess. They weren't serious, he said, but he did enjoy her company. She worked at the Waffle House on Highway 5 outside of McCaysville.

I pursued that woman. I took her out every night I could. My love for her was deeper than old man Riley's well, which took three weeks of solid drilling before they hit water. Her presence opened my life to joy like a lily pad unfurling to the spring sun. She encouraged me to develop my dream of writing songs. We spent many evenings sitting in the lawn chairs on the flagstone patio behind my trailer, strumming chords on my old guitar.

It was heaven on earth. During those days, the sun was never too hot and the moon was always bright with love and romance. But try as I might, I just couldn't write a good song. The closest I got was, "Hound Days." I liked that song.

"Lazy days are hound days,
Whether June or May.
Gone are the sad days
If you'd only stay."

When I couldn't reach in and stir my soul, Tess saw me as who I was. She knew I was riding life on her shirt tails. A dead weight to keep her from soaring.

The two leaves on the puddle bumped together one last time. The dried one ran aground on the asphalt, the green one twirled on the water. I looked down at my half-finished cup of coffee. I set down the cup, put two dollars on the table, and sighed. I looked at Tess for a long moment and sighed again. I stood up and walked out of the restaurant humming,

"Gone are the sad days
If you'd only stay."

165

O, Georgia!

It's Never Too Late
by Leona Peffly Martin

It was barely daylight when Ruby Whaley first awakened, but Barney was already up. She could smell coffee and hear the sizzle of bacon. He didn't need such a big breakfast now that he was no longer walking his mail route, but he was set in his ways. At least she had convinced him not to fix her breakfast. She preferred her orange juice, raisin toast and hot tea, but later. She pulled the covers over her shoulders and went back to sleep.

Ruby woke again to the high-pitched whine of the trimmer. Why did he need so many gadgets? Until he retired, she had done all the garden work, and all she'd wanted were hand tools.

She loved her garden. She loved setting new plants into the moist soil or growing them from seeds she had gotten in trade at the garden club. She enjoyed her colorful flowers and her green borders brimming with hosta, Solomon's seal, spurge and lungwort, but most of all she loved the process of creating this beauty.

It was barely nine o'clock when Ruby finally made her way into the yard, but obviously Barney had been busy for hours. He had finished the trimming, but what else had he done? The lawn was littered with the corpses of plants.

She surveyed the damage. Her hands tightened into fists and her teeth clenched. Then she screamed, "Barney, Barney Whaley, what have you done?"

Barney came around the corner of the house, a hoe in one hand. "Keep your shirt on, Ruby," he yelled. "What are you so worked up about?"

"My plants, my beautiful plants—-"

"I did some weeding," he said. "What's wrong with that?" He stood there looking at her, like a big kid.

She noticed he didn't have his hat on. How many times did she have to tell him? The top of his head would get sunburned. He'd end up with skin cancer. His shirt was already soaked with sweat, his belly bulged over his belt, and his wrinkled cut-off khakis failed to cover his knobby knees or his hairy legs.

"I didn't have that many weeds," she told him. She started

across the lawn, with him trailing after. "You've pulled up my marigolds," she said.

"Don't marigolds have yellow flowers?" he asked.

"If you give them a chance."

She gave a little cry and knelt in the grass. "Why did you pull up my ornamental cabbage?"

"Vegetables in a flower garden? That's crazy."

She didn't have the heart to go on, but stayed on her knees, looking about the yard. "You're the crazy one," she said. "You don't know beans about gardening. Why couldn't you leave it alone?"

He threw down his hoe. "What do you expect me to do? I can't just sit around. You don't want me to shop. You don't want me to help around the house. You talked me into retiring—-"

"It would've been crazy to refuse that offer," she said. "Six months extra pay—-"

"I liked my job. I liked walking my mail route like I'd been doing for thirty-five years."

"They wanted you to use the Jeep."

"I would've hated that. Anyway, that's water under the bridge. I can't go back. But I gotta have something to do—-"

She suddenly felt ashamed. They were only plants. "Maybe we could go on a trip."

"You know I hate being cooped up in a car."

"You could get a job—-"

"Doing what?"

"You could get a job at a grocery store."

"You want me to be a bag boy at my age?"

"Lots of old men do it."

"That's what you think of me? I'm an old man now?" He stomped off without looking back.

She sighed and stood up, watching until he went into the house. Then she turned back to her plants. There was no use trying to repair the damage. The plants were withering already—might as well add them to the compost.

She thought of Barney as she worked. She knew now it would've been better for him if he'd kept his job. Still, they would've forced him out before long. But what to do about him? Everything she suggested, he nixed.

The rest of the day they barely spoke to each other. He went for a long walk, then parked himself in front of the TV. She tried to keep busy with her usual activities, but she wondered what to do about Barney.

Finally, she said to him, "Barney, I'm sorry."

"What're you sorry for?" he growled.

Ruby sat down on the arm of his chair and ran her fingers through his sparse hair. "I'm sorry I got so mad at you. It wasn't that important."

"It was important to you," he mumbled, looking away from her. "I should've left your garden alone."

"It's your garden, too."

"Nah, it's always been your garden."

"Maybe you could start a vegetable garden," she said somewhat hesitantly, wondering where they could put it.

He shook his head. "I'd probably pull up the carrots and cultivate the weeds."

"You know I don't think of you as an old man."

He looked up at her with a crooked smile. "I guess that's what I am. At least, Social Security thinks so."

"We could still have some good times, Barney."

He sighed. "That's easy for you to say. You've always had so many interests. All I had was my job."

"You coached Little League and Pop Warner when the boys were young. And you used to fix things around the house and even go fishing sometimes—-"

He sighed again. "Nothing seems to matter anymore. Time just drags by."

"Remember when we were first married?" Ruby asked. "We went dancing on Saturday nights, and bicycled into the country to picnic—-"

"That's when we were young. It makes me tired just to think of it."

"We were going to see the country," she said. "Remember

169

that? We were going to buy a motorcycle and take off together——"

"Yeah, and then you got pregnant. First there was Rosie, then Joyce, and Larry and Paul."

She laughed. "Well, you had something to do with that. Do you regret it?"

"No, they're good kids. The grandkids, too."

"But do you regret we never took that trip?"

He looked up at her, and he was smiling now. "It would've been fun. Out on the open road, the two of us—we were just a couple of crazy kids."

"You were happier then," she said.

"I was younger then."

She got up from the chair and walked over to the window. She stood looking out at the garden for a few minutes before speaking. Then she turned to face him. "Why couldn't we do it now?" she asked.

"What are you talking about? Do what?"

"Buy a motorcycle. Go on that trip around the country."

He just stared at her, his mouth half open. Then he shook his head. "Woman, you're crazy."

"Am I? Do you think I want to spend the rest of my life with a grouchy old man?"

"Are you really serious?" he asked. She just looked at him. "Yes, you are, " he said. "You'd do that for me——"

"It could be fun," she said tentatively.

He grinned at her, then laughed out loud. "It would be great. Wouldn't the kids be pissed?" He laughed again.

She hadn't thought of the children. But look at him now. How long had it been since she'd seen him that animated?

The next morning he shook her awake. It was hardly light out. "What's wrong?" she asked.

"Were you really serious about the motorcycle trip? Would you really do it?"

She looked up at him. "You want to?"

"You don't know how much."

"Well, let's do it, then."

170

He lay down beside her and took her into his arms. She snuggled close to him, enjoying the warmth of his body.

"I love you, Ruby. You're a good old gal."

"Cause I'll go motorcycling with you?"

"That and the forty-five years we've spent together. And everything."

"Well, I like you, too," she said. "What time is it?"

"About five, I guess."

She groaned.

"We'll need to get a tent," he said.

"Barney, God invented motels so people wouldn't have to sleep in tents."

"You didn't seem to mind when the kids were little."

She pushed away from him and sat up in bed. "I did a lot of things for the kids. Isn't the motorcycle enough?"

"More than enough," he agreed.

"Well, then." She lay back down. "Let's talk about it later."

Later, he wanted to visit some motorcycle shops he had looked up in the Yellow Pages. She didn't want to go with him—what if some of her friends saw them?—but she couldn't tell him that. He was like a kid looking forward to Christmas. But when he was ready to go, she was doing something else, and he didn't seem to mind going without her. He was more subdued when he got back.

"There's so many different models," Barney explained. "I don't know the first thing about choosing a motorcycle. Maybe I'll talk to Jimmy about it. He's been looking at motorcycles for himself." Jimmy was their eighteen-year-old grandson.

Ruby felt alarmed. "Why is he doing that? Isn't he going to start to college in the fall?"

"As a matter of fact he wants the motorcycle to commute to college on," Barney said. "It'll be cheaper than driving a car. I think it's a good idea."

"I'll bet he hasn't mentioned it to his mother," Ruby said. "Rosie would have a fit."

"No doubt," Barney replied.

The next thing she knew Barney had put money down on a

motorcycle and the delivery date was set. All of this was moving too fast for Ruby. She had halfway expected Barney to confess he was only teasing her about the motorcycle, but now she knew that wouldn't happen.

Ruby was glad when Joyce and Peter invited them to help celebrate their son, Stevie's, tenth birthday at the lake cottage. The cottage belonged to Peter's mom and dad, Jane and Ernie Barker. All of Jane and Ernie's children and their families would be there, as well as Ruby and Barney's four children and their families.

Ruby and Barney didn't get away as early as they had expected that Saturday morning, and the rest of the clan was already gathered. As they got out of their car, several grandchildren ran up to hug them, and Jane and Ernie came out to bid them welcome.

The lake cottage had a long, wrap-around porch, and most of the adults were out there, the women in the rockers, while the men lounged against the rail or sat on the steps. Ernie carried more chairs out to the porch, while Jane brought out tall glasses filled with ice and a pitcher of tea.

"There's beer in the kitchen," Ernie said. "You'd rather have a beer, wouldn't you, Barney?"

"Sure," Barney said and they went in together.

Ruby leaned back in her chair, sipping her iced tea, filled with a feeling of contentment. She could hear the children down at the lake, splashing and screaming, and several others were playing in the tree house that Ernie had built for them.

Jane came over and sat down beside her. "Isn't it nice to see the cousins enjoying each other?" she said.

Ruby smiled. "I love these get-togethers, even though sometimes it's pure pandemonium."

Sally and Kitty caught Ruby's attention. Her two daughters-in-law were whispering together at the end of the porch.

"No, I don't believe it," Kitty exclaimed, and laughed hysterically.

Sally tried to hush her up, but it was no use.

172

"What are you girls carrying on about?" Ruby's eldest daughter, Rosie, asked.

"Nothing," Sally said, still trying to get Kitty to calm down. "It's nothing at all."

"Oh, come on, no secrets here. Let all of us in on the joke," Rosie insisted.

"Oh, I really shouldn't say anything," Sally said, and Kitty went into another gale of laughter.

"Come on," Joyce said. "You've got to tell us."

"Maybe you should ask your mother."

"Mom?" Joyce said.

"I'm sure I don't know what she's talking about," Ruby said.

"Oh, I knew it wasn't true," Kitty said. "I knew they wouldn't do that."

Ruby felt her cheeks grow hot.

"Wouldn't do what?" Rosie asked.

Kitty and Sally looked at each other. Kitty giggled nervously and Sally said, "Buy a motorcycle."

Ruby wished there was someplace to hide as Rosie said, "Well, of course not. What an idiotic idea." Then there was a sudden silence as everyone looked at Ruby.

From his perch on the porch railing Jimmy whispered, "I didn't tell, Grandma. Honest."

"Mother," Rosie said, "tell me this isn't true." Then she turned to her son. "And you knew about it? You knew, and you didn't tell me?"

"Ah, Mom," Jimmy said, "I promised Grandpa I wouldn't."

Barney stepped out onto the porch, surveying the group with a puzzled expression as everyone looked at him.

"I told you we should have told them," Ruby said.

"The cat's out of the bag, is it?" he asked with a rather pleased look.

Peter started laughing. "I'll tell you one thing," he said. "If Mom gets a motorcycle, I'm getting one, too."

All the men joined in the laughter, but Ruby was quiet as she saw her girls staring at her.

"I can't believe you'd let Dad do a thing like that," Rosie said. "What were you thinking of?"

"Well, actually," Ruby said, avoiding looking at the girls, "it was my idea."

"Mother," Joyce said, "have you lost your mind? This is the most harebrained scheme I've ever heard of. You haven't actually done it yet, have you? I absolutely forbid it."

"You forbid it?" Ruby's voice was quiet. "Just who do you think you are to forbid us anything?"

"Now Ruby," Barney said, "the girl's just upset. She didn't mean that."

"Oh, yes I did. You can't do such a thing. It's not right and it's such a bad example to the children——"

"Oh, be quiet," Rosie said. "Let me handle this."

"And how do you intend to handle it?" Barney asked.

"Dad, let's discuss this reasonably. It doesn't make any sense for you to buy a motorcycle at your age. What would you do with it?"

Ruby stood up. "We plan to go on a trip around the country," she said emphatically. "The motorcycle is being delivered on Monday. We plan to leave in June, right after Jimmy's graduation."

Ernie started clapping, and after a few seconds the other men joined in. "Good for you," Ernie said. "That sounds like one hell of a trip."

Jane came over and hugged Ruby. "Don't let them bamboozle you, honey. These kids think they own us."

Ruby suddenly felt proud as she saw Barney smiling at her.

"Mama, I can't believe it." Joyce's voice had gone up two octaves, but Rosie just stood there looking at them.

"What's going on?" Stevie yelled as he ran up from the yard. "I thought this was supposed to be my birthday party. Are we going to have cake and ice cream? When can I have my presents?"

"Hey, young man," his Grandfather Barker said, "come with me and we'll get the hot dogs and hamburgers on the grill. Lunch before dessert, you know. And the presents last of all." They went off together.

"We were going to tell you," Ruby said. "The time just never seemed right."

"Your mother was afraid you wouldn't approve," Barney said, "but you know we don't need your approval."

"Of course not," Paul said. Their youngest son came over and hugged them, then Larry did, too.

The rest of the group drifted off and left Barney and Ruby alone with their two daughters.

"We're just worried about you," Joyce said. "Don't you know how dangerous this will be?"

Barney took his pipe out of his shirt pocket and fished out a pouch of tobacco. Nobody said a word as he filled his pipe and tamped it down. Finally he spoke: "Give us credit for having some sense. We're not reckless kids. We'll stay on the back roads. We won't go too fast and I'll be careful. Do you think I'd do anything to hurt your mother?"

Rosie put her hand on his shoulder. "So many things could happen——-" she began.

Barney raised his hand and she stopped. "Nobody can control everything. Did you hear about that guy in the next county? He was in his own bed on a Sunday morning when a tree crashed through the roof and killed him instantly. Thirty seconds before, his wife had gone downstairs because the wind was banging a door. Who could figure something like that?"

"But you don't have to go looking for danger," Rosie said.

"We're not. Just a little novelty, something to remember. You can't stop us, so don't spoil it for us. O.K.?"

They got up early on a bright day in June. The sun was just coming up, but for once Ruby didn't mind. They had packed everything the night before. Her stomach felt a little queasy. She couldn't believe they were really going to do it. If only the girls weren't so upset with them.

After eating a light breakfast, they went into the garage. The sun shone into their eyes as the garage door lifted, so the voices

175

shouting "surprise!" caught them off-guard. Then they stepped into the driveway and saw their children, their grandchildren, and half the neighborhood gathered there.

Rosie stepped forward. "We wanted to give you a proper send-off," she said. She put her arms around both of them and hugged them hard; then the others crowded around with hugs and kisses, bon voyage cards and little gifts.

Ruby felt as though her cup was overflowing. Their daughters' disapproval had been the only thing to take the shine off their adventure. She could see that Barney was embarrassed by all the fuss and couldn't wait to get started. Ruby perched on the seat behind him, her arms around his waist. The motor coughed once, then roared. They were off. Hundreds of balloons lifted into the sky and grandchildren raced after them laughing and yelling.

The wind was in her face. The road was unreeling before them. "Isn't this great?" Barney said. "Isn't this fun?"

"Wheeee——" Ruby replied

Painful Memories
by Larry G. Rader

As I look back on times that stand out in my memory, February, 1968 has to be high on the list. Most Americans were at odds over the involvement in the Vietnam conflict. I had a little different opinion about the situation. This might be because my view was through the gun slot of a machine gun bunker in Vinh Long, Vietnam. From the view that I had, I could not see political differences, and I could not see young people demonstrating. As a matter of fact, I hadn't even seen the news on television in over a year. Opinion in Vietnam was based on another concept. In fact, the most basic concept here was surviving for another day. Survival meant kill before you are killed.

Why was this time any different from our daily routine? Actually, I was trained as an airplane mechanic. Although this was my primary mission, in this environment there were some additional duties. These included flying on combat missions. The primary mission of survival made it necessary to spend a lot of time defending our perimeter from frequent enemy attacks. We had become so accustomed to late night mortar and artillery attacks that it had become quite routine. Returning to bed or going back to work within minutes of these attacks was normal. Death itself was part of the routine. Instead of stopping to mourn the dead on a daily basis, we had a scheduled time once a week to have a memorial service for our lost comrades. At this time the names would be read at a common service. The morning of February 20 started out at two a.m. with an enemy mortar attack of unusual severity. The norm was for the enemy to fire for only a few minutes then disappear before being hit by our attack helicopters.

A very different day had definitely started. Instead of a hit and run attack, the shelling of our position lasted much longer. Hour after hour the shelling continued. The source of the enemy artillery and mortar fire came from every direction. There was no doubt that we were surrounded by a large force. At sun-up a reconnaissance airplane was able to assess the situation. The report was that we were surrounded by as many as 3,000 men and that reinforcements were increasing that number. The total of all men on our airfield was less than 500. The odds didn't sound good at all. Our armed helicopters were our primary defense, but by this time it was not possible to take off because of heavy enemy anti-aircraft fire. Little changed during the day as steady streams of bullets were exchanged and neither side moved.

When another day had passed, it became apparent that the situation was, in fact, changing. I looked out the back of the machine gun bunker and got quite a shock. In a nearby area where all the vehicles on the airfield were kept, all that I could see was fire. Looking down the flight line where all the aircraft were parked, I was not able to see any that were not on fire. The only buildings visible from my position were leveled to the ground. This was the beginning of some sad realizations. We were aware that all of our ammunition and food were running out. The only source of supplies was the Air Force cargo planes that were able to land on our short runway. These planes had not been able to land in several days because of the enemy anti-aircraft guns. Soon the only ammunition left was that in our individual rifle clips. At this time we began to fire only defensively. Our enemy quickly realized our situation.

Desperation was quickly setting in on our troops. We saw men who never showed signs of faith before begin to pray. The officer in charge of all the guard positions was sent to tell us which way we were to retreat when the enemy overran our position. We were shocked by the fact that he didn't say, "if"—he said "when." This was about the time that our enemy decided that it was time for their big move. An airfield is a large area to protect. That meant that our positions were spread out quite a bit. It was normal military logic that if forces were massed at any given point there wouldn't be enough people to defend that point. So it came as no big surprise that the enemy forces were massed into one group. This happened in plain sight of our position, but we were not able to do anything about it. Thousands of armed men stood in an open field shoulder to shoulder. As they poured across the field towards our lines, only light gunfire was heard; our men were out of ammunition. In the moment that we waited for our end to come, something completely unexpected happened. Suddenly a lone fighter plane appeared over the horizon. The pilot apparently saw our predicament and quickly acted. He dove straight toward the tightly grouped men and released a single large bomb. We watched in disbelief as human bodies flew into the air like particles of dust. It was close enough for us to see bodies flying hundreds of feet into the air. All who weren't killed made a hasty retreat. In one sense it could be said that the battle was over. In the minds of all present it would never be over. The picture of thousands of dead men lying on the ground ripped to shreds would be permanently etched into every mind. The contest was over, but no cheers of joy erupted. Men in a near state of shock silently tried to understand how man could be so vicious. They tried to understand how a person could kill another human who they not only did not hate, but didn't even know. To them the answer would never come.

O, Georgia!

The Sea King
by Linda S. Kirkland

The sea king, king of the world, shall take your aching heart that weeps
and gather you into his rolling arms of salt
to rock the pain and grief away, and soothe
with surge and sweep of love like waves
your hurt and ache, and give instead
all joy and light,
the sun upon the sea at dawn—
the brilliant light, so soft
that colors all the world to see
with green and rose:
(your silver steps race down the foam
to touch the sun)
and fill the hollows of pain and loss—
the sea king, whose strength is deep
is always so and shall remain,
and all the tears you weep
can only add to depth and breadth and height
and never be to us so clear
as when we finally weep the most, and all our sorrow
add to his, and follow the curl and surge of love
out to sea, out, farther out—
run deep,run far and then
rise like columned clouds at dawn
to tower over the waves of night
catch the first bright flare of light
and brim with gold and rosy sun
and know that all life comes to this:
the surge and flow and warmth of pain,
the surge, the flow, the warmth of bliss.

O, Georgia!

Lapidaries
by Margarita D. Moldovan

We are the
tombs
they leave behind

Youthful warriors consumed
by a
death
worse than
fate.

We shall carry their spirits
'graven within us

and our hope shall be
as buttercups;

weeds

the Gardener could not kill.

O, Georgia!

Times And Places
by Jeanne S. McPherson

The cat jumped lightly up on her lap and draped himself over her thigh, settling down to nap. Julie could feel his heart beating its comforting rhythm against her leg. The birds sang their morning song. She could see the cattle just at the horizon behind the house. The cattle must have heartbeats like the thunder she heard in the distance. She had settled in the chair in the backyard to enjoy the morning with her coffee. The cat had found her. The cattle didn't know she was there. She was immensely content.

The earth was washed with the frequent rains, everything green and clean. Soon she would go into the house and make sure it was presentable for Bill's visit. It was the first time he had visited since she left a year ago, seeking the peace of the country. The first time he would see her in this old house so familiar to him. She and Bill were close and then they weren't and then they were again. It would be wonderful to see him. They had a long shared history, indelible common experience. Not much to do, really. He mainly noticed clean kitchens and nothing else, as far as housekeeping went.

When she finally heard the doorbell, she was surprised at the strength of her feelings, which hit before they could be catalogued and filed away.

"Well, hello." he said in that familiar voice. The keen brown eyes, that half smile, the military bearing, that comfortable presence filtered by the screen door.

He had sat in his car looking at the place for several minutes before going to the door. Still just as neat as he had always seen it. The hedge just so, the yard close-clipped and raked, the house shining white in the sunlight. The out buildings had the patina that came with years in the south Georgia sun and rain. Knowing she was in that house somehow brought things full circle, boyhood, manhood, the long sortings out of life—so much of which had happened within a few miles of this shining white house where she now stood.

She held open the screen door and said, "Hello, yourself. Come on in. Have some tea." The wood was still dark, the hall still squeaked in the same spot, the kitchen, so simple and small, looked out on the pastures which stretched behind from his aunt's house just up the road. "Excuse me a minute." she said. "I've been petting the cat." She washed her hands in the kitchen sink and tried to look at him at the same time. "Have you eaten? I made bread yesterday."

"I'm fine, just fine." Some of the things in the kitchen, the feel of the kitchen were hers and not the things of his childhood visits. The Kitchenaid mixer, the Cuisinart were beyond his great aunt's time or interest. The little things she hung on the wall were hers. Her habit of keeping the dish detergent on the counter behind the sink was not the great aunt's habit. The old Garfield mug held her smaller cooking tools while a shelf over the sink held vaseline glass and luster ware from her family. A sweet potato sent its pointed leaves up the window frame from what had to be an imitation cut glass goblet. Aloe was pushing its babies out of a small plastic pot. Statis leaned against each other in a pottery pitcher. A stained glass iris hung just over the sink. There were pictures roughly based on chickens on one wall. There was a small cross stitch sign announcing, "A clean house is a sign of a wasted life."

"Too bad there isn't room for a dishwasher," he said as he scanned the old kitchen.

"The only time I miss a dishwasher is when I have lots of company, and that hardly ever happens here." She must have been singing again in the evening over the warm suds; Patsy Cline, a couple of Sarah Vaughan's that she could manage, show tunes, Gladys Knight and the Pips, whatever suited her mood. No, the dishwasher probably wasn't missed.

"I need to stretch." he said. "Let's drink our tea outside." He opened the door to the small stoop. Plants lined the edge of the stairs and clustered to the sunny side, the containers as varied as the plants in them. Hens and Chickens were outgrowing a mixing bowl. A spider plant hung over the top step from a small iron pot. Moss was spreading over the shady sides of the pots like water color, fading down the concrete.

186

As she preceded him over the grass to the fence, he couldn't help but notice that she had lost some of the weight of her days in the city. Her old familiar blue jeans only caressed the body they used to adhere to. Her step was quick, her banter lively. Obviously, she was enjoying whatever she had here. The breeze lifted her hair around her face as she gazed out to the cattle in the field before them. Must get it done in Atlanta, he thought. No one around here would know how. The color was lighter than he remembered. The old feeling of sanctuary came over him. He wanted to move toward her until they were the same person, seeing everything the same, feeling the same. It was a delicious sensation. He caught himself.

"Aunt June is teaching me to tend the cows. I just love them," she was saying.

"This land never changes," he said, leaning on the fence. "I wonder how old that live oak is? Older than Aunt Mary was. It will be here when we are dead and gone."

"Yes," she said. "Not much changes. Look at the clouds. Afternoon showers as usual. How long are you going to be around? Do you have to be somewhere?"

"I'm on my way home. There's no big rush. We've had our annual reunion at the beach. You remember, with my Marine buddies. I had to see how you were doing. I still can't believe you are living here." He felt strangely uneasy, almost annoyed.

"I mentioned living here to you several times. You always thought I was joking and said the idea was preposterous. Actually, I suggested both of us living here and you always said you could never earn a living here. I love it. Nothing happened in Atlanta as far as I'm concerned. I guess this just fits my boring personality."

They laughed comfortably at this in the way of people who shared stories. "I've always amused myself, you know. I'm writing and I'm beginning to sell some pieces to magazines. I dust off the camera once in a while. It's great," she looked at him with a smile.

The wind was picking up and the dark clouds cast shadows on the pasture before them. She felt the excitement she had felt from childhood at the approach of a storm. Having him there only added to the feeling.

She could tell he hardly remembered the conversations about the house. She had been fighting a persistent discontent, needing some forthcoming change to pull her along. She had thrown out her idea as both an interesting idea and a test of the waters. He had thrown it off. She had not. The long, curving sandy road leading to nothing but the homes of the quiet people who were part of his family was in her mind like a siren song. Beautiful, alluring, peaceful. There was no trash or beer cans on this perfect road. The fence ran through the green fields, undulating into the distant cloudless sky. The air was soft and without incident. Surely, this place was isolated from happenings in other, more hurried places.

The two of them left the trappings of Christmas behind one year on a pilgrimage to his boyhood home. He showed her the house where he had lived, where he pruned the camellias and mowed the grass. The little brick building where his grandmother had run a general store was now a beauty shop, but it still stood. The railroad no longer came through town, the tracks had been taken up.

Then, they had gone out a two-lane road and turned where there was no road to find the shining track that led to so much. He had stopped at the second house and knocked at the door, standing at the far edge of the flagstone porch, waiting. The woman who opened the door looked familiar...soft features, soft body. Bill had said, "Hey, remember me?"

The woman stood still for a moment, then said, "Well, Bill. Of course, I recognize you. There you stand looking just like yourself. Come on in." Aunt Jane's voice was as soft and pleasant as the rest of her. Julie had gotten out of the car and been accepted into the house with Bill. It was a wonderful house full of family treasures, a wonderful, unpredictable house. They sat and spoke of family for a long while. Julie was comfortable there with this stranger. She wanted to go around the house and look closely at everything, but that wouldn't be polite, so she sat and listened to family stories. Aunt Mary had been summoned from her house down the road, so she had met her just before she turned 100, a sharp

188

mind in an old body. Another of the treasures of the house.

"When are you going to put some chickens out here?" Bill was saying. "There is plenty of room."

"Aunt Jane says they would just be food for the foxes, and I've learned to listen to her."

The grass rippled in the direction of a huge clump of orange daylilies bobbing and waving in the sunlight that broke through the clouds. A hydrangea covered the far corner of the house with blue and green. A fig tree obscured the other corner and blocked the view of the road. Pine trees, sweet gums and dogwoods claimed the land beyond that. A garden had been dug, where the cabbages and lettuce were going to stalk, and tomatoes and squash plants promised summer vegetables. At the end of the fence and at each fence post, she had planted clumps of gladioli. She always planted things where a hole was easy rather than where they looked best. He had to admit that they looked good against the fence, nevertheless.

"The cat got a baby rabbit the other day. There must be a bunch of them in the thicket. He ate the whole thing, I'll say in his defense. He hasn't lost the knack that kept him alive when he was a stray."

Big drops of rain began to plop on the leaves and the two of them made it to the back door while the rain's edge advanced across the grass of the pasture toward the house. He put his hands on her shoulder, and hurried her into the kitchen. "You're going to get wet," he said as if that would somehow break his heart in some small way.

"Are your windows up?"

"Yeah, I was running the air conditioner all the way." He filled his glass with tea and sat at the small kitchen table. They spoke of old friends, projects he was working on, stories and articles she hoped to sell. It was wonderful having him across the table, rambling on about everything. "You sure are keeping this place up."

"I live here alone and I'm not a messy person. Also, when life is quiet, cleaning things gives me something to do. Helps me

189

think. Willie is still around and he can do the front yard with his eyes shut by now."

"Willie? He must be eighty by now." He would love to talk to him. That ageless black face under the hat he had worn since he became a man. Not everything had changed.

"Must be. He still mows for Aunt Jane and me, though." Julie looked toward the window where rain now ran in sheets down the pane. She got up and checked the back door.

"Show me what you've done to the house." Bill said, moving toward the small living room. "Your furniture looks like it was made for this house."

"It's the same era, just a different family and place." Shelves and pictures were asymmetrically arranged and still looked right. Family treasures kept company with garage sale finds. The piano took an inside wall, as usual, a safeguard against drafts and humidity, as she had explained to him long ago, while a cast iron boy perpetually tuned his violin on the back of it. Yes, it was hard to sort out whether he felt more of his old childhood memories or his memories of times with Julie. The living room was familiar in the same double-edged way. Time was telescoped, a double exposure.

The bedroom was the same, exactly the same. He said he felt he could look out on the street in Atlanta, the dogwoods, the lawn, the streetlight would all be there.

There was a small window in time when she could have moved away and kept a distance between them but she would not. This was Bill. He said, "Can we lie down a little while? O.K.?" Contained in his arms, she was no longer expanding into the atmosphere like a balloon out-distancing gravity, she had boundaries and form. In his long absences, she couldn't conjure even a fantasy of what it was like to be with him.

She was so solitary without him, getting along, but with him she was another creature, reaching out, wanting, drawn to him with his every breath, spent, finally, drained of some unknown need, some ghost, some unnamed wound closed. She lay there breathing his breath, easing back into her body, apart, but not separate, not yet. A move from her brought a tightening of his arm. Soon he began to snore deep in his throat. She lay there while he slept, feeling his body his heartbeat, conformed to him. She wished she could store this, all of this, for the long times in between. Soon they would arise and move around each other in their own private spaces again.

He left some time later, giving her a warm embrace on the old porch, with the rain dripping on the roof, the air saturated with moisture. She watched his car disappear down the track and closed the door, the house quiet again.

That evening, she lay on her bed, secure in all her pillows. So familiar and comfortable. From it she could see things from her childhood, the secretary with the paperweights, the old clock with its hypnotizing tick, the table with her old doll having a tea party with the silver tea set. Some of the smells of her youth came with the old furniture and old memories came back unbidden. The bed never seemed too large, but it was roomy enough. Would she want to share it all the time, even with the most companionable man? Her books and papers usually took up a third of the bed, but when she wanted one of them, it was less than an arm's length away. Sometimes she was awakened by sliding papers sloughing to the floor, but it was a familiar sound and never startling.

Great Aunt Mary had lived to be over a hundred years old in this house. Many seasons, many nights lay ahead with only her breathing to keep her company, waking and sleeping, if she did the same.

Bill drove back down the sandy road and it gradually ran into hard top which led to four lane highways. Soon, he was sliding in and out of traffic on the interstate in his air-conditioned Mercedes, the rain increasing the buffer from the heat and glare of the road. He turned off, finally, at his exit and drove the familiar way to his house, through the lush green curves of his neighborhood, up the hills to his driveway lined with azaleas, rhododendrons, dogwoods and hardwoods into the cool cave exposed by his garage door opener.

He walked up the stairs, through the shining kitchen, through the dining room with its glass table and copper accents, up the stairs through the browns and blacks of the main floor, past the brass railing to his office on the top level. His desk was still piled high with work in various stages. The telephone by his grandmother's old platform rocker blinked with messages. He opened the sliding glass door and went onto the roof. A red-tailed hawk circled below in the updrafts from the river and the lush green hillsides below him. He watched the hawk circle silently on the currents, push and glide. Beautiful. He went back to the phone and dialed her number. She answered with that familiar languid voice. They wished each other sweet dreams. In the air between Eulalia and Atlanta, they hung and circled like the hawk above the river.

Acquittal
by Anne Webster

I wear my guilt like a wool dress on a warm spring day,
never forgetting the wrongs I inflicted on you, my son.
From the moment in the delivery room when I sat on your head,
pushing out of my body, receiving the saddle block,
you have suffered to have such a mother.
Still a child myself at your birth, you,
a new toy, were at my mercy.

These are my confessions:
I smiled the day you were born,
hiding the evil thought:
I don't want to be *anybody's* mother.
I still cringe, at how I slapped your wiggling bottom
during diaper changes,
spanked to break you of comforting bedtime rituals
when your daddy went away to fly jets,
shrieked at you, like a kitten tugging on my leg.
Leave me alone!
I wanted adult games; you demanded I watch you turn a flip,
ride your trike, do magic tricks.
Always jolly, you forgave with kisses,
told me you wanted to live with me forever.
Your childish voice still rings in my ears
as it once pealed across grocery store aisles:
Mommy, I love you!

O, Georgia!

But wait, I have worse sins.
I swatted your legs with a wooden spoon when you bullied your sister,
forgot your chores.
I told myself not to worry,
you would have plenty to tell your therapist at thirty-five.
Now, nearly that age, a businessman,
you call me at noon, your voice shaking.
There's just *one thing* I can't forgive, you say.
As if in a car rolling over a precipice, time slows.
A deep breath, almost nausea.
Tell me.
The time Hank Aaron hit his record-breaking home run,
and you wouldn't take me, here, in Atlanta, to see it.
"Oh, that's it?" I say, and hang up, smiling.

No Man Is

by Sean Taylor

Dinner at eight. Sex at nine-thirty — ten at the latest. Depends on the service at Roberto's tonight. If we get that lousy mid-western kid again, it could be as late as eleven before we're out of there. Really, Roberto ought to fire that kid.

Should it be the skimpy red velvet one tonight? Maybe the navy blue leather one — Warren says I look really sexy in the blue one. What would he know? He'd say I look sexy in any of them. Just play along, that's what he thinks, just play along and feed her a few compliments and he'll get what he wants. All stars are like that . . . small minds, I get so sick of them.

Another interruption. Just great. I really ought to talk to someone at that answering service. Too many of these things slip through.

"Hey darling. I've got some bad news."

"Really. What? Having trouble matching your bow tie to your socks again?"

"Worse."

"Your polo pony caught something from an undesirable filly and won't stop scratching?"

"Hilarious. You're a regular riot. Now would you please shut up and listen?"

"Yeah, sure."

"Look, Dad's entertaining some Arabs tonight, and one of them has a daughter ready to hit the big three-oh. It's a favor for Dad. Really. She's a tramp, true dog meat. Got nothing on you, sweetheart."

What, no screaming fans at every corner? No number one re-mixes? Dry up and die, Warren.

"Yeah, whatever. Maybe tomorrow night."

"OK . . . Hey, thanks for understanding. Blood's thicker than water, you know."

I hang up, listening to the bath water lap against the sides of the tub while Boots swats at the bubbles. I imagine the same bubbles swimming in my nose, throat, lungs. Boots licking my hand,

giving up, and slinking off to the bowl by the refrigerator. Rest . . .
"Here Boots. Let Mommy in. Cats aren't supposed to like
water."
  Nice night for a walk. Maybe afterwards.

  Tramps, all of them. Whatever happened to real heroes?
When I was kid, we had the Shadow, Lone Ranger, even Batman
and Robin. Now it's these sex-crazed musicians. Self- proclaimed
Messiahs for a new generation.
  At seven-thirty, I'll call it a night. Been on the corner all
day anyway. I'll be back tomorrow morning, shouting and scream-
ing. "Repent! Repent!" It used to be so clear, easy to tell them.
Now they can't hear me for all the noise those headphones are pump-
ing into their ears.
  Just like Ellis, every one of them. Not one of them goes by
that I don't see a little bit of Ellis in their eyes, hear a little bit of
Ellis out of their mouths. Ellis cursed his father, too. Even cursed
me on the note he left.
  One more show tonight. Gangster rap crowd. They think
they're cool. I can tell by the walk.
  About four of them. The biggest one's got a knife. He doesn't
know I know, but he's got it anyway. Right up against his wallet.
Probably a butterfly. That's where Ellis kept his.
  "Yo! What's up, old man? Why ain't ya preaching no more?
You all out of things to say? Or did you change your mind all of a
sudden?"
  "Yeah. I got something real smooth jammin' right now. Real
smooth . . . 'Ooh baby . . . give me what you got . . . ' Wanna hear
it?" The short one offers me his headphones.
  "Repent!" I say. "Repent! Quit following the gods of that
trash you're listening to. 'Thou shalt have no other gods before me.'
That's what the Bible says."
  "Ain't got no time for the Bible. It don't rhyme."
  "Can't dance to it either."
  "Listen," I say, "You'll dance soon enough. Dance right on

into Hell. Dance forever. No stopping, then. All these zealots of immorality will be dancing with you then. But you can outsmart them. Repent! Repent!"

They don't like what I say. The one with the knife pushes me down. I think each one of them gets a chance to kick me as they go by. That'll hurt in the morning. But bruises heal.

They yell something at me as they run off. I can't hear it clear enough to make it out. The sounds don't separate themselves in my head when the darkness comes in . . . they just mix together. Maybe I'll go in at eight or nine — whenever I wake up.

Some listen. Some don't. All I can do is all I can do.

I'd turn on the radio, but I get so tired of hearing my songs over and over again. I used to think it was so cool to hear the radio playing something I wrote, something I sang, because I knew then that they thought I was good enough. Now it doesn't matter, and I know it. They'll play any old crap I give them. All it needs is my name on the CD.

Let's see—jeans, raggy t-shirt, Papa's fishing hat, a ski-mask if I had one, and these old Nikes (the old-fashioned ones I bought before the air pumps). Maybe this windy city will be blowing so hard nobody'll notice me. Sometimes a girl needs to be alone. Without the whole crazy world chasing her down like she was wearing a sign that said "A MILLION BUCKS - - JUST CATCH ME TO WIN!"

Wonder if I'll see Warren and that Arabian princess tramp. His Dad does enjoy showing off the city whenever company is in town. Driving down the strip in his stretch limo. Guess he doesn't quite realize that those things are a dime a dozen nowadays. Oh well, Warren wouldn't recognize me if I weren't wearing something kinky anyway. It's a perverted kind of tunnel vision he's got.

Better call George downstairs. See if he can't let me leave by the loading area again. The winos make great company. Don't ask a lot of questions.

"George."

197

"That you, Miss Diva?"

"Can you sneak me out back again tonight? Last time, I promise."

"For a kiss."

"Don't tempt me, George. Your heart rate alone would kill you. And I wouldn't want that on my conscience. Besides, I might not find anybody else who'd let me use the back door."

"It was worth a try, anyhow. Sure, come on down. You gonna use the service elevator?"

Dear sweet George. I bet he hasn't seen a single one of my videos. He probably wouldn't be so sweet then. Come after me like I was the anti-Christ, jump on that "she's ruining our kids" bandwagon. Thank God Salem was a hundred years ago.

"Yeah. Bought my new album yet?" I hope he's blushing.

"Naw. Not on a security guard's salary. It'd be a little too new for me, anyhow. No Benny Goodman on it. I'll meet you downstairs in a few minutes."

"Thanks, George."

Well, Boots. You up for a little walk down the strip? No? Well, keep an eye on the apartment for Mommy. Wouldn't want to lose anything. On second thought, let someone take it all. It would be a welcome change.

The lights spin like showgirls, rapt in their performance. I try to focus, but the showgirls keep dancing, teasing, taunting, twirling around, all glamor and frills.

Something dark that reeks of a night's sweat comes between me and the lights.

"Hey, mon. You okay?"

He's a big black man, close to six-and-a-half feet, no joke. And he's got those long dreadlocks growing like ropes from his scalp. Very unnatural.

"I say, hey mon, are you okay?"

I gurgle something out to him, noise mostly, that he at least pretends to understand. He reaches out to help me up, out of the alley.

"Thank you," I say.

"Don't mention it. You need a ride somewhere?"

"No thanks. I live here." As I say it I realize he probably assumes I'm talking about the alley . . . that I'm a boozing, vagrant wino.

"Okay, mon. Take care!"

He's gone before I can correct him.

My watch beeps faintly, one of those cheap twelve dollar, made-in-Taiwan kind of beeps, alerting me that it's ten till eight. I always set it ten minutes fast.

The loading bay doors of The Regal open. Probably some college kid carrying out the trash . . . No, it's a rent-a-cop checking the alley. No drugs here, I start to yell to him, just a beat-up old preacher, trying to save a few souls.

After he comes out, he holds the door for this kid who was behind him. Rough looking kid. Faded blue jeans, full of holes, baggy flannel button-up covering an old undershirt, and an ancient fishing hat. Fashion is something I'll never grasp.

The kid kisses the rent-a-cop on the cheek, makes him cross his heart on a whispered promise, and then jumps from the loading dock to the alley. I'm going to assume the best, that the kid is just leaving work from one of the shops downstairs at The Regal, and takes a shortcut home through the alley. Only walks a few feet after the door closes behind the rent-a-cop. Leans against a wall, pulls a pack of cigarettes from the pocket on the front of the flannel shirt, lights a match on the bricks of the wall, and sucks a cigarette like it was a straw. Blows smoke rings, too. Darn good ones.

Ellis used to blow rings, too. He used to try to catch them on his finger, score a point for each one he caught. Scored thirty-eight points once. His room smelled like smoke when his mother and I cut him down. Unfiltered smoke. It made his mother sick. Me, I just ignored it, washed the odor out of my clothes, and threw up later. But first we had to turn that music off.

The kid looks over at me, offers me one.

"No thanks. I like my lungs."

"Suit yourself. Gonna die anyway. Fire's as good as ice, or something like that. I never can remember."

I want to tell this kid to repent. Throw away those smokesticks, and breathe the fresh air of Jesus. But I can't — my lungs and ribs hurt too much. One of the hoodlums must've been wearing pointed shoes.

The kid finishes the smoke, then puffs down two more without missing a beat.

The fresh air smacks against me like a kiss, shooting me up like morphine. No pain. No memories. No anything.

I finish the third stogey, and crunch the butt under the heel of my Nikes. The wino looks at me, still shaking his head after declining my offer of a cig. Well, at least I'm not sleeping in some alley with a bottle of Jack, or whatever guys over sixty-five who live in dirty alleys drink now. I wish he'd stop looking at me that way, accusing. If I wanted that, I could just grab the Lear and fly back to Iowa to Mom and Dad. Even they would hug me first before condemning me.

Maybe that's why I hang on to Warren.

Three to get ready, and four to go, so I light up one more, and start walking out of the alley. The wind has other ideas, lifting Papa's hat, whisking it back over to the wino. He's nice enough, picking it up and knocking the dirt from it. I pop my neck, stretching the muscles, and slide my fingers through my freshly cropped hair. Kind of a long flapper cut . . . it's starting to grow on me. The wind tickles my scalp, triggering the night's rush again.

"Thanks."

He doesn't answer, seems shocked that I'm a girl underneath the street urchin clothes. Oh well, thought I'd made a friend. You win some, you lose some. Nothing new under the sun. I take the hat, tuck my hair back up under it, and head incognito into the street.

Then, all Hell breaks loose. The wino starts screaming at me.

"You! You're that high-fashion harlot of music that's running this country's morals into the ground! Diva! My God, what if everybody's little girl grew up to be like you?"

Great. So much for incognito. In just a few seconds, people start gathering like maggots on dead meat. Thanks a lot, old man.

"Taxi! Hey, taxi!"

People, paper, pens. No matter where I look they're all around me. Stupid old preacher. Go ruin somebody else's night. I've got enough problems.

"Hey, everybody! Look! It's Diva!"

"I think you're great."

"Can I have your autograph? It's for my cousin."

I wonder if this is what a lab rat feels like, having to push all the right buttons while the guys in glasses and white coats stand around and watch. Only now the glass between me and the crowd has been removed, and they're squeezing in, huddling in tighter to touch me, pull me apart, get a piece of me, carry me home as a souvenir — *"The Night I Touched Diva!"*

"Taxi!"

"Please, just a few autographs."

Can't think. Can't feel the night air. Won't you please leave me alone. You don't want me . . . you want Diva. I'm not Diva. I'm not Diva. I'm . . . My God, who am I?

"Sure, just a few. Anything for my fans."

A blur of yellow rescues me. I fall inside less than gracefully. In the back seat, I cup my hands to hide my face.

My God, Ellis. Is this what you saw when the floor danced beneath you?

The attention she commands. The worship she craves. A pimp in black leather selling sex to children. And once they're hooked, they beg for more. Not one kid in the crowd is older than eighteen. Most look at least thirty, padded and curved, showing off the adultness of their bodies. But they're children. And begging at her feet like pets, ready to play.

"Repent! Repent!" I say, but I know they can't hear. All I can do is all I can do. My sermon gets lost in the thunder they give her. Try as I might, I can do nothing here. God forgive them for they know not what they do. If anyone causes Your little ones to stumble, oh Lord, have mercy . . .

A cab sweeps in, screeching recklessly next to the curb. She crawls in, bowing first to soak in their praise. The yellow door slams behind her, and the cab screams off.

It takes a good fifteen minutes for the crowd to fully disperse. Most of them linger, trading stories of how close they got, what her clothes felt like. Two girls in the front lie on the sidewalk, passed out. I guess they actually touched her.

Might as well get a cup of coffee before going home. Henry's place is only two blocks away. Let the commotion die down a little.

When I enter, the smell of hot coffee is solid like a wall. Just being here cheers me up, even makes my side feel better. Sid and Gladys wave, ask me for a soul count. Marty looks up, nods, then looks away, finishing his grilled cheese and Maxwell House. Two drunks are passed out in the corner booth. I stuff a Gideon New Testament in each one's shirt pocket, and order them each an omelette plate and some fresh coffee for when they wake up. Henry will see that they get it.

"Here's twenty bucks. It'll get them each a night at the shelter," I say to Henry as I sit down, "Don't let them have it till after I leave."

He takes the money. "The last two blew it on more liquor. What makes you think these two won't?"

"Just got a feeling this time, Henry."

"You had a feeling last time."

He's right. Most of them drink it all away. Probably end up right back in the corner booth, drunk and passed out. Some don't.

"Didja hear the news, Wilson? About Diva's new album being banned in two stores in Mississippi?" Henry asks me. And as he does, I remember the color of her eyes when I handed her the cap, deep brown like Ellis', before they became dulled from drugs.

"Well, preacher, didja hear me? Diva's new album was

202

banned from two stores in Mississippi."

I ignore him as much as I can. "Ham and cheese omelette. Grits and toast, too."

"Bet those libs'll be making a stink about their first amendment rights again. Yes sir, this time it's got the smell of a lawsuit all over it."

Henry keeps talking to me, but the words get lost somewhere between us. Eventually, he gives me the omelette plate, and I join the two drunks at the corner booth. One stirs as I sit, shows me a picture of his wife, then passes out again. My watch lets me know it's ten till nine.

O, Georgia!

My Sister

by Yuval B. Zalkow

I washed my hands in the bathroom and then pressed my wet thumb and forefinger against my closed eyes. "I'm going to be fine," I told myself. I dried my face and hands with a towel and I looked into the mirror. The excessively bright halogen lighting exposed every last wrinkle on my face. A new wrinkle appeared every week, or at the very least, an existing wrinkle grew longer. "One more night," my lips pronounced in the mirror.

They stayed in the basement, which gave us some distance from *him*, but still not a comfortable distance. Across the world was a comfortable distance. I heard my husband shaking up another gin martini for himself. The ice rattled within the aluminum container. It was round three for him, though we had just begun eating. Not a good sign. He's a pretty good drunk all in all, but I just feared a possible flair-up of his temper. It is just that religion thing that sets him off. Once he actually told a Rabbi to "shove his dogma up his asshole" at a panel discussion at the university.

"But just do this for my sister," I had asked him that night. "You have so much family and history here in Georgia, but for me it's different. This is the first time anyone from my family has even come to this country. I really want Ahuvah to be comfortable here."

I stepped out of the bathroom and into the hallway leading to our kitchen. I turned my head, briefly observing the watercolor painting of the wall to the old city of Jerusalem. On the wall was a green smudge of a plant. I forget the name, but this plant manages to grow in the dry heat, out of the cement that holds the stones together.

Walking through the kitchen, I gently rubbed my hand across Victor's lower back, exactly over that disintegrating vertebra where he enjoys my touch. His head quickly turned toward me and his lips attempted a smile, but his eyes kept wandering back to the Beefeater.

As I entered the dining room, the thickness of the carpet almost engulfed my momentum. My sister, Ahuvah, and her husband, Shai, sat at the table, across from where Victor and I would soon sit. They spoke of how great the *challah* tasted. Shai even kissed the bread before the second bite to demonstrate its tastiness. The loaf of bread sat on a paper plate, as did all the food, because Shai wouldn't eat from our non-kosher dishes. The paper plates and plastic dishware seemed to glow against the soft beige tablecloth. I wiggled into my seat and looked up at the piece of wallpaper peeling from the top corner of the wall. Ahuvah's gaze followed mine, to the ugly masking tape that failed to hold up the wallpaper. She asked me why it looked so tacky.

"I figure the tape is so out of place that it would *have* to hold up this damn wallpaper," I answered in Hebrew.

She laughed and laughed at this statement. In fact, I couldn't remember the last time I heard my sister, the oldest of my mother's four daughters, laugh so much in one night. The sort of laughter that I hadn't heard in probably fifty years. The sound stuttered out of her nose while she kept her mouth nearly closed, leaning her head back; and then it began coming through her mouth as she leaned forward. It brought me back fifty years ago, when I lived with my three sisters and our parents in a single room in the poorest section of Jerusalem. My mother was always proud to say that we were the sixth generation born in Jerusalem.

"Simcha, where did you get this bread?" she asked me while her husband searched through his prayer book and hummed a vaguely familiar tune of my past.

"At the farmer's market," I told her. "We have to go there before you leave. You would not believe what they have. We buy everything there."

How I miss that sort of soul connection we had – the way we could relate to each other on everything from shopping for things we could not afford, to crying for our lost loves, to gossiping about Sarah, with the blue eyes, who had menstruated for the first time during morning prayers. I imagined what it would be like if we lived in the same place, as adults. No one in America had been a friend in the same way. One night when we were children, we stayed up all night writing our conversation on paper so we wouldn't wake up the family. We had thirty pages, front and back, by sunrise. The conversation dealt with all those things that used to seem so important—boys and our homework, music and romance novels. When I laughed, she laughed, and when she cried, I cried. We were mirror images of each other – not knowing who was the original and who was the image. In fact, we truly believed that we were twins, separated by two years and eighteen days.

My husband walked into the room with careful steps, holding his martini in his hand, as if he were holding his own heart. He put his glass down, and then sat himself down, moving slowly at first, but then falling to the chair abruptly. He quickly picked up his martini glass, which, on this third serving, actually contained some ice cubes. The ice cubes hit the martini glass and produced a rare and soothing ring. During Victor's entrance, my sister and I focused on him with peripheral attention while we looked at each other vacantly.

"But not the fish," my husband said, followed by a loud sip from his glass, one olive being sucked into his mouth.

"What?" I asked him.

He held the glass in front of his mouth, with all his fingers around the stem, and said, "We buy everything at the farmer's market, *except* for the fish." Behind his glass, I could make out his soft smile and fuzzy cheeks.

"Oh yes," my sister said with a rising smile, "Simcha tells me that you are an excellent fisherman."

"*Fly* fisherman," he corrected her.

"What?" she asked, fiddling with the bronze earring that dangled from her ear lobe. Its design ended in a stone – a green tear-shaped stone, hand-made just for her.

"I *fly* fish," he said, and then proceeded to describe this so-called art by recounting his most recent expedition. It involved a bit of embellishing and merging of stories, but no matter. Ahuvah watched him without blinking her eyes. Her jaw nearly dropped to her plate on some occasions, like when he told about being carried by the current and sucked up by an undercut rock, remaining underwater for an eternity.

"I tell you," he said, nodding his head, "My adrenaline was

pumping but it sure as hell didn't help me get out of the water any faster!"

I don't think my sister knew what the English word "adrenaline" meant, but she held her breath from excitement. And every time my sister picked up her fork, she had to put it back down – Victor was skillful at timing the high moments of his story to prevent his audience from becoming distracted by food. And his sexy Southern accent only sweetens his stories.

Meanwhile, my brother-in-law kept his full attention on eating. He spent minutes at a time arranging his food into separate divisions; I would swear that each pile contained the exact same number of grains of rice. After the troops were lined up on his plate, he forked them up to his mouth, never looking up until he needed seconds, and then thirds. And during those moments, he really didn't look up. He just looked further down the table as necessary and reached out his hands, like a spoiled child, to signify what he needed. His focus astonished me. To think that I spend hours studying meditation techniques, all to get to a point where my mind is as focused as this insincere bastard! This man who steals neighbors' newspapers at 5 a.m. on the way to his morning synagogue service. This man who says that women don't have the intuition required to own and operate his lousy electronics store in Jerusalem, because they can't sell things at profitable prices. This man who stares at young girls coming home from school like God gave them to him, as desserts.

My husband concluded his story, nearly out of breath, by standing up and pretending to carry a suitcase in his hand while saying, "So Larry actually had to get on the plane with twelve fish in his carry-on luggage!" He sat back down.

My sister covered up her mouth and said, "Oh my goodness!"

Shai had finished his food by this point and had actually begun to watch the conversation. His main focus, however, was given to sucking particles out from between his teeth and pulling on his white, rabbinical beard. His eyes, and the discolored skin around them, sunk into his head like two bruises. The skin immediately around his eyes looked infected. Surely, with those eyes, he could not see anything beautiful. And oddly enough, even though he considered himself a member of the chosen people and thanked God countless times a day in prayer for the wonders of the world, he despised the world. Perhaps he had learned this bitterness in Hungary, around 1944.

"You know, zee Torah portion zis veek," Shai started, his strong Hungarian accent always present, "is very, very interesting."

"Shai!" my sister said to him quietly, but forcefully. "I was talking to Victor. That is rude to interrupt!" She put her hand on Shai's shoulder and looked at me with squinted eyes. Her exhausted eyebrows implied, 'you see what he does to me!'

While my sister fabricated some chit-chat with my husband, Shai continued to pull on his long beard, though it appeared that his stiff hairs were firmly rooted into his chin, making up for his bald head. And finally, after a pause of closure from my sister, Shai said to her, "Now can I talk?"

"Yes," she said, with a hint of exhaustion that had yet to leave the wrinkles on her forehead. "Now it is okay."

He blew a sigh of frustration into my sister's face, and she closed her eyes and squinted as if a diesel truck had spewed out its exhaust onto her. Shai's stretched hands captured the prayer book on the table, one hand on top of the other. He smiled and tried to muffle his yawn.

"The Torah portion is about how the Jews built a tabernacle when they were wandering in the desert – "

"Oh. It's the *old* tabernacle story," my husband said with an arrogant chuckle.

"What?" Shai asked as he leaned toward Victor. A moment

209

later, Shai pulled away, probably realizing Victor's sarcasm a little late.

I looked at Victor with my "angry eyebrows," as he calls them. He did not even need to look at me before changing his tone. "Uh – nothing Shai, I'm sorry to interrupt. It just reminded me of another story I heard."

"Anyway," Shai continued, mostly confused about Victor, "this tabernacle was built so they could have a place of worship. It was very complex to build you know. They could only the use the wood from the acacia tree and each of the ten curtains around it had to be just the right shape and size – 28 cubits tall. And the table had to be covered in gold with gold rings hooked to the corners..."

He kept detailing the specifications of this tabernacle, correctly translating every bit of it into English, so that Victor could follow. (But I still don't know what the hell a cubit really is – and surely Victor doesn't either – both the Hebrew and the English are meaningless to me.) Shai spoke mostly to Victor, but often he looked slightly above him, especially when speaking about specific details. Victor just ate his food, with only occasional glances back at Shai. Victor's eyes would open widely at times, and he would nod. Then he'd eat some more food.

Shai continued, "It took almost three months for the Jews to build this tabernacle, but when they did, a thick cloud sat over it. This was God. The Jews followed this cloud for thirty-nine years through the desert. If the cloud did not move for a year, they did not move for a year; if the cloud only rested for an evening so too did the Jews."

"Thirty-nine years!" Shai repeated emphatically. He held up the back of his hand with his fingers curled around his outstretched thumb. To further demonstrate his story's importance, he waved his hand in the air with his wrist, just like a fly fisherman would whip his rod back and forth.

Silence. Nobody said a word. The spirit of his tabernacle story lingered in the room uncomfortably. No one knew how to deal with such an image. It did not belong at the dinner table, as the story of the fisherman had. I felt perspiration under my arms and

210

then realized that I forgot to put on deodorant.

"Yes," I said to him in a monotone, "I remember studying those details in the Book of Numbers with Lalee, the wife of Rabbi Eldar. Is that where it is from?"

"Yes, yes," he said as his voice trailed off, and he began looking more and more towards my husband with each bob of his head.

My husband sat and ate; one hand gently rested on my lap. Otherwise, his presence utterly disappeared from the table. Shai ignored my distraction and pointed a finger in Victor's direction. My husband looked up at him, just as his fork had penetrated the salmon.

"You don't even care, Victor," he said with dismay, like a grandfather preparing to tell his grandchildren what is wrong with their generation. "You can talk about fish but not of the Torah. You know Victor, you should at least spend a few minutes every Shabbat and read from the Torah. Just ten minutes a week!" Again, his gesture with the hand. "Then," he continued, "you will really know what Shabbat is about." Shai smiled, one out of the 613 good deeds specified in the Bible was accomplished.

My husband's hand tightened against my thigh. His fork, which was staked into the salmon, crashed onto the plate loudly and mangled the smooth form of his dinner. He looked at his poor, pink salmon; then he looked at Shai.

"I prefer to do *other* things," my husband said. The verbally italicized word "*other*" lingered around the table.

"But Victor," Shai said, "you don't even listen when I talk about the Torah. What kind of Jew are you?"

My husband squeezed my thigh even tighter. I could see blood rush to his head. I quickly put my hand over the back of his cold, moist hand, and massaged it with the soft tips of my fingers. I heard the timer ding in the kitchen. My memory shot back to past tense moments with my husband. Like the time he ripped the shirt off of our son because he told Victor to shut up.

"Don't you dare tell your father to shut up!" Victor had said after ripping our son's t-shirt off his back with one sharp pull. "What

211

have you done in life to make yourself worthy of telling your own father to shut up?" His eyes were fierce and unrelated to the man I love.

My son yelled back at him, "You are such an asshole," and then ran to his room. I repeated my son's last words and Victor stormed out of the house, disappearing for half the day. He returned quietly, with the instability in his eyes that read, 'don't bring up the incident'. And so I didn't.

Then there was the time he called me a "fucking imbecile" because I didn't know where Lapland was. I mean, who the hell mentions such a place in context?

But these types of incidents had passed years ago. Not that I credit our shrink for resolving these issues, but time seems to calm a man down, some men later than others. Or perhaps the people around him had simply learned to tiptoe down certain dark corridors. Either way, the end result is the same – I just think of these incidents as mere departures.

At this point, I looked at my husband and I witnessed something amazing. He stared directly at me – patiently – and he did not alter his expression as I held his gaze. Under the table, I discovered it was *he* who had the upper hand, holding my own. His warm hand gripped my hand firmly and gently. As I had just crept through these dark scenes, he had crept with me, he accompanied me. Soon his gaze penetrated too deeply, so I probably blushed, and I looked at my empty plate. But this moment between us was unmistakable.

He lifted his glass to finish off the martini with a big gulp, keeping the last olive in his mouth. I took a deep breath while Shai watched Victor's slow response, as if this *act* of inaction floated like a stagnant cloud over the table. I smelled a burnt pound cake in the oven.

"Did you ever look inside yourself before becoming so critical of others?" my husband asked him, rolling the olive in his mouth and speaking so calmly that I almost jumped out of my seat to hug him. While he spoke, all the wondrous undertones of brown and pink returned to his face. He looked under the table at our hands and then at me and then at Shai.

212

"You know what I think?" Shai asked.

"What do you think?" Victor said, without maliciousness, but with the energy of someone who realized that he had already fought the battle that marked the turning point.

"Shai!" my sister said, this time loudly, "don't tell him how to live! That is not nice! We're the guests in this house!"

My sister was very embarrassed, as she often is when she has to excuse her husband. She held her plastic fork like it was a metal knife and slowly shook her head back and forth.

Shai threw his long, awkward arms up in the air. "I am sorry. What can I say?" He left the table and went down to the basement.

I also got up from the table. As I stood, I could still feel, and savor, the places on my thigh where my husband had gripped. The charred remnants of the pound cake went into the trashcan and I offered my two remaining dinner guests ice cream instead. No takers. They wanted to leave this dinner table as well. I noticed that the wallpaper had peeled down a little further.

Ahuvah and I talked later that night. She came in the living room, where I was reading *Lolita*, on my favorite couch – leather, the color of coffee with too much milk in it. She remembered my insistence upon finishing my text appropriately before beginning a discussion. So, she sat on the couch beside me and waited while carefully removing her long earrings. I read one more page, delighted by the way that Nabokov used the word 'unattainable' in the last sentence on the page, and then I closed the book. It fell through my lap, down my smooth dress, and onto the thick, white carpeting – where I let it lay.

"I should have divorced him 40 years ago, when I first found him cheating on me," she said, holding her earrings in her fist.

Her frown turned into a partial smile and she looked right past me. "Your husband is wonderful, Simcha! I love to listen to him. And it breaks my heart when I see him put his hand on your lap. I never got to experience such a thing! Shai has not held my hand since I was pregnant."

"Oh, Ahuvah," I said, as I pulled her head to my chest. She sobbed on my chest as I cried quietly above her. Echoes of her moans reverberated between my breasts. I smelled the unpleasant aroma of my sweat and feared that she would too.

I didn't know what to say. What do you say to a woman after a miserable marriage of more than 45 years? Oh I told her to leave him on plenty of occasions... At first, she said she had to stay with him because of the children, then because he was sick, and now because she doesn't want to be alone at sixty-five. But I had noticed that she had a different set of jewelry on everyday, so I knew there were other reasons that she did not leave him. The women in our family have a history of being the unnoticed victim behind their religious husbands. That's why I left home in the first place.

Ahuvah's children excuse their father's actions, and tell her to excuse them too, particularly the more religious children. After all, they argue, Shai survived the Holocaust, a Rabbi's son born in Hungary in 1930. At 14, he witnessed his own parents' death in the gas chambers. How can anyone get beyond such a thing?

But does that really allow this man to make a pass at *me*, his own wife's sister, while his wife is in labor? He can pray all he wants; it does not seem to guide him anywhere but deeper into his brooding and torture. I just wish I had the courage to tell my sister that he made a pass at me 35 years ago.

Perhaps it is time, I thought to myself. I felt her heat and melancholy against my chest and I saw a reflection of my face in the naked window across from us. My sister confessed it all as my clothes and my skin absorbed her sorrow. Meanwhile, I continued to build a thick film of dishonesty to protect myself from the world. When I left Israel 30 years ago, I somehow left myself behind. So perhaps it was time. If I couldn't tell her, then maybe I could write it. That was more concise and true, as I recall. But I still have some copies of our letters from decades past – did I want to risk immortalizing *this* conversation as well? Probably not. But regardless, I felt ready to release at least one secret of mine. Though the outcome would no doubt seem bad at first, it could bring us closer in the end. And maybe time has altered these issues, we have gotten quite old, and the healing would have to begin at *some* point. Or more accurately, my own healing. My reflection in the window watched me with a drooping frown. I sensed the lower lip in the window twitch, and felt my own lip tremble. For a moment, I forgot that Ahuvah concealed herself within my bosom.

She lifted her head off of my chest and looked at me – an excessive amount of eyeliner dripped down her face. Without taking her puffy eyes off me, she moved her loosened fist over the glass coffee table beside us and released her earrings in one placid motion.

"You were very quiet tonight," she said, "I felt like you weren't even there. Like you were just taking notes. Are you okay?"

A few seconds passed as I sat there silently. The air-conditioner turned on and blew against my head as swirls of mad thoughts spun around me.

"Yes," I told her, "I am fine."

O, Georgia!

Arpeggio
by John Bush

In this bright darkness

I want to rest

with your deep incipience,

between cold, then warm threads,

beneath eider dreams,

to meet

your assembled bareness,

your constellation.

And while you sleep, halfway,

to feel

your little goddess touch,

your thin nails massaging my simple skin.

I want to preserve this increasing

memory

this accomplished glimpse of your horizon,

your newborn world,

O, Georgia!

to mingle with your infant dreams

                         -your reflection pronounced in her-

and to complete your crescendoed outline,

which forms both sets of primaries, a flourishing sharpness and

power.

and I

watch and hold

 your striking and particular concentration

of

perfect whiteness

perfect smoothness

perfect roundness,

your skin a landscape

a length and breadth suspended above all

that invents, again and again, hues, waves, and intensities.

and at the threshhold of extension

where skin touches skin,

where line and color converse openly,

I feel your dowel toes,

                  moving like a symphony,

arrange my skin

as your knees

rise to your stomach and

conduct my body to all points of lightness

And

In this abundant moment,

this immensity that a curve of air can never separate,

I catch ecstasy

as you stir, unawake still.

and

I,

hearing your face in your sounds,

your breathing low like a candle,

know we dream the same dream,

one

that will never lull,

that is a verse of memory,

O, Georgia!

that is a closed secret that

we inhale,

a music weaving a universe

of precise moments

into quickening notes

into fastening silence.

In The Jardin
by Roseanna Almaee

In the Mexican town they

wander wide-eyed

and spend, as they can,

the coins in their bags.

So it was with surprise

that a poor one intruded

on the Gringos brief time

in the San Miguel shops.

Having so much

is so normal to those

who have little known hunger

or hardship of life.

In the Plaza Jardin

she sat in the cold

wrap'ed in her shawl

hand out to the world.

Seeing only the beauty

and closed to the other,

the needs of the people

do not readily come

In her broken, cracked speech

she called to the passers

for help or assistance

from life's cruel measure.

To ones at their peaks

of good life and good living,

there's no time to be witness

to the sufferings of some.

"Please sir, please ma'm,"

she begged for small change,

from ones passing by

closed to her misery.

O, Georgia!

And on the small mat
a bone-thin hand
encircled her own
not more than three years.

How dare she disrupt
their holiday trip
and burden their thoughts
and their carefree world.

The child curled tight
in old fetal mem'ry
without mother-shared cord
to keep hunger away.

"I know you have money!"
the old beggar shrieked,
frustrated by hunger
and lack of attention.

In vain effort to seek
what warmth may come
the two starving bodies
pres'ed close as one.

She called and reached out
to Gringos who looked,
but warded her off
and never slowed down.

The tourists shook off
the ancient one's grasp,
offended by touch
and brief intrusion.

Young girls made the sign
of the cross as they passed,
averting their eyes
from the wretched old one.

For they knew full well

only one brief trouble

and some day they, too

would be here and then,

Their hands would stretch out

to the soul-less crowds

for food or release

from this merciless life.

And the sun's weak rays

touched the ancient one's skin

unable to warm

or fill the great need.

So she cried and implored

to the gods of the crowds

as winter approached

and her anguish increased.

But not one of the mass

took a moment to ease

the burdens of such

so small in their lives.

A useless old woman

thrown away by time

to live on stone steps

of the church San Miguel.

O, Georgia!

A Token Of Grace
(an excerpt)

by Mary Anna Bryan

Margaret woke to the song of a mockingbird in the crepe myrtle tree outside her window. For a long time she lay listening to the music and staring at a patch of sunlight on the gray tongue-and-groove wall opposite her bed. The patch was alive with colors, swimming and coiling together. She thought of fairies dancing on a spot of cool green moss in the woods at the bottom of the hill.

She got up, dressed, and went to the kitchen. No one was there, but Ida had left a dish of canned peaches on the table. Margaret poured cornflakes and milk into a bowl and dumped in the peaches. She sat down, planted her elbows on either side of the bowl, and slurped down her breakfast. How pleasant to be eating alone, with no grownups around to complain about manners.

When she finished, she wiped her chin on her sleeve and returned to her room. She took out the old sewing basket Maggie had given her and dumped its contents—rocks, sycamore balls, dried okra pods—into the middle of her bed. Taking the basket to the dining room, she selected the reddest apple from the bowl on the sideboard, dropped it into the basket, and went outside.

"Where you headed, Biscuit?" Ida said. She was hanging out wash near the chinaberry trees.

"Moss time!" sang Margaret. "I'm going down in the woods and dig me up some fresh moss for my garden."

"Moss time nothing," Ida said. "This here snake time. Day like this every snake on the hill be out of its hole looking to bite you."

"Aw, there aren't any snakes on Cardinal Hill. Just the old rat snake, and Sam says leave it alone because it does good and not harm."

"'Cause you ain't seen none don't mean they ain't there."

Margaret changed the subject. "I'm going to see if the scuppernongs are ripe."

"Well, they ain't. But wasps and yellow jackets is. And they got their stingers out."

225

Margaret didn't answer. She'd tramped through the woods around Cardinal Hill for as long as she could remember. The only snake she'd ever seen was the rat snake. She'd been stung by wasps a few times but never by yellow jackets.

She crossed the yard and climbed over the stile into the pasture. Chickens around the feed trough made a to-do as she passed, swinging her basket. The cows were too busy munching fresh grass sprouts to notice her when she passed. But Cherry's calf bolted away on long, stiff legs, and she glanced up to see what had caused the commotion.

When Margaret reached the fence on the far side of the pasture, she followed it to a small gully. Crouching low in the gully, she ducked under the fence and started down the hill.

The day was brilliant. The sweet scent of pine lay on the air. She passed a clump of huckleberry bushes and started when a brown rabbit darted out at her feet. She searched the bushes, hoping to discover its warren and babies. But all she found was a pile of fresh droppings. Halfway down the hill she came to a tall pine with a thicket of jessamine vines at its base. She crawled into the thicket and leaned back against the pine to eat her apple.

A black beetle wandered over to examine her skirt with its pincers. Margaret broke off a crumb of apple intending to offer it, but it hurried away. She finished the apple and laid its core on a piece of pine bark as a treat for three large red ants that were scurrying about. Then she crawled into the sunlight and continued on down the hill.

Near the bottom, scrub oaks gave way to Carolina cherries and hickories. Farther on, along rotten logs and in low, spongy places grew the smooth, emerald moss she wanted for her garden.

Suddenly, there was a cry like an animal in pain. Margaret stopped. The cry came again from somewhere to her left. Stealthily, like an Indian, she slipped from tree to tree, making her way toward the sound.

A clump of bushes lay directly ahead. She circled it and darted behind a large pine. Peeping out, a few yards away she saw a girl squatting on her haunches, holding onto a pine sapling with both hands. Her thick orange hair fell in a mat to her shoulders. The skirt of her gray broadcloth dress spread about her like a tent.

The girl moaned and leaned forward, then pulled back and swung her head from side to side. She sat on the ground, putting her arms out behind her, and leaning back on them. She cried out again.

Margaret thought she should go to her and ask what was wrong. Instead, she stayed where she was.

The girl turned toward Margaret. Margaret ducked back, but not before she'd seen the girl's face. Her eyes were pale blue or gray; her skin was as bleached as the sand. Something about her—the dull expression, the dress—was familiar. Then Margaret knew who she was, or rather, where she was from.

Cardinal Hill was six miles from Georgia Instructional School for Mental Defectives, or Hope Forest, as most people called it. Margaret had been there once with Maggie to deliver Christmas stockings knitted by the ladies in Maggie's church circle. While Maggie and a woman talked in an office, Margaret had watched some young women milling about in a room across the hall. They all wore gray broadcloth dresses; their faces all had the same dull expression.

The girl was on her haunches again, this time making a low growling sound in her throat. She pushed the pine sapling so hard that its needles brushed the ground.

Margaret's breath came in gulps. She started to run to the house. Then she ran back to the tree.

The sounds grew fiercer and closer together. The girl flung her head back and forth, orange hair tossing about like a rag in a dog's mouth.

She's having a fit, Margaret thought. She'd once seen a kitten have one.

The girl let out a long, piercing scream and collapsed to the ground. There came a faint mewing sound. The girl raised her head, muttered something, and looked down. She drew into a ball. There came no more sounds.

Margaret sat down to wait. Presently, a blue jay landed beside her and turned its head sideways to study her face. Then it flew off. Above, in the radiant sky, two hawks glided like tiny black crosses.

The faint clang of the dinner bell came from the house. If Margaret didn't get back soon, Ida would be out yelling, "You, Margaret!" loud enough to be heard clear to her father's office downtown.

She picked up her basket, and started up the hill. She turned to look one last time. The girl hadn't stirred.

After lunch Margaret returned to the woods and tried to find the girl. She located the bent pine, but not the girl. She started back up the hill and as she drew near a cluster of scrub oaks, she noticed what seemed like a bundle of newspapers lying beneath it. She went over; it was a petticoat. She unfolded it carefully. Inside was the tiniest baby girl she'd ever seen. Its nose was almost flat, its eyes were closed tight, its umbilical cord lay like a ravaged worm on its stomach. She touched one hand with her finger; the hand curled around it. She moved her finger away.

Smudges of red-brown lay under the baby. Margaret moved it to a clean spot, and it made a slight squeaking sound. She covered it back up with the petticoat and sat down to wait for the mother.

The sun hit Margaret's shoulders, making them burn. She shifted herself and the baby deeper into the shade of the scrub oaks. The baby slept without moving.

What if the mother didn't come back? Then she'd take the baby to the house and let Maggie and her father decide what to do. They'd probably send it to an orphanage. But if they did that, the mother would never find it.

Margaret leaned close to the baby. "How long should we wait for your mother?" she whispered. "One hour? Two hours? All afternoon?"

The baby made no response.

Margaret picked up a twig and began to play tic-tac-toe in the sand.

After ten games, she spoke again to the baby. "If your mother tries to come back, she might have trouble finding you." She smoothed a few wrinkles out of the petticoat.

Then she said in a voice too low for the baby to hear, "But if your mother really wanted you, she wouldn't have left you."

Margaret rose to her haunches. Supporting the head the way Junie had supported Dexter's head when he was tiny, she picked up the baby and stood. "Finders keepers," she announced to the world. She started back up the hill.

As she drew near the pasture, Margaret slowed down. "I sure wish I'd brought my basket," she said. "I could put you inside and nobody'd even know you were there. Nobody thinks anything of it when they see me with my basket."

She came within view of the fence. "Now, where shall I take you? The barn loft? Sam might hear you cry and come up. My room? Maggie or Ida could come back any time. The best place is the lockup."

The lockup was across the porch off Margaret's bedroom. It had once been the kitchen. The door facing the house had been boarded up long ago, but the door on the back side had not. Margaret could come and go without being seen.

She went through the woods around the pasture and came out at the big water oak behind the lockup. From there to the lockup was a short distance.

Hiding as much of the petticoat as she could with her arms, she sauntered toward the lockup, hoping anyone who noticed would think she was just strolling about.

For years the lockup had been used only for storage. Ida said it had rats. But Margaret had played there many times and had never once seen a rat—although she had come across a few mouse pills. Furniture and boxes were piled everywhere. Margaret had made a path through them that came out at an oak table near the back window. A pane was out of the window, which helped, since the room had a strong musty smell.

Margaret had created a little room under the table, with two cushions on top of an old rag rug. She laid the baby on one of the

229

cushions. It started to cry. Not with Dexter's lusty howls, but with a soft mewing sound which would never be heard outside the lockup.

"There, there, little girl," Margaret said, patting the tiny shoulder. "Hold on a minute, and I'll get you some warm milk."

She pushed one side of the cushion against a foot locker and pulled boxes around the other three sides—Junie said you always had to be sure a baby couldn't roll off from where you left it—and went to the kitchen.

"What you doing dirtying my pot?" Ida said. She was at the counter mixing up cornbread. "I'm heating some milk for a barn kitten."

"A barn kitten don't need no milk from you long as it's got its momma to nurse on."

"Yeah, but I'm trying to tame this kitten so it'll come when I call it."

"Get on out of here. I'm fixing to start my supper on that stove."

Margaret took the saucepan of milk to her room. She dug around in the bottom drawer of her wardrobe where she kept her old doll things until she found a baby doll bottle. She took it to the bathroom, washed it good with soap and hot water, and poured in the milk.

When she got back to the lockup, the baby was sleeping. Margaret picked it up and held it close, the way Junie held Dexter when she nursed him. Gently, she poked the nipple between its lips. The baby frowned but didn't open its eyes. Milk ran down its chin, and Margaret wiped it away with her skirt. The baby coughed. Margaret lifted it to her shoulder and patted its back.

Junie always gave her baby his bath in the morning. But since Margaret's baby was busy getting born in the morning, it'd have to have an afternoon bath.

Margaret went back to the kitchen and hung around until Ida stepped out. She grabbed up a brown paper bag and the big roasting pan used for Thanksgiving turkeys. She went to the linen cabinet for a wash cloth and towel and an old sheet to tear up for diapers. Then back to her room for safety pins and doll clothes. She

230

put everything into the bag, ran warm water into the roasting pan, and snuck out to the lockup.

Junie always stuck her elbow in Dexter's bath water before she put him in. She said if you couldn't feel anything on your elbow, the water was just right for the baby. Margaret stuck in her elbow. The water was too hot.

While she waited for it to cool, she picked up the baby and laid it in her lap. The baby opened its eyes a slit, as if to see who was holding it.

"What a sweet little girl you are," said Margaret, stroking one tiny arm. "You're just like Moses, only I didn't find you in the bull rushes, I found you in the scrub oaks.

"You know what I'm going to do? I'm going to take care of you and raise you and you'll be my own little girl. And I'll never, ever, ever go off and leave you. Or die, or anything like that. I'll never do that, I promise." She gave the baby's foot a slight squeeze to emphasize what she'd said.

"Now, what shall I name you? After somebody in the Bible? Esther or Mary or Elizabeth? How about a movie star? Shirley Temple, Deanna Durbin? No, let me see, I'm going to give you the most beautiful name in the world—Alicia. Patricia? Which do you like best? Tell you what, I'll give you both names."

Alicia Patricia kept her eyes closed. But she raised her brows a little, and Margaret could tell she liked her new name.

She stayed in the lockup until supper. Alicia Patricia slept the whole time, but Margaret talked to her anyway, and sang her songs.

It was Friday night and Louisa had a date with Frank Varnedoe. On nights when she went out with Frank, Louisa was always excused early from supper. That night Margaret asked to be excused right after Louisa got up and left.

"Sit at your place until the meal is over," Jim Norman said.

He glanced at Louisa's empty chair. "Oh, all right. This one time."

She had to get away from the table before he did; she needed the flashlight from his night stand and a pillow and sheet from the

231

linen cabinet. She couldn't take those things off her bed. If Maggie found her room empty the next morning, she'd think nothing of it, Margaret often went outside early to play. But if Maggie found the pillow and sheet missing too, she'd know something was up.

Alicia Patricia was still sleeping when Margaret returned to the lockup. Margaret checked her diaper. It may have been damp, so she changed it. Alicia Patricia opened her eyes a crack, then went back to sleep.

Junie always said, "When the baby sleep, I leaves him be." But if Alicia Patricia didn't take in more food, she'd never grow big. Margaret picked her up and gave her the bottle. Milk ran down her chin; she couldn't tell if any ran down her throat. Tomorrow she'd go to Stumpy's and buy a proper baby bottle.

One more thing from the house: a cardboard box for Alicia Patricia to sleep in. Ida had told about this woman who went to sleep next to her baby and rolled over on it during the night and killed it. Margaret didn't want anything like that happening to her baby.

When it was time for bed, Maggie had to tell her only once.

When Maggie came back to kiss her goodnight, Margaret pretended to be almost asleep. Maggie put her hand on her forehead.

"You feeling all right? It isn't like you to skip dessert."

"I'm just tired," said Margaret. "I wasn't hungry."

The house was dark and still when she crept from her room to the lockup. The baby lay like a pearl in her box. After adding one more "God bless. . . " to her prayers, she kissed the small head, and settled down for the night.

Somebody was jabbing her side with a club. Margaret reached down. She was lying on top of the flashlight.

She sat up. Her whole body ached from having slept scrunched up on the floor. Outside, the sky was still dark. She turned the flashlight onto Alicia Patricia. One tiny hand had worked from under the doll blanket Margaret had laid over her. If she'd cried during the night, Margaret hadn't heard.

When a runt was born in a litter of pigs, Sam brought it to the house, and Maggie put it into a box on the back porch and fed it with a rag dipped in warm sugar water. Soon the piglet was as healthy as its brothers and sisters. Margaret would feed sugar water to Alicia Patricia.

She tucked the hand under the blanket and left the lockup; she needed to be through in the kitchen before Ida arrived.

She was cooling the pot of boiled sugar water under the spigot, when she saw Ida leave her house and start across the field. Quickly, she poured the sugar water into a jar. Ida had almost reached the house when she sneaked through the front door and around the side of the house to the lockup.

Alicia Patricia raised her chin when Margaret touched her lips with the rag dipped in sugar water. Margaret squeezed some drops onto her lips. Alicia Patricia stuck out her little pink tongue. Margaret squeezed sugar water into her mouth. Alicia Patricia opened her eyes.

"You like sweet things, do you?" Margaret said, stroking the tiny head with one finger. "So do I, darling Alicia Patricia."

"What you doing out this early?" Ida called from the kitchen window.

Margaret had forgotten to go around the side of the lockup that couldn't be seen from the kitchen.

"I've been looking for that hen's nest to see if her biddies have hatched yet," she said. Why did Ida think she needed to know everything that went on in the world?

"That nest be down near the barn," Ida said. "Go wash for breakfast."

Margaret sat down at the table. Her eyes itched; her body felt sore. She peeled the banana Ida had set out next to a box of raisin bran and a bottle of milk. The outside of the banana looked fine, but the inside was mushy.

"This banana's rotten!" Margaret said and threw it as hard

as she could toward the slop bucket under the sink. It missed the bucket and slid along the floor until it hit the wall. "Now what am I going to put on my cereal!"

Ida picked up the banana. "Ain't nothing wrong with this banana till you done gone and ruined it. And you don't need nothing on that cereal. It already got raisins."

"I don't like raisin bran without banana!" Margaret picked up the bowl and was about to dump its contents into the slop bucket when Ida took hold of her arm.

"You set back down and eat what you fixed. How come you all prickly this morning? Ain't you got enough sleep?"

Margaret sat down and ate her breakfast. But she slopped milk on the table and didn't wipe it up. When Ida spoke to her, she wouldn't answer.

As soon as her father and Louisa left for the office, Margaret took a dollar from her bank and started out for Stumpy's Store to buy a baby bottle and some baby oil; Junie always rubbed Dexter with oil after his bath.

And if Stumpy asked why she was buying those things, she'd say the bottle was to feed a stray puppy and the oil was to mix with lemon juice to put on her face; she'd heard it would get rid of freckles.

But Stumpy asked her no questions. So she told him no lies.

Alicia Patricia had soiled her diapers. It wasn't much more than a pigeon's droppings, but as Margaret cleaned her, she told her what a smart girl she was and that pretty soon she'd be making big messes like Dexter.

Alicia Patricia kept her eyes closed.

The day before, when Margaret bathed her, Alicia Patricia stayed awake and made small squeaking sounds. Today, she hardly opened her eyes. Margaret patted her dry on the towel, rubbed her with oil, and dusted her with some of Louisa's sweet-smelling bath powder. Then she dressed her in a doll's soft, white batiste gown. Alicia Patricia slept through it all.

Margaret poured the sugar water into the new bottle and picked up her baby. She carefully pushed the nipple into her mouth; it was so huge, Margaret was afraid she might gag. But Alicia Patricia kept sleeping. Margaret tickled her foot. It twitched, but Alicia Patricia wouldn't suck on the nipple.

"You're awfully good at sleeping, little miss," Margaret said, "but you've got to take your bottle. You've got to grow big and strong so I can teach you all the things I know about." She wiggled the bottle; Alicia Patricia didn't respond.

Margaret set down the bottle and unbuttoned the top of her dress. Gently, she pressed the baby's mouth against the flat brown spot on her chest. "Dear, sweet little girl, please nurse me," she said. "I love you so much."

"What you keep fooling around that lockup for?" Ida said when Margaret came to the house for lunch.

"Oh, I'm just playing. There's some sour grass growing back there and I'm trying to pick the seeds."

"Huh," Ida said.

After lunch Margaret hung around the house, making sure Ida saw her every few minutes. After a while Ida took the vacuum cleaner and went to the parlor; she'd be busy in there for some time. Margaret heated a little milk which she planned to mix with the sugar water and went back to the lockup.

The baby was lying exactly as Margaret had left her. Margaret slid her hands under her to lift her. The baby felt stiff. Margaret slid out her hands and tickled the foot. It didn't move. She brushed her fingers over the lips. She stroked the cheeks and head. Alicia Patricia was as cold as a lamb on a tombstone.

"Dear God! Dear Jesus, please help me! Make her move, make her open her eyes. Don't let her be dead. Please, dear God! Please, please don't let her be dead!"

O, Georgia!

Outside the lockup window, a honeysuckle vine with trumpet-shaped flowers grew over a fence post. Beyond the vine loomed the dark water oak. To the right of the oak lay the field. Behind the field stood Ida's house. Over them all stretched the infinite sky.

Target
by Carroll V. Springer

Love became real to me when I was nine. It was a blisteringly hot Georgia July afternoon when Billy Barbee and I were riding our bikes home from getting fresh flattops from his dad, the local barber. We were on the curvy dirt road leading to his house when out of the corner of my eye I saw a dog peel out of the woods on an intercept course with us. He caught us pretty quickly and fell into a relaxed lope just as if he was where he was supposed to be. He didn't bark at us or seem mean or anything like that; he just ran with us because he wanted to, I guess. He wasn't even much of a dog: dirty, about the size and color of a large beagle but with longer legs and hair. We stopped; he stopped.

For some reason, he stopped beside my bike...not Billy's. He just stood there panting and staring at me.

"Get away from here," I yelled, "go on home!" He just wagged his tail and kept staring at me. Billy hollered something at him, but the dog never took his eyes off me. We both dismounted and laid down our bikes, so we could check out this inteloper. He had no collar. He didn't have anything. No tags. No nothing except an obvious desire to go with me wherever I was going, and he didn't seem to care where that was. I started to walk down the road just to see what he would do. He trotted along about a foot behind and off to the right of me so that every time I looked down to see where he was, he would be looking up at me with his head cocked a little to one side - just to see what I would do.

I stopped and tried to run him off, but he maintained his poise and just stood there in his stoical pose. I threw a rock at him, but I missed. He simply retrieved it and dropped it at my feet - wagging his tail all the time. I'd been adopted. I knew there would be trouble when my folks saw him.

Sure enough, my Dad said that he probably belonged to someone and that we should take him back to where I had found him. Since I had not had time to become really attached to him, I agreed. It was quiet around the supper table that evening.

After supper, the dog and I jumped into the bed of our rusty old pickup, and I told Dad where we had found him through the sliding window in the rear of the cab. The dog knew something was afoot; he scrunched up as close to me as he could and put his muzzle under my arm, hiding his eyes. We sat in a front corner of the bed out of the wind as much as we could. I felt like I was in the "family car" following a hearse, and I looked up to see if the cars following us had their headlights on. His tail never completely stopped wagging, but it was only the very tip of it that moved. I always wondered how he did that.

It was only a few miles to the woods behind Harold's store where he had latched on to me. Dad stopped the truck, and I climbed over the tailgate and jumped down.

"I know you like him, but he's just not ours. Some other little boy might be his owner, and he'll be missing his dog," Dad said. Made sense to me but I didn't have to like it. I lifted the tailgate latch and the gate swung down. The dog just stood there in the bed with one of those "you are making a big mistake" looks on his face that dogs make when they want to make their owners feel bad.

"Jump on down here," I said, and he did.

"Now," said Dad, " just throw a rock over into the woods as far as you can and while he's gone to get it, we'll leave." I picked up a nice agate off the shoulder of the road and showed it to the dog. His tail wagged furiously, and he seemed to know exactly what would happen next. He turned around and looked back over his shoulder at me as if to say, "Ok, Pal, do it now."

I threw the rock as hard as I could, and he bolted after it almost before it left my hand. Dad was already in the truck with the motor running, and all I had to do was junp into the bed. He took off, and just as we started picking up speed, the dog came out of the woods with the rock in his mouth. Making a quick value judgment, he dropped the rock and came charging after us. He really stretched out those long legs, and he flew faster than anything I'd ever seen on four feet. He locked in those brown eyes on our truck. By God, he was not going to be left behind. His tongue came out and flailed back beside his jaw; dust and gravel flew up as his feet clawed the shoulder of the road, and his body lowered down into high gear. He ran with a passion that I had never seen before in any living thing. My mouth fell open, and I felt a sudden and unfamiliar emotion that made my hand go to my stomach. I wanted to make Dad stop, but I knew better than to try.

The dog's attention was so solidly focused on our truck that he failed to notice the old Jeep waiting to make a left turn behind us after we passed by. The dog was going so fast that he appeared to only be touching the ground every now and then when the left front tire of the Jeep struck his head. Dangerously, I stood up in the back of the truck as I saw his body go spinning around and around in a whirlwind of dust and dirt and gravel.

My heart stopped and that emotion in my stomach turned into an instant knot. "Stop, Stop!" I screamed, and my dad glanced into his mirror just in time to see what was happening. His first thought was for me, and he managed to stop the truck without throwing me out of the bed. He got out and stood beside me behind the truck; we feared the worst, and he hugged me tightly while we looked back at the motionless dog. The man in the Jeep had stopped and gotten out to see about the dog, and he noticed that we too had an interest in him. He motioned us over, and my father and I cautiously approached what appeared to be the lifeless body of our self-appointed pet. We just watched for a minute or two. As we did, his tail moved a little. Then he wheezed and panted for a minute or two and seemed to be coming around. He got stronger before our eyes and in a few more minutes, he was trying to stand up. Unbelievably, he managed to do just that. He just stood there wobbling for a while until he spotted me. Then he sidled awkwardly over to me and gave my hand a lick as I reached for him. He had a lump on his head where the Jeep had literally knocked him out, but other than that, he seemed to be fine.

My Dad said, " Now I feel guilty for sure. We almost got him killed by trying to get rid of him, so I guess we should just keep him safe until someone claims him." I looked up at Dad just in time to see him turn back toward the truck. He had a finger up to his eyes. Didn't fool me, but I didn't care either. We took him home, and he spent the next few days sleeping off his brush with disaster.

Not long after his arrival back into our home, he was sleeping on the pad that my Mom had made for him when along came my little brother, Charlie. He had a small toy truck in his hand, and he dropped it right on the dog's head. Of course, the dog jumped up like he'd been shot or something — much to Charlie's joy! True to his character, however, all the dog did was lick Charlie right in the mouth.

My Dad watched the whole thing, and he saw what was coming, but he wasn't quick enough to prevent another lump on the dog's head. What he did do was proclaim that the dog's name was Target since he tended to be in the way of fast moving, dangerous articles. All agreed.

Target started going to school with me the next day. It was November, and the late fall leaves were blowing through the woods that we used for our shortcut. Target had a great time catching leaves in his mouth as we went. It was only about a mile to school, and Mr. Taylor, the principal, said he didn't mind the dog being there so long as he stayed outside. Mom made him another pad, and I fixed him a place next to the furnace room chimney where it was warm. He stayed there all day until he heard the bell ring, and then he would come around to the front door and wait for me. We'd play all the way home, and he'd be so tired when we got home that he would usually head for his pad and catch a nap before dinner. That routine went on for the next two months of my third grade class.

It was one of those cold gray days with wind whistling through the trees in the wood. Target and I had been running to get away from some fifth graders who had mischief on their minds, and since we knew a short-cut through the woods, we had managed to elude them. I was a little tired, so I paused for a minute to sit down and pop "smoke bombs." I still don't know the proper name of the plants, but they look like dark brown paper wads, and when you hit them they produce a powdery "smoke." I popped one on my right side, and I had just started to turn to my left when Target came snarling and growling by me with his teeth flashing. He scared the life out of me. Those teeth looked the size of those in the mouth of a large lion to me, and I jerked back just as he brushed by my face. He was focused again, this time on a large copperhead so close to me that I'd almost sat on it. Target did not know the intricacies of killing snakes so he just kept biting and slinging the snake like an old rag. But the snake was getting his licks in too. Target paid no attention to the snake bites and just kept after the job at hand until he had crushed the snake's head in his own jaws.

Satisfied that it was dead, he came over to check me out. He sniffed me over good and then headed off down the trail. I'd seen him get bitten several times, but he seemed okay as I watched him, so I hoped for the best as we started for home. He yelped one time and licked at a place on his hip, but he kept leading me along toward home. Not far from my house, he stumbled as one front leg went out from under him, and his muzzle pushed into the dirt. Quickly back up, he looked at me, and then his hind quarters collapsed. He looked at me again as I struggled to pick him up, but I could only get his front end off the ground. I wiped the dirt off his nose, and with his rear quarters dragging behind, I ran as hard as I could for home. I soon ran out of wind and had to walk for a bit. As I did, I looked at his swollen face, and our eyes connected for a few seconds before he just went limp in my arms without a sound.

I sat down on the path by the old ball field and put Target down on the ground. He didn't move, but then he didn't move when the Jeep had hit him either. I was too tired to carry him any further, but I didn't dare leave him, so I just sat there and fiddled with his ears and paws. That knot in my stomach had returned, but I tried to ignore it, unsuccessfully. I don't know how long I sat there, but Dad soon came down the path looking for me.

"Where in the world have you been?" he said. "Your mother's

241

worried..." He stopped talking abruptly when he saw Target. "What's the matter?" he said.

I told him what had happened, and that I thought Target was tired or sleeping. Dad looked at Target and bent down and put his ear against that big chest. He listened. Then he stood up without speaking and turned toward our house, walked a few steps before he stopped, then put his hand out and leaned against a big poplar tree for a few seconds. Then he turned around and walked back towards Target and me. He looked at us and turned around again. He did that for a few minutes. Finally, he turned around, came back, and sat down beside me. He turned his reddened face towards me and said, "Target's not asleep, son. He's dead. The snake bites killed him."

It's been many years since that day, but when I think back to that time, grief still settles on me — but at nine years old, all I could ask my Dad was, "Why did Target have to die?"

"He didn't have to, son," Dad said to me that day, and he reached those big arms around me and looked at me the way Target had for those few seconds when I'd held him in my arms — and I understood.

Poem From My Dying Father
by Kalynn Sharkey Vernick

Waterfall and willow tree
Pale light and shapeless sea
My loyal safeguards follow me
To the center of my most alone
Moving somewhere close to home.

Ragged clouds break high below
Slanted rain melts shaded snow
My loyal safeguards let me go
In the center of my most alone
Staying somewhere close to home.

Focus inward, facing you
A family circle and single view
Inviting dreams lead me to
The center of my very own
Resting somewhere close to home.

Waterfall and willow tree
Vision of mist and greenery
My loyal safeguards cover me
Watching over mine alone
To keep, forever, safe at home.

O, Georgia!

So Much Like Love
by Holly Barrios-Gayman

So much like love
This sweet, sweet rose
Its tender hue softened by end of day
Now pale shades of memory arrayed
In golden twilight.
A tint of heartbreak,
A hint of heartache
Glinting from beneath its fragrant breath.

So much like love,
This sweet, sweet rose
Drawing all attention to its splendid crown
Of enchantment,
Of entrancement by some lusty dream.
Love's rippling streams
Nestled deep within its prickly heart.

Those luscious petals wait before me now
As I gather them to my breast,
For my heart's been pierced by Cupid's bow
And my dark blood drips silently
And slow,
As I arrange the lovely stems,
Just so.

But I'll not dwell on what lurks below
This velvet's bliss,
But touch the magic with my kiss
And keep my eyes above
Those wicked thorns.

This sweet, sweet rose
So much like love.

O, Georgia!

On A Clear Day
by James L. McVay

It was cold Saturday. Even under the lee side of Sawnee Mountain, the wind whipped, gray clouds swirled over the house, seemingly at roof top level. It rained Sunday. I spent the morning putting the rebuilt carburetor on the '52. The car had sat for several months awaiting a transplant, but now it was road-worthy again. But the freaky winter weather pattern we experienced in North Georgia this year caused Monday to dawn clear and sunny as I backed the old car out of the garage and headed over to Buford to pick up dad.

As a kid growing up, I never saw my dad display any interest in things mechanical. But he seemed to enjoy riding in the old car, driving over the back roads in North Georgia while trying to convince me why central Florida was a better place to be than Georgia. I picked him up at Flanighans, and began the slow trek back to Cumming, around the south end of Lake Sidney Lanier. We stopped at Buford Dam and watched the sun sparkle off the lake's wind-ruffled surface.

My dad, his father, and his two older brothers didn't talk much in each other's presence. As a kid I remember them sitting around my grandma's kitchen table, listening to Detroit Tiger Baseball's Ernie Harwell, playing penny ante poker, and passing a whiskey bottle around once in a while. The only conversation were those words necessary to conduct the card game. They were comfortable in each other's presence without much conversation. These men's adult lives had been shaped by the Great Depression, and they didn't waste much. Not even words. So, long periods of silence between dad and I were not all that uncommon.

Below the dam, where the Chattahoochee River regains her full song, was the park where I had brought him, some years ago, to let him convince himself that driving a car was no longer something he could do safely. Recovery from that first stroke had been remarkable, but his coordination had not returned to a level where driving a car was an option. That was a hard lesson, but once he had seen it for himself, he could accept it. As I remember, it's been that way for him all of his life. It was never enough to tell him something. He had to see it for himself. He could be stubborn until he convinced himself about most things. But he had a soft side too. I remember waking up during a childhood sickness, in a dark room, to see him asleep on the floor next to my bed. Apparently, he had stayed with me until my fever broke and he was sure that I would be all right.

He loved the water. He had grown up around it as a boy in Northern Michigan. One of his triumphs, worked hard for as a young Boy Scout, was winning a motor boat ride around Black Lake with Judge Mountain Landis, the Commissioner of Baseball. The Commissioner had a summer home on Black Lake, and the boat ride was a prize for something to do with the Boy Scouts. In fact, as a youngster my dad saw and met several of the professional baseball players who were outcasts because of the Black Sox scandal in the thirties. They had barnstormed under assumed names and played some games at Onaway, near Black Lake. Apparently, the Commissioner had some pity for these players who had been banned from the game for a lifetime.

We continued our ride in the '52 over to Bald Ridge Marina, where we used to keep our boat. The surroundings there reminded me of old Charlie Hanna back at Black Lake, who, it was rumored, would rent his neighbors' row boat or even their summer cottage without the owner's knowledge. Old Charlie had seemed to be a remarkable person to me at age twelve, which was when dad introduced us. Dressed in a wrinkled shirt, with pants rolled up to his knees, the barefooted old timer told us to take any of the still serviceable rowboats beached next to his dilapidated boat house. There was to be no charge for the rental of the boat that week, Charlie had said. He was just happy to relive old memories again with dad. I noticed that my dad, who had been president of his high school senior class, but did not graduate, seemed to affect a lot of people this way as I was growing up.

Our ride in the '52, ended as I brought dad's ashes home from Flanighan's Funeral Home to Cumming. In a few days he would

248

take his last trip with us. Back home to Florida, where he had lived most of his retirement years, and where we would hold his small memorial service. He had died on that cold, cloud swept Saturday morning two days earlier. He was eighty-nine years old. His ashes would be placed next to mom's at the cemetery in downtown Mount Dora, Florida. Where spring's renewal is already in evidence.

These last few years were not good years for dad because of the dementia and poor physical health. He had some good days, but not many of them. But he is remembered by his family. And particularly by me, his son, who wishes there had been more sunny day rides with this shy man about whom I should have known more.

O, Georgia!

Erosion

by Sean Taylor

The breeze that blew the dust around seemed to whisper rumors that a storm was on its way. I'd only swept off about half of the porch, and I wasn't even close to being finished yet; after the porch came the back storage room. Since I was just a few feet away from the open doorway, I could hear Pa whistling, but the wall hid him from me. He'd done a lot of counting in there all week.

Big Bull stood silently on the porch, and watched intently as I worked. His stare never ceased, never turned. It was as eternal as the thin flat frown the woodworker had given him. He had skin like rust mixed with mud, and his outfit was a rainbow montage of feathers and animal skins. The man who made him was an Indian, too.

Three years ago, Pa had finally bought that store he'd always dreamed of owning. To Pa, Nettle's General Store was the culmination of years of hopes, and the end of the elusive vision that never materialized, yet had continued to tease him mercilessly. Most of his time, free or otherwise, was spent in that store. Neither my mother, sister, nor I saw much of him after that, except sometimes for supper. Meticulously he'd walk each aisle of the small store and stoop to check every bin of merchandise, neglecting nothing at all. Every yarn or straw doll, knitted scarf, Mr. Goodbar, everything was accounted for and inventoried.

Dust flew and danced around me in the breeze while I swept. Every few minutes, whenever his counting brought him to where he could see me out front, Pa would yell out to me to get on with it, or to tell me that I missed a spot. He wasn't a big man, but he had a big voice. Most of the time he just kept to himself, staying busy with his inventory list.

"Hey, Pa! You need any help counting them yarn dolls?" I yelled, hoping my words would sneak around the doorway to get his attention. "Miss Barnes says my adding's about the best in the whole class." I gave him a few seconds to show. "Hey, Pa!"

"What you yelling about now, Midge?" Midge was the nickname given to me by most of the other kids at the schoolhouse.

251

Short for midget, it never let me forget that I was less, at least in stature, than my peers. It was the only name by which most folks in town knew me. "Say, you ain't done with this porch yet? Dang, son...Quit fooling around with that Indian, and finish the porch."

"Yes, sir."

The wind played tag with the dust, and kept me sweeping twice as much as I should've just to get done. When I did finish, I gave my broom to Big Bull, leaning it beside his spear. He was surely a sight, that proud warrior, carrying a war spear firm and ready to fight, and there propped up against him was a ramshackle excuse for a broom. If only a real heart beat underneath that chest of oak, it would've burst wide open from humiliation.

"So...who are we gonna get after today, Big Bull? Billy the Kid?"

Indian eyes gazed straight ahead, seeming to point visibly at a victim for the day. Up main street, like the naked emperor in that Hans Christian Anderson story, walked Kyle Lovett.

"Good idea..." I told Big Bull, "Good idea..."

"Hey Mee-uhge," Kyle teased, dragging the nickname into two syllables, "You and your Indian chased any rustlers out of town today?"

Kyle stopped in the middle of the street to make sure I didn't ignore the remark. He looked different than usual. Clean. Dressed in his Sunday suit. Even his brown, mangled hair was combed. He didn't look like the same Kyle who had bloodied my nose two years ago.

I knew it was stupid to provoke him again, but I couldn't help it. Besides, Big Bull was with me. "Kyle? Hey, Kyle? What you all dressed up for? Today ain't Sunday, and there ain't a funeral in town or nothing."

"Look here, Midge," he shook a fist at me, "What I wear is my own business, not yours, runt."

That was the Kyle I was used to, no matter how he looked. That was the bully who had been responsible for getting me and

252

Big Bull together in the first place. When he had pounded my nose, Pa had been busy in the back of the store, and my mother had been up visiting my aunt and uncle in Missouri, so where else had I to go but to the Indian? He didn't tell me to hush up my racket, or that I was too big to cry. He had just listened and let me wet his feet and legs with my tears and the blood from my nose. By the time I'd finished, the swelling had gone down, and most of the bruises weren't sore anymore. Pa had sure been mad though; the blood wouldn't wash out, so my shirt had been pretty much ruined, and it was a gift from my cousins.

"I just wanted to know. Didn't mean to make nothing of it."

"Well, it ain't none of your business anyhow...but if you go telling everybody, I'll get you like last time." Satisfied, he spun around, facing away from the big Windham house at the edge of Chattville, and strutted off like the only rooster in a house full of hens.

Sometimes Big Bull and I would pass the afternoon hoping for a new General Motors' car to drive by. Most people who owned a car had an older Model T from ten or twelve years ago. The Windhams owned the only General Motors' vehicle in town, but they only got it out when they went to another town. Mostly everybody walked since Chattville was so small.

Before Kyle's dust could settle, Molly Windham came skipping up the street, her red hair pulled off to the sides of her head in pigtails, each one bouncing without rhythm, beating softly on her neck.

"That you, Midge?"

Molly was fourteen, three and a half years older than I was, but it didn't matter much. Especially standing there in her green party dress, made up like she was grown, not just a girl.

"Sure is."

She bounced right up to the porch, grinning like the cat from Wonderland.

"Midge..."

253

"Uh-uh."

"I just got the best news in the world." Her lips were painted with bright red; they were two roses, growing on her face. "And I'm so excited I feel like kissing somebody."

And she did. Molly Windham leaned over and stuck her two roses right on my forehead, and puckered like a fish.

I thought the stars had fallen from heaven, and were dancing around me.

While the stars danced, Molly twirled off the porch, and straight over to the dressmaker's shop. She jangled the bell beside his door a few times, spinning and jangling, jangling and spinning, until Sam Miller finally came out and yelled something I couldn't make out before pulling her inside. The echo from the bell drifted toward me and Big Bull.

"Did you see that!?"

The Indian didn't answer, but I knew he was listening, and that he hadn't missed any of it.

"Pa...Pa...Guess what!"

"You done with that porch yet?" Pa had come out to the screen door, tapping his pencil hard against that list of his. "There's plenty more sweeping to be done inside."

"Pa..."

He slipped his pencil into the front pocket of his work apron, and pulled his watch and chain from out of his pocket. As he flipped it open, he nodded, "Now, don't 'Pa' me. You know it takes a lot of work to keep this place going. That means all of us."

"But Lucy doesn't have to."

"Your sister's busy enough taking care of your mother. She don't have the time."

"But,"

Pa was starting to get mad. His eyes narrowed like an Asian man, and his ears began to turn a little red under where his hair was cut. "No excuses. First the back room, where the feed is. After that, we'll see about letting you play some more with that Indian."

He held the screen door open until I got the broom and trudged inside, dragging it with me. His eyes didn't leave me until the door to the back room slammed shut behind me. I know. I peeked back out as he turned.

My wooden friend waited patiently while I swept out the back room. He hadn't changed a single expression while I'd been gone. Just like always. He was there waiting.

"How much do you think flowers cost, Big Bull?" I kept watching for Molly to leave Sam Miller's shop. After a while nobody went in or came out anymore, and there was still no sign of Molly.

"Special flowers, I mean. Something better than I could pick out of somebody's yard."

Directly, Sam left the shop too, and locked the door behind him. He left two empty buckets outside the shop's door like he always did, just in case anybody needed to borrow one late in the day. His brown suit was pulled tight over his round frame making him look like a sausage with a lump in the middle.

"What kind of flowers do girls like now, anyway?" They're always so hard to please. That's what Pa says. He ought to know...he's known my mother a long time and all."

Sam had to walk down by the store to get to his house, and as he waddled by, I waved to him and said hello.

"Well, if it ain't little Midge. Say, you got you a girl for the dance next month? Surely your Pa and..." He made a face like he'd swallowed a horse. "Surely he's gonna let you and your sister get out to it."

"We ain't so good at dancing, Mr. Miller."

"I ain't so good myself." he said, and he was right. Round men who bounce when they walk looked twice as silly dancing. Even though he waltzed like a bag of potatoes, he always went. The girls said he made the best dancing gowns in the state. "But I wouldn't miss seeing all the pretty girls in their new dresses I've made for them. Just today Molly Windham ordered one of the most difficult gowns I've ever had to put together. Old Man Windham said not to worry about how much it costs. It's a dressmakers dream, Midge."

"What color is it, Mr. Miller?"

"Color? It ain't just any color, Midge. I've gotta order the cloth clean out of St. Louis."

"They got different colors in St. Louis than here in Chattville?"

"No. Now don't fool with an old man's funny bone. It's red, except it's the same color red as Molly's hair, lighter in spots, and shiny when the sun hits it right." Sam pulled on a gold chain that disappeared into the fold-over of flesh and suit where his pocket should have been. Out flopped a gold pocketwatch. He opened it. "I'd better go. Mrs. Miller will be wondering were I am. Hope you get to go."

I waved goodbye.

"Roses. Red roses. The reddest we can find."

I knew Big Bull approved.

Pa said no when I asked him about the flowers. I told him I'd work harder, and even stay away from the gumballs, but he still said no. That he was spending too much on the store already, and with my mother's fever still not breaking, even though it had been two weeks...

The wind was picking up, turning a calm kiss-like breeze into a cold slap. Some papers announcing the dance floated across town in short hops, then flew on, bullet-like, when the stronger drafts got a hold of them.

The porch was warm underneath my weight, but when I touched it in a new place the wood was cold. The moisture on my hands would chill and then thaw in a fluid motion. I looked back at Big Bull.

"Sure was nice of old Joe to let me work for the flowers."

I held the two flowers, roses, red as Molly's fiery hair and the lips that had kissed me. They had cost me every cent I had plus a promise to work down at Old Joe's flower shop once a week when I wasn't helping Pa at the store. It was a high price, but worth it to see the look I knew would be on Molly's face when I asked her to the dance.

It had seemed like hours until dusk came. Now that it was here, I could hardly wait. But the timing had to be perfect. I had to show up right after the dishes were put away. If I arrived early, the surprise would get lost in the cleanup shuffle; if I was too late, the effect would be interrupted by the family time around the radio listening to Amos and Andy.

"Wish me luck," I said, and dashed from the porch.

Roses firmly in hand, I hurried down to the house at the edge of Chattville where Molly and her father lived. Her mother had died of tuberculosis when Molly was a baby. I could think only of my dream, my vision, waiting for me there in her red party dress, the fringes dancing in the evening breeze. My heart seemed not only to beat, but to pound with a steady, driving, big jazz rhythm like Benny Goodman or Louis Armstrong was directing its music. Time hardly passed at all, it seemed before I was there, suddenly staring at the heavy oak door.

Mr. Windham answered the door quickly after my small closed hand gathered the resolve to knock. His herringbone suit hung comfortably loose off of his tall thin frame. When he recognized me, his small mustache twitched and his eyes focused down onto mine.

"Why Midge, what a pleasant surprise. What can I do for you?"

"Is Molly in, sir? I'd sure like to see her. I/ve got something for her."

"Sure she is. Right in the den with:"

Kyle Lovett. Mr. Windham didn't have to say it. I knew it the minute I walked in. He was sitting on the couch with Molly, holding her hand. How could she? Didn't she know what he was like? Kyle Lovett.

257

The roses were trampled underfoot as I choked on the anger rising in my throat, and ran away to Pa, dragging a cracked and tender heart behind me.

"Pa! Pa!" as I pounded at the door with my small fists, knowing he would be locked away in the back office, listening to the clickety-clacks of the adding machine.

The sky had blackened since I had left Molly's, and had given its first few drops to warn me that a big storm was coming. Rumbles sounded in the distance, but grew a little louder each time. If I'd had sense enough, I'd have let the winds blow me straight up the street to my house, safe from the weather.

"Pa! Please let me in. There's a storm coming, Pa. Pa!"

As if it had waited for my announcement, the thunder and rain let loose on the earth like God was trying to punish us the way the Pastor down at the Missionary Church had said. The rain began to pelt down, soaking the dirt of the road, and beating it into a shallow layer of mud almost instantly. The papers that had been blown all over town were drenched and wrenched apart by the combined power of the wind and water.

Across the street was the wall of clay we all climbed on in the summer. At least we tried to climb it. It went about sixteen feet straight up, smooth as a polished stone. The only way to make it to the top was to take two pocketknives, and edge your way up, one jab at a time. Only the oldest and strongest boys ever made it all the way. The rest of us could hardly even stick the knives in the wall, since the clay was so hard and set.

The storm washed it down to sixteen feet of mush pretty quickly. Anyone who tried to climb it now would probably drown in the river of wet clay eroding down the face of the wall.

The wind lifted Sam Miller's two buckets, and sent one through the candy store window, and the other into the outside wall, where it dented and fell, waiting for another flight.

Although the porch kept me safe from most of the wind, it offered me no protection from the worst of the storm. The rain invaded in solid bullets of water, spreading out and joining together to make lakes and reservoirs that ran down between the cracks, only to be replaced by the new puddles that continued to build.

"Pa!" I yelled, but the thunder swallowed my cries. Big Bull stood firm. Since he was so heavy, the wind couldn't shake him, not even a quiver. The rain soaked into the wood, but that only made him heavier, more secure. It also darkened the colors, and brought him closer to life.

Through the curtain of water, I saw every cut, every strain of artistry on Big Bull's frame. In each carefully carved inch of his face, pain rested. His eyes were deep-set and sunken a little in sorrow, but somehow friendly in their darkness. The mouth was closed in an eternal silence, and the wrinkled carvings surrounding the flattened frown revealed a subdued bitterness that flamed, no doubt, beneath the painted exterior. Though he held only a single spear, his muscles were tensed and rigid, ready to answer the call to fight, eager. Big Bull captured well not only the hurt and anger of his people, but their strength as well.

So I hid from the storm.

The Indian's figure kept me dry for the most part. Patches of rain managed every now and then to sneak around his legs and hit me, but I was separated from the worst part of the weather.

In time, the fury of the storm faded away. Its terrible threats and banshee screams died into quiet darkness. The sun had abandoned its post during the attack, leaving Chattville lighted only by the incandescent glow of random windows. Sleep, like a desire for death, found me, and I curled around Big Bull's wooden feet.

"Midge...Midge...Get up. You'll catch a death of a cold out here."

The blackness lifted from behind my mind and eyes, and I saw Pa trying to help me up.

"Pa..."

"Yeah, it's me. What were you doing out here in the middle of that storm anyway? I thought you were home with your mother and sister."

    I didn't answer. Instead, I reached for the handle of Big Bull's spear, and used it to pull my worn-out body to a sluggish stance. Pa immediately reached out to keep me from falling again to the porch, but the spear supported me well enough.

    "Let's get you inside. I've got some hot cider going if you want some. It'll sure help warm up your insides."

    I felt Pa's overcoat as it was put around me to keep me from shivering. I expected it to engulf me, but it barely spread across my shoulders. He was a much smaller man than I had imagined.

Dying Will

by Jessica L. Nettles

Rose awoke to a steady beep-beep-beep. She looked around slowly, taking in the cluster of tubes, wires and machines surrounding her bed. Her body felt light and airy as she sat up, pushing her silver curls from her face. Hanna, her daughter, was keeping vigil by her side. She held on to her mama's knobbed hand in silence.

Rose leaned over and kissed Hanna between her gray eyes, stroking her golden hair. She couldn't feel her daughter's warmth and Hanna didn't notice her mama's touch. She peered through the wall and watched Jeremy as he talked to a nurse with intense interest. Rose chuckled to herself—even as a small boy he was a charmer, picking flowers to the roots and bringing them to make his mama smile. He was such a good boy. She had always wanted the best for both of her children.

The door opened, bleeding blue light into the dimness of the room. A young, raven-haired girl with porcelain skin entered. She smiled at Rose.

"I told you I would come back," she said.

Rose climbed off the bed, away from her static form and asked, "Is it time to go? Can I leave?"

"Look, I know you're ready to rock, but you know I can't help until the machines are gone. Rules are rules," replied the girl. She sat down on the floor allowing her ebony skirt to spread around her. She fiddled with the miniature scythe on the chain around her wrist.

Sitting down with her friend, Rose whispered, "Jeremy begged me to get a living will. Of course I was always busy doing something and never got to it. Now I'm ready to die and I'm hooked to these damned machines. Why can't you do anything? After all, you are Death."

Death sighed and looked down at the floor. "Rose, we've been through this already. I can't do anything to the machines. I can just escort your soul. I'm just as frustrated as you are about this situation."

The two of them sat in silence watching the pump force air

into Rose's lungs, and the heart monitor count the meter of her life; she should be dead, but the doctors refused. For the last six days whenever the physicians visited, she did everything in her power to get their attention. At first she was furious, but Death had assured her that was not the solution. Fury gave way to the fear of being on machines for months or years. Today, day seven, she had accepted her fate whatever it may be.

The nurses came and went so many times, Rose lost count. She peered at the clock on the wall, to get a sense of time but the numbers on its face were jumbled. This must be limbo, God's waiting room. Rose hated to wait. She got up and marched over to her inert body, first looking into her own face, which had a blue transluscent quality about it. The tubes going in and out of her nose and mouth intensified Rose's alienation from her earthly form. The mockery of life under her gaze made her glad to be separate. She reached over the head of the bed and tried to turn off the machines herself. Her hand passed through the wall effortlessly, causing her to almost fall on top of the body in the bed.

"Remember, you are spirit, Rose," said Death.

"Damn it to hell!" Rose spat through her tears. After her tears evaporated, she looked at Death, who was still sitting calmly on the floor. "You can't help, I can't do anything. Who can end this? I'm tired of waiting," she said.

Death smiled wryly. "Your kids can, if they're pushed. Push them, it's what you do best. In the meantime, I have other people to visit," she said. "I'll be back."

Blue light passed through Rose as Death made her exit. The next time the door opened Jeremy entered. He looked so tired and rumpled. Rose wanted to straighten his tie and smooth his mussed brown hair, like she had all of his life. Sadness darkened his face as he sat by her form. After what could have been a long or short time, he dozed in the green hospital chair, allowing a sort of peace to wrap his body. Rose remembered the ghost stories that her daddy told her when she was a child. Many of those stories mentioned ghosts appearing to sleeping people. Jeremy had always laughed at her "haint" stories. He was one who needed proof. She closed her eyes in prayer to God, *please let him believe this one time.*

"Jeremy, rise and shine," she bellowed, just like she did when he was a boy.

He startled, his bright-blue eyes fluttering, "Mama!" As he looked around the dim light of ICU he mumbled, "Must have been dreaming." Shaking his head he got up and paced around the room to revive himself.

Rose jumped in front of him and yelled, "Look at me, Jeremy!" She had to get through to him.

"I need coffee." He shivered and strode right through her to the door.

Jeremy was exhausted and angry. Mama had been in a coma now for a whole week and the doctors could do nothing for her. He knew that her age had finally caught up with her indomitable spirit and that he should be more understanding about her dying. Something inside of him kept whispering that if she had held on this long, maybe she could pull out of the coma. The machines kept this false hope alive the same way they kept her body alive, in an artificial but acceptable way.

He passed through the entrance to the hospital cafeteria in search of caffeine and relief from the awfulness of ICU. The sign above the carafes read "Now proudly serving Starbuck's Coffee." Jeremy poured himself a cup, wincing as he took a sip of the strongest cup of Sumatra he had ever had. The taste made him think of Mama's chicory brewing on the stove early each morning before school. He sat down at a table next to a huge window that framed a lovely garden with roses of various shapes and colors glowing in the early light of morning. He imagined that Church Street was flooding with commuters and buses by now. He should call Delia at the office and tell her to pass his docket to Magnus, his partner, again today. Thank goodness he understood.

He put his head in his hands, as the caffeine tingled through his bloodstream. The dream flashed in his mind. There was Mama, jumping up and down in her flowered nightgown, bellowing for him to wake up just like when he was at home.

Mama had pushed him hard as a kid to do the best he could, much more than Hanna, who was expected be a mama herself. She pushed him to work hard at school, to focus on his future.

He wanted to play football and have girlfriends, but he yielded to her desire, focusing on good grades instead. Once he arrived at college, her drive became his inner voice. Even when he didn't speak to her for weeks at a time, he could hear her voice in his head. He began to believe he was the best, and the payoff was rewarding. He had a reasonably successful law office that overlooked Glover Park and had a clear view of the stylish courthouse where he practiced his craft. At forty he was still single. She tried to find women to suit him, but he rid himself of them pretty quickly most of the time. He loved her in spite of her demanding nature and had lunch with her at Shillings every Wednesday until last week. He had drawn up a living will for her but he could never get her to sign it. She complained about how he was nagging her about something that might not come for a long time. So, not wanting to make her unhappy he dropped the subject. Without the living will, the doctors could keep her from dying indefinitely. Jeremy clung to the hope of recovery. He needed her.

He raised his head and was caught off guard by a young woman sitting on the other side of his table drinking chocolate milk. The girl looked at him with deep, dark eyes that seemed to peer directly into his soul. Jeremy looked away, mostly to hide any truths she might see. She smiled and set down the milk.

"Hey, mister, that stuff will kill you," she said pointing at his cup of now cold coffee.

He looked up at her, confused. "Do I know you?" he asked.

"Hearsay, mostly. Rose and I have become close in the last week," she replied.

"My mother has been in a coma the last few days. You're from the psycho ward, right?"

"Your mama wants you to know that she loves you. She also wants you to stop being selfish and let her die," she said quietly. She took another sip of chocolate milk, her black hair falling

264

into her face.

"Look, I don't know who the hell you are, but how about going back to your rubber room, okay?"

"Just make the doctors turn off the machines. She needs to go; you need to let her. You owe her that much dignity," she said, looking directly into his face.

Jeremy turned away. "Who are you to be saying these things to me? Now, please leave or I'll call security." He spoke with an edge in his voice. Whoever she was, she knew exactly how to upset him.

She stood, stared at him and frowned. The natural light from the garden encircled her body like a halo. She pointed a pale finger directly at him.

"Hear me out, Jeremy MacAfee. This isn't about you; this is about your mother. Let her go," she said.

"SECURITY! SECURITY!" Jeremy called, as he backed away from her.

Two nurses ran from the entrance of the cafeteria to Jeremy. He pointed in the direction of the woman, and said, "That woman needs to be removed."

They looked around, but saw no one. Then they made him sit down and take deep breaths. The taller and prettier of the two comforted him. She looked at her companion shaking her head. "He's the son of one of our terminal cases in ICU. Poor guy, he's been here for a whole week. I'll take him upstairs and get him a light sedative."

Once upstairs, she stopped to grab a blanket and pillow and then led him to the family room; they passed Rose's room. Jeremy paused for a moment then followed the nurse silently.

"I'll wake you if anything new happens with Miss Rose, okay, Mr. MacAfee?" the nurse said with a professional smile.

"Sure. Thanks for your help," Jeremy answered.

As he drifted off into a gray sleep, he wondered if he had really seen the strange woman at the table. He dreamed of his childhood again. He smelled the morning chicory. He ate breakfast watching his mama flutter around the kitchen, eggs on one plate, bacon on another. He then dashed out to school, where all the girls had the face of the girl in the cafeteria.

"Let her go," they chanted.

Behind the girls was one face that was different. It was Hanna. He reached for her to no avail. "Hanna!"

Hanna brushed Rose's thin, white locks away from her grayish face with a hairbrush. "You should always look your best. You never know who might see you," she whispered to the wire cluttered body of her mother. She smiled, and thought of the many times Mama had made her change her clothes before going out of the house, using those very words. Hanna wondered if mama could hear her and was chuckling. The doctors had told her that coma patients could hear everything going on around them. Maybe mama could hear, too.

She knew that she was not her mother's favorite child. Jeremy disagreed, but it was true. Mama loved her differently, pushed her in different ways. She was never driven like Jeremy anyway, being more comfortable around horse farms and babies than cities. When she married Patrick, they moved to Paulding County as soon as they found a house with acreage. She had fulfilled her destiny, to be a mother. She remembered how mama beamed when she held each of her four grandchildren after they were born. Mama seemed pleased for her, but they never had the closeness Hanna wanted.

Hanna gazed down at Rose. She was so frail now, not at all like the woman who had raised them. Mama was loud and boisterous—not afraid of anything. She wondered if mama was singing "All Hail the Power of Jesus' Name" right in death's face, the way she taught Hanna to do when she was afraid. Mama's heart had stopped briefly on Wednesday, but the nurses brought her back. Since she had no living will, they could keep doing that, even if it seemed futile. The lack of color in Rose's face told Hanna that her mama was not really there. Keeping her on these machines seemed ridiculous to Hanna. She shivered as a cool breeze brushed at her arms.

"Hanna, angel baby," whispered a familiar voice.

She turned around, looking for what couldn't be possible. There on the hard, green hospital chair sat an apparition that resembled her mama. It was wearing mama's favorite flowered nightgown and robe combination. Its hair looked like it had just been done, all curly and styled. Its eyes had the same twinkle they had when mama looked at the boys.

"M-Mama?" said Hanna, not believing her senses.

The ghost nodded its head and smiled. "I'm so glad you can see me. I tried to talk to Jeremy but he wouldn't listen."

"But mama...are you dead? Or am I dreaming?" Hanna asked as her mind raced to put words together.

She reached out to touch the face of the being in the chair. Her hand passed through it. Hanna sat down at its feet and looked up like a small child. She wasn't sure whether she should be afraid or just accept the idea of talking to a spirit. After all, it was mama.

" Mama, you look great, really. Uh, mama, are you dead or not? Why aren't you in heaven? Isn't that where people go when they die?" the words seemed to flood out of her mouth.

"It's those damn machines. I want to go, but they won't let me. Baby, help me." Hanna could see traces of tears on her mother's face.

Her own eyes darkened in a storm of sadness, not knowing what to do except talk. She needed to call Jeremy; he would see things in a logical fashion.

"Let me get Jeremy. He'll know what to do," she said.

"Jeremy won't even see me, sweetie. He won't believe you anyway, never could believe in haints. His feet are planted solid in the world. I'm glad you were the one to see me first, you've always had more heart. Listen to your heart, you've always been good at that," mama said with a smile.

Hanna smiled too, and she thought of how many strays she had brought into the house as a child. "You used to say that when I brought in all those strays back at home," she replied.

"Baby, you have the gift of caring, which is something rare in this day and age. It makes you more special than you know," Rose said as she placed her hand on Hanna's head without really

267

touching her. "Now, I saw Jeremy talking to that pretty nurse out-side. Is she interested in him? I can't always make out what is happening on your side."

Hanna looked at her incredulously and then laughed, roll-ing her eyes. "Mama, when are you going to leave him alone?"

"When I'm dead and gone, which I hope will happen soon if you two will help," Rose said.

"How? Please don't ask me to turn off the machines, I don't think I can. The idea of killing you is too horrible to bear. What if they arrest me, what would happen then? Oh, mama, isn't there an easier way?" Hanna asked as she paced across the room.

"Hanna Raquel, stop whining. This isn't murder, I want you to do this," answered Rose.

Hanna closed her eyes and absorbed what was happening to her. She was sitting in a hospital room talking with her mama's ghost trying to decide whether or not to commit a mercy killing. She got up off the floor and stretched her legs. Then she took one more look at the shadow of her mother.

"I need to talk to Jeremy," she said as she moved toward the door.

Mama nodded and said, "I'll be here."

Hanna backed out of the door into the flourescent bright-ness of the hall. She called Delia at Jeremy's office, but he had not come to work nor even called. She asked the nurse at the desk if she had seen him and she led Hanna to where he was sleeping. Hanna followed quietly, trying not to be angry with the nurse for what was happening to her mama.

When they got to the room, Hanna slipped in and peered at Jeremy's sleeping form on the cot. Jeremy seemed to sleep peace-fully, and Hanna hated to wake him but touched his shoulder anyway.

Jeremy was trying to get to class on time. He was late be-cause he was trying to escape the young women who kept following him. He turned an unfamiliar corner and was confronted by his mother suspended by ethereal chains over his head. She was weep-ing, "Jeremy, free me…let me go. I can't move on…help me."

"Mama, hold on a minute," he shouted.

He reached up and up, but when he reached the lock on the chain, he discovered that he didn't have a key. Then he heard Hanna's voice in the distance. "Jeremy, I have the key!"

"Where are you, Hannie?" he called using the name he had given her as a child.

"I'm right here, are you okay?" She asked as she shook him awake. He was startled at her presence.

"Is mama all right?" he asked catching his breath.

"She's the same. Sort of. You've gotta come with me. Promise you will listen," Hanna said.

"Hanna, you haven't seen a strange girl trying to get into mama's room have you?" he asked, as they moved toward the hospital room.

"No, but I talked to mama just now. Or her ghost, I mean."

"You can't be serious. Mama is still alive, so she can't be a ghost even if there were such a thing."

"Hey, I know this is hard for you to swallow, but just listen." She said this as she stalked up ahead to the door to mama's room. Why couldn't he take anything on faith?

She opened the door and there was mama sitting on the edge of the chair, tapping her fingers. Mama had never been patient. "Hi, mama. Jeremy is here," she said loudly and slowly to the ghost.

Rose covered her ears, "I can hear just fine. No need to shout anymore."

Jeremy looked around the room but only saw the same view he had seen for the past seven days. He gently took his sister's hands. "Maybe you should go home and get some sleep in your own bed, Hannie."

" I'm not seeing things, she's right here," she said, emphatically pointing to the empty green chair by the bed.

"Let me get the nurse in here. I'm sure she can help," he said in a soothing voice.

Rose paced back and forth. "Dammit, why won't he listen!"

Jeremy was too busy trying to call a nurse to hear her comment.

The door opened to a space of blue light. Jeremy had hoped it was the nurse, instead it was the young girl from the cafeteria. Jeremy stood between her and his mother, " Don't touch my mother."

"Hey, I'm not the enemy here, Jeremy. I just want to do my job. Any questions?" She shot back at him.

Rose stepped between the two of them and reached up, stroking Jeremy's ruffled brown hair. "Now baby, she's not gonna hurt me. She's here to help."

Hanna stood toe-to-toe with the girl, "Who the hell are you?"

"I have many names, but most people call me Death," the girl answered, as she spun around watching her skirt billow out.

"You said you were here to do a job? Well, do it, mama doesn't like waiting."

"I can't. The machines won't let me."

Hanna looked at her mama, who nodded in agreement as she hovered around Jeremy.

Jeremy shivered. A cold draft had passed through his messy crop of hair and he didn't know why. He went and sat in the big green chair. He felt the draft follow him.

"Why is it so cold in here?"

Jeremy felt the chair sigh with the added extra weight. He looked again around the room and then right next to him. He jumped back in bewilderment as his mama's dancing eyes met his. "Oh my God, mama."

"In the spirit. Hey, I'm still funny."

"Mama, what are you? You can't be a ghost. What am I saying?" he asked.

"Baby, you were always my logical child. Everything had to make sense. Hanna was my spiritual child, more in contact with the unseen. Some things, like this, aren't logical. You have to follow your heart."

"Mama, we can't just unplug you. There are laws..." Jeremy whispered.

"Jeremy, I am ready to do whatever it takes. Mama is ready

270

to go, who cares about the law?" asked Hanna.

"There's no logical way to make this work," Jeremy said.

"Then ignore logic,"said Hanna.

"Finally, someone makes sense in here. Look, you guys make your decision. I'll be waiting outside for you, Rose when you're ready," said Death. She patted Hanna on the shoulder as she exited. "Listen to your heart, girlfriend."

Hanna felt hot and cold at the same time. She looked into Jeremy's face but found only anguish. He turned his back to her.

"Do what you think is best and I'll do my best to support you."

She closed her eyes for a second, then opened them and moved toward the bed and her mother's body.

"I love you, mama."

She looked over at the green chair where Rose had taken a seat again and smiled. Hanna noticed mama was smiling that smile she had worn at both of Jeremy's graduations. Only this time the smile was for Hanna.

She quickly found the red switch that would shut off Rose's life forever. As she pushed it, she blew one last kiss to her mother. Jeremy got up and pulled her toward the door, his eyes welling with tears. The constant meter of the heart monitor was replaced by a single long beep and mama's body let out one last, relieved sigh. Death was waiting as she said she would. She smiled at Hanna and Jeremy as Rose joined her.

Doctors and nurses raced around them like they were invisible. Rose embraced her children one last time, kissing them between their eyes. She loved them forever.

Death smiled and turned to leave, then turned to Jeremy, "Hey, remember that coffee will kill you."

The wall opened up and Death and Rose exited into the bright, blue light of eternity.

Jeremy held Hanna close hoping to absorb the depth of her sorrow through the numbness that encased his heart. He prayed for the first time in ages and thanked God for the chance to be with his mama one more time. Some things just defy logic.

O, Georgia!

July Fourth, New Orleans
by Genevieve Nicholson-Butts

We follow the centerline of the uneven street
Its paint faded, cracked
Sun-pulled flake by flake

The air here is wet, you say

Crumpled bills we pull from pockets,
Hand to the street vendor in exchange for crimson, rum-loaded drinks
Thin plastic cups bend in our grip as we greedily suck straws

Today, a holiday

Storefronts quickly accumulate crowds of loiterers
Vacationers form haphazard circles around portrait artists
This heat will melt the charcoal right off the paper, you say
Only deliquesced faces, blurred forms to remain

The pavement ends abruptly, and so we've lost our guide
Behind us loom synthetic structures and concrete-covered ground,
Before us stretches a rare tangle of nature preserved,
    Trees age-gnarled, stones earth-carved, paths foot-worn,
    The grass thick, an unearthly green,
Beyond this, the river shines, its currents calm

In this place stuck between asphalt and water,
Dozens of people sprawl, sun-soaked,
    College students sleeping with backpacks for pillows, sandals kicked
    off at their sides
    Preteen girls, tank-topped and short-shorted, giggling at
    shirtless men passing by
    Old men, wrinkled and weathered, hugging their brown-bagged
    whiskey

O, Georgia!

One sole stander, a twenty-something male,
Wears nothing but cutoffs,
His arms outstretched, cheeks sunken, ribcage protruding
We hear his voice, elevated above the clustered chatter

I will die soon
This could be you

We notice blood-crimson lesions on his shoulders, chest
Wet, blazing, heat-drenched with sun-sweat
Sun-kissed sarcoma, sun-sucked, sun-pulled

We've seen this before
But never in public, you say
We know what silence equals

Death
Don't let this be you
Don't let this be you
Save yourself

People milling in the street, lounging in the park
Napping, laughing, drinking, chatting
The river, like time, passes slowly today

But not for this man,
His course raging, near its end

Today, a holiday,
But a day this man won't celebrate

Country Medicine Man
by Maxine Hamm

Mr. Eric fills up with grins as he opens the door to the wardrobe and looks at the rows of bottles on the top shelf. Green bottles, brown bottles and a row of small clear bottles stand side by side like an army waiting for a command. He reaches for one of the brown bottles and puts it on the table, then turns to one of the green bottles and lines it up beside the brown one. He stops to admire the row of clear bottles and takes out a jar that has a measuring spoon in it. He pulls a sheet of white paper from the roll on the table and places it beside the bottles. Carefully opening the brown bottle he dips in the measuring spoon and puts the boric-acid powder on the paper. Next he takes the green jar and pours a little distilled water on the powder and with the spoon turns it around in a little puddle that begins to look like a tornado. Turning back to the wardrobe he gets a clear bottle, scoops the ingredients into it, and pours water from the green bottle until it is full. Putting the lid on tight he shakes it until it foams and sets it aside to settle.

He gets that same grin on his face every time he mixes his eye-water. It makes the hairy mole that is perched on his cheek stand out on his road of wrinkles. His blue eyes flash like he is still a young man and his hands are as steady as the day he was twenty, except for the pinkie on his right hand—it moves up and down in a jerk and seems unaware of the rest of his body. His life has been good these sixty-five years. He turns to the man in the room and says, "Bout how much y'all want?"

"That'll do. Just 'nough so it'll do sum good. My kid she ain't never got no sore eyes like this 'fore and she just keeps on a rubbing them and I tells her to quit it but she don't pay me no mind." He reaches for the bottle as his right hand feels in his pocket for some change. "It's still twenty-five cents, ain't it?"

"Yep, that's all it is," he said.

"Well, I gotta be going. Much ablige to you." He hands him the change, tips his hat and walks out the front door to his truck. Mr. Eric following behind stops on the front porch and sits in the old rocking chair.

275

The screen door opens and Maude comes out wiping her face with her apron, her hair strung up on top of her head with pins—looks like gray ribbons hung up on a clothesline. "Hit sho' is hot, I tell you. What'd he want?" she asks as the man drives away.

"Just a little eye water for his kid. Says she might near can't see."

"I sho' don't see how that stuff you got in them there jars makes a difference in opening eyes."

"Well, I don't know either, but it does. Did you see that Carmel girl? She was a sight to see. She could barely get about until she got my eye-water and then about three or four days of them there drops made a difference. It must be something."

"Well, I'm going in and finish supper. You been trying to catch a cold, so don't sit out here so long. Ya hear?"

"Call me when it's fixed."

The porch is quiet except for the sound of crickets and the occasional sound of a car on the dirt road.

"Eric, come on in ya hear, and le's eat 'fore sommers else comes."

He takes his time about doing it, looks one more time down the dusty road and pulls his chair in the corner of the porch, just in case it rains, and goes into the kitchen.

"You know one day Eric we gonna buy us a good table to put here in this kitchen. You can have this un to put in the back room for your eye water and get rid of that old board table you made. It would be a good mixing table. I gets tired of having to pull out a metal piece in a cabinet to eat off of."

"I like the board table myself. It's not too big and not too little. Sides, I nailed it together with boards from this here house. If you get tired of eating off the metal table we could just eat in the dining room. I kinda like it in there myself."

"That's fur company."

"Company? What company? We ain't had no company since I don't know when."

"Sides, it's just too much trouble. In the winter time its too cold in there and in the summer I'm just too plain tired to fool with it. I just scrambled us up some of them eggs to eat with the bacon and biscuits we had."

"Sounds all right to me. I ain't too much for eating when it's hot."

"Well, why ain't you sitting down and eating now?"

She hands him his plate of eggs and bacon and pulls her chair beside his. "Well, I'll declare I plum forgot the biscuits. Trying to keep them warm over there and us talking and all, I just forgets." She stands up, gets the tin pan of biscuits out of the oven with her apron, throws them on the table, pulls her chair up by the sides with both hands and balances herself to sit down. "You ain't gonna eat no bacon?"

"Don't think so. The last time I did I had the heart burn so bad, I said to myself, you don't need that to eat."

No sound was heard except the chirping of crickets outside and the constant banging of forks and plates. "I believe I hear another car out there, Eric."

"Can't say as I do," he replies.

"You just keep on a eating and I'll see who's out there." She pushes her chair back and wipes her hands on her apron before moving down the hall to the front door. "Eric, you better hurry up and swallow down that there food cause there's somebody out here."

"Y'all just come on in ya hear. We just eating a bite of supper so y'all come on in and sit down," she says opening the screen door.

"No ma'am, we can't stay. My little girl needs some eye-water and they say this here stuff is real catching. It must be, cause my other kid's eyes are already getting red. I need to get enough for all of them. Is Mr. Eric busy?"

"I just said we're eating our supper."

"Well, I'll just wait here on the porch till he's through."

"I'll tell him to hurry. Here he is now. You through with supper?"

"Yeah, mighty good too. What can I do for you Mr. Cox?"

"My kid out there has the sore-eyes and my other one is a rubbing his too so I thought I'd better get over here 'fore I had to

277

see a doctor."

"Come on in here, I'll have to mix sum up. Your kid in the car?"

"Yeah, she's sitting out there."

"Well, bring her on, in—I ain't seen her for a long time and I bet she's 'bout grown."

"They sho' do get away in a hurry. I wuz just telling my wife other day how soon she'll be gone from home and it'll just be me and her." He goes to the door and hollers, "Hey, Mr. Eric says you can come on in."

The door was already open, so she jumps out, runs up the steps, tugging a doll in one hand and a bottle in the other.

"You sho' grown up since I seen you last. It's been a long time. What do you have there?" asked Mr. Eric.

"That's my doll," she says holding it up for him to see. "She's had the sore eyes for a long time. Can you make her well?"

"I believe I can," says Mr. Eric as he winks at the man. "Well, ya'll come on in and I'll fix you up." They go through the hall to the long back room. "Oh, I haven't cleaned up my mess from my last fixing today. Just give me a minute." He rolls up the paper and lays it on the table, tears off a clean sheet and puts it down to start mixing. Mr. Eric takes out clear bottles, green bottles, and brown bottles. The little girl goes around the table touching everything in sight and even the things that aren't. Laying the clean white paper on the table he measures from each of the jars and puts the boric-acid on the paper. His little finger seems to be giving him trouble again. He doesn't know if it shakes because the child makes him nervous, or if it is just determined to shake.

"Mr. Eric, smell of my medicine," the little girl says. "See, I'm a doctor too."

"Just a minute and I'll have this mixed for you." His little finger seems to be giving him more trouble. She grabs the old paper and pretends to mix medicine like Mr. Eric and opens her bottle.

As he mixes the powder on the paper the child sits her bottle down beside the paper. "Let's don't put that here till I get through," he says. He starts to pick up the bottle but his finger got there with its shakes first and turns it over on the table.

"All right in the car. You're making Mr. Eric nervous," says the man.

"Can I help you clean this up?" asks the child.

"No, I'll do it," replies Mr. Eric. "What's in that bottle anyway?"

"Just something the kids put in it, probably water," the man says.

"Let me get her in the car and I'll be back. Just throw that ole bottle away. She don't need it no how." He hollers at the kid plundering around the house. "In the car, I say." She runs to the door and down the steps to the car. "You just wait there till I get through, ya hear?"

Mr. Eric wipes up the spill before putting a clean sheet of paper over the dirty one to mix the powder. Carefully he tightens the cork on the bottles and sits them back in the cabinet; all except the brown one. He picks up the powder that is left on the paper and dumps it back in the brown bottle and says, "Well, that's done." Placing it back in the cabinet he goes back to the front of the house as the man is coming in the front door. "Well, here it is. That'll be twenty-five cents."

"Sho' saves me a lot, I tell you. Well, much ablige to you and Ill see you later"

"Just glad to do it for you."

Mr. Eric goes back in the kitchen where his wife is finished cleaning up from supper. "I tell you that kid's a mess. I could hardly do a thing for that little one."

"They probably ain't had no learning at home. Guess it's just as good that we ain't got none. Are you 'bout ready for bed? I'm 'bout ready to turn in."

"Can't say that I am, cause it's so hot, but we need to get some rest."

"Well let's turn in then. I have a few things to finish right here, so you go on and I'll be there in a minute."

He is already snoring when she ties back the curtains to let in the air. All she can hear is the sounds of crickets, frogs and the small fan that will purr back and forth at the foot of the bed until first light.

"I knew we'd do it. Eric, we slept too long. Eric, do you know what time it is?" she says as she turns over to wake him up. "Eric, now where did he go? Guess he couldn't sleep cause it's so hot." She grabs her housecoat that is strung across a chair and ties it around her. As she walks toward the door she hears voices from the porch.

"That's just the way it is. I'll have to check all your bottles cause the child's eyes are might near out. I hate to do this but, you know the rules about this kind of thing."

"I know how it is but, I've been fixing eye-water might near thirty years and I ain't never had no complaint. I go by what it says on the bottle."

"I know that."

"Well, seems if you gotta do it, you might as well git at it. She's up 'bout now so just come on in."

"Here I am Eric. What is the matter?"

"You know that kid that was here last night?"

"How could I forget that kid. What's the matter?"

"Seems that last night she just gotta screaming and hollering so bad that they had to take her to the Doctor. Said she had sumthing in her eyes she wasn't suppose to have. They saying that hits my eye water. I ain't never had no trouble 'fore."

Mr. Eric and his wife go to the back room and the Sheriff's Deputy follows. Mr. Eric starts pulling out the bottles. "That's all right. You don't have to do that. I'll just get your dirty paper and some of the bottles. I sure do hate to do this, you know. I'll let you know as soon as I find out something." The Deputy reaches in the cabinet, pulls out some bottles, puts them in a box, and shakes Mr. Eric's hand before hurrying out the door.

As he leaves, Mr. Eric walks back in the kitchen where she is. "I can't believe they said it was my eye-water that hurt that kid. I ain't done nothing different for thirty some odd years and I ain't never hurt nobody."

"Well, you can't trust nobody these days. I just guess they

scared or something."

"I think I'm going to ride to town awhile and see about getting some more plants for the garden. Wanna go?"

"No, I'll finish up my work here. What time you be back?"

"Don't know. Before early afternoon."

"You be careful. Them roads are so dusty you can't see who's
coming or going."

"I know how to drive." she follows him to the kitchen door
and watches as he drives off.

"Be careful, I say."

She fastens the screen door, walks back to the bedroom,
raises a window and scrambles through a basket of clothes. "I might
as well do this mending since I hate to do it but it's gotta be done."
She picks up her needle and thread that was stuck in the pants leg
and begins to darn the torn place in the leg. "Every time I turn
around I'm mending these here pants. He must work hard trying to
get holes in them." She sits half-way rocking, half-way mending
and half-way thinking out loud. "I just know he didn't put anything
in that there eye-water. He is forgetting a lot though. And his poor
'ole finger just won't stay still. It's hard for him to measure good,
but that shouldn't make no difference."

"There come that there dust again." She jumps up and pulls
down the windows. "It don't do me no good trying to clean with all
that dust. Well, it's that there Deputy again stopping out there. No
need to sit down. I'll just see what he wants."

She gets to the door just as he jumps two steps at a time and
is at the screen door. "Is Mr. Eric home?"

"No. He went in to town to get some plants for the garden.
Won't you come in?"

"I'll just wait here on the porch,"

"Did y'all learn anything:"

"Yes, and what time did you say he'd be back?"

"I didn't say."

"There's the dust over there. Could be him."

The old car drives up by the yard and she is out there before
it stops. "They didn't have a thing I went there for. Just told me to

come back Friday. Oh, I didn't see you up there," he says as he looks up at the Deputy standing on the porch. "Do you have any news?"

"Yes, we do, Mr. Eric. That brown jar had alcohol on the outside. Just a trace mind you but, it was what the girl got in her eyes. No wonder she was screaming. I'm sorry 'bout this Mr. Eric, but they tell me to bring in all your jars. You know the Sheriff told me to do this and it's my job."

"You have to do what you have to do," Mr. Eric says. "Can't see how that happened we ain't even got no alcohol in the house. Let's get it over with."

They all watch Mr. Eric hurry up the steps and throw the screen door back and walk down the hall to the back room. He stops as he looks at the old wardrobe that has all the quilts from his family for the last hundred years, that same wardrobe had hidden the Christmas presents for as far back as he could remember. The old wardrobe is so special. They stand and watch him. He moves his hands across the edge of the shelf and feels the smooth finish of the wood and slowly takes out brown jars, green jars, clear jars and the little measuring spoon that he uses and sits them on the table. She turns, pulls the spread up, looks under the bed and hands him three shoe boxes to put them in. "I just can't see how something like this could happen," he says as his little finger keeps trying to move away from him and he carefully puts the bottles in the boxes. "Could you just spare me the bottles back, I'd kinda like to keep them."

No one answers, so he hands the boxes to the man. "Is she gonna be alright?"

"Oh, she's fine. Has been all day. Just that thang last night. Sheriff said to tell you Mr. Eric that you couldn't make any more eye-water."

"How can I when you take my stuff with you?"

"You know I have to tell you what they said."

"I don't blame you fur this, it's just that's what I've done for thirty years."

"Well, I'll be going now." They follow the Deputy back to

282

the porch as he carries the boxes close to his body with his eyes stranded on them. He never looks back but they look at him till he is gone and the only thing left is the dust.

She puts her hand in his and says, "I think we better get some supper now."

The night is long as he tries to find work to do. He goes back to the wardrobe and looks at the top two shelves where most of the bottles had been, then his eyes wander to the shelves that his daddy put in so they would have a place for the quilts. Then he sees the box with all the family pictures and the family Bible. He takes the quilts out, one by one, unfolds and looks at each, then seeing himself infringed by the patterns of his life, he carefully refolds and returns each one to the wardrobe as if he was putting a baby to sleep. He picks up the small box with his family's pictures, places it on the top shelf, runs his hand across the wood where the bottles had been sitting and smells of his hands. The noise of her slippers makes him turn.

"It's about time to eat Eric."

"Don't believe I want nothing, think I'll take to bed a little early tonight. I feel kinda tired. I guess it's the ride."

She watches him and neither speaks. He goes to the room and pulls the windows down. It was a little chilly now. He stands and looks out into the night. The moon shines in through the window and gives a light of hope across the room. The crickets and frogs give him their sounds but he does not hear. He pulls the cover back from the bed and lies on his back and pulls the cover over his head, so that only his eyes and forehead are showing. She follows him. "I don't think I'll need supper tonight neither," she says, as she props her knees on the bed to reach the cord and pull out the light before sliding in beside him.

"What in the world is that noise out there? Must be sumbody drunk. Listen, they are just blowing their horn. Eric, do you hear that? Wake up."

They sit up in bed, grab their housecoats and run to the door. There is that Deputy again. He is banging on the door. "Do you know what time it is?" she asks. "It's about one in the morning and we trying to sleep." Mr. Eric just stands behind her and doesn't say anything.

"Oh, Mr. Eric, I just had to come and tell you even if it is late. You know that little girl? Her Mama found this concoction that she made up. It seems it had some alcohol in it. That little girl got it mixed in with water and made herself some eye-water for her doll like you did. She had put some of it in a bottle, which she said you took from her, so she fixed some more and her mama caught her. She told her mama that the baby doll cried and she wanted to show her that it didn't hurt like her mama does. She put a drop in her eyes and that's what caused all the burning. It was a burning and she was a screaming and she wasn't about to tell her mama what she did, cause she wasn't suppose to be in the medicine cabinet in the first place. Ain't that just like a kid? She even told her mama that it had been hurting before but it just got worse. That's how the doctor saw her. Screaming and pitching a fit. He scared the daylights out of her when he ask her what really happened. I know the Sheriff will let you have your jars back. Anyway I think you'll be practicing medicine again."

"I don't think I'll be doing it again. My finger is a little shaky and I don't want to hurt some little child."

"Well, I better going. See you Mr. Eric and you sleep good tonight, you hear?"

"Good night," they say together.

They both walk back into the hall and she starts hooking the screen door. "Let's close the wood door tonight, you never know what somebody might do," he says.

"Yes, we better start closing the door when the weather is hot, too. You just never know," she remarks.

She turns and he takes her hand. "Why don't we get one of them there quilts and put across our feet tonight. I don't remember when we ever used them."

They turn and go to the back room and she gets out the quilt that had been given to them as a wedding present from his Mama and carries it to the bed. She lays it across the foot of the bed—the heat is too much to pull it up—and crawls in beside him.

"You know what," he says.

"What's that Eric?"

"Sometime the medicine we need is not in the bottle."

"Yeah, you're right, but you'll always be my country medicine man."

O, Georgia!

Traffic Light Free Association (April 11, 1998)

by T. Kyle King

and the light turns red and so I stop and, while I'm waiting for the light to turn green, I catch a whiff of postmortem pine from the back seat, which is where I put the Christmas tree, shrouded in a great big bag since the day after New Year's and languishing on our back porch ever since, since the apartment complex wouldn't let us dump our Christmas tree in the trash compactor, forcing us to leave it, bagged and half-forgotten, on the back porch, uncertain what to do with it, out of sight, out of mind, except when the wind kicks up outside and the sound of rustling plastic raises the infuri- ated question once more in my mind *what the hell am I going to do with this thing* because it has long since been too late to take it by Home Depot (although they might well still take it, but there is the embarrassment factor to take into account, as well, since you know damned good and well they'd laugh at me, and I would much rather suffer my shame alone), only now I no longer have a choice: the family will be in town tomorrow for Easter, and, whereas I might be able to suffer it silently, she will not have our parents visiting us for Easter and us not have our Christmas tree taken out yet, al- though, by me, on the back porch ought to be plenty "out" enough, and there certainly ought not to be anything theologically problem- atic about linking Christmas (season of birth) with Easter (season of rebirth), and, hell, who knows, maybe, just maybe, if we became the first couple in history to keep their Christmas tree around until Easter, it might rise up anew, resurrected, restored to life, once more green *green like I wish this light would turn* turns out, though, my wife is convinced that all my philosophical forays are just a lame attempt on my part to cover up for the fact that I'm too damned lazy to take out the Christmas tree, which is probably true, because I know she's usually right about me when she calls me on stuff, although, oddly enough, that wasn't what first endeared me to her, no, that was something altogether different, something I did not truly fully comprehend that first time I saw her shelving books in the university library when I asked her where I could find Kant or Kierkegaard or one of those guys, something I did not even start to see until nine days later, the first time I took her to dinner at Bennigan's, which was where I used to take all my first dates, figuring it was at once classy enough to be impressive yet not pricey enough to be intimidating, but, given my prior and singular lack of success with women, I had decided to go a different route this time, only, when the wait at the pricey classy place I had picked turned out to be too long, I asked her where she'd rather go instead, and, even though I gave her several choices, still she picked Bennigan's, not knowing until much later the significance of her selection, so I just accepted that it was fate and took her there, which was where I began to see it for the first time, still shadowy indefinite and hazy yet still there: having met her in the staid confines of the library and found that she stood out from those surroundings as an extraordinary woman in an ordinary setting, I had expected her to blend into the more extraordinary surroundings afforded by a nice restaurant, and yet, as I came to sense that night and have seen again and again with increasing clarity and stupefaction in the years since then, she always remains two notches above her environment, shining all the more as the places and people and scenes around her begin to shine themselves, and that was when I began to become aware that the word "extraordinary" just didn't cover it, and, more amazingly, that no word I knew of did, and that realization *I don't know the word for the woman who outglows the lights around her no matter how brightly the lights around her glow* enthralled me, for, as one who loves the language, I found myself fascinated by my own inability even to describe her, and I knew I loved her when I found I lacked the vocabulary to put what it was about her into words and how here I am, bound for the city dump on the eve of our first Easter as a married couple with plenty of planning left to do groceries to buy meals to prepare rooms to clean and it's starting to get later than I'd like it to be for me to still be out and about and what time is getting to be anyway *5:49* damn these digital watches anyway when I was a kid, we had nothing but analog watches—of course, back then, it wasn't called analog, it was just a watch—but it was easier with analog, with a watch that had hands, why, I can still remember using it while I worked in that awful warehouse that

288

long hot summer after my senior year of high school, man, what a miserable experience that was, all lifting and loading and endless mindless repetition, when it was the watch that got me through as I carved the day up into fifteen-minute segments, thirty-six of them (counting the hour for lunch), and I would punch in at 8:00 and focus on 8:15, only on 8:15, and each sweep of the second hand was a scythe slicing into that first fifteen-minute eternity, one layer at a time, one lift one load at a time, until I had just broken a sweat and focused just hard enough just long enough, had lifted loaded gotten distracted enough that it was 8:15 and that wasn't so hard and that was one down already and just thirty-five more to go and now 8:30 was all that mattered in the world 'cause once two were down and just thirty-four were left, well, then that was something, that was one-eighteenth of a day right there and that wasn't so bad and now 8:45 seemed a reasonable goal, three already gone and just thirty-three remaining, one-twelfth down the drain in practically no time (not forty-five minutes but fifteen and fifteen and fifteen, you see) no time, no sweat, actually plenty of sweat, but that was how I made the time pass in lifting and loading and keeping my focus and now it was on 9:00, on four parts overcome and thirty-two yet to be surmounted, one-ninth of the way home, but then along came digital and there was no more sweeping second hand, no fifteen-minute increment no carving up the day into easy pieces using a watch with no hands, it couldn't be done without hands, not any more than the lifting or the loading could be done without hands, so all focus was gone, all compartmentalization segregation differentiation distinction done, just complete capitulation, surrender to the flow, no fifteen-minute portions, no focus on fractions, just life moving by without even the clear consistent comfort of a second hand's somber and serene circumscriptions, minute by minute, second and by second, instant by instant, one moment running into another in one big long silent screech of the warehouse whistle, lifting and loading in indistinguishable identical mechanical motions made without thought or reflection or even hope of release until the quartz crystal showed 5:00:00.0 and it temporarily ended, but by then we didn't wouldn't couldn't even care, having by then been enslaved to specificity in the great leap backward from the amorphous analog to the definitive digital which was perpetuated in order to enforce reassert with baldfaced boldness the narrowminded certitude of the Bohr model of the atom, the conviction that we could know a nanosecond in its totality without rendering it diffuse and inconceivable as we once believed we could observe a subatomic particle without affecting its speed and location, but, for my money, give me an electron cloud model and a watch with hands, and watch me be content to know there's an electron somewhere in that general area and we're somewhere in that segment between 9:00 and 9:15, which is close enough for me, only now it's all digital and I have no idea where in the bloody flaming hell the electron is, it's just *5:50 ten of six ten of six tenor sax* I used to play a little saxophone, not much, not well.., mind you, but just enough to know why musicians (and I was not one, mind you, not. in any meaningful sense) do so well with the ladies: women understand, instinctively, intuitively, that what a man can do with a musical instrument he is apt to be able to do with the female form as well rhythm tempo larghetto adagio vivace allegro crescendo *tenor sax tender sex you will regret not keeping up with your piano lessons* they say music makes you good at math, too, although my math skills didn't seem to have suffered when I was dividing my days into fifteen-minute sections, but, then again, I never could figure out when Easter fell, it just was when it was, but there's supposed to be some science to it, something to do with the spring equinox (which always falls on March 21, even when the spring equinox doesn't really fall on March 21, something to do with that age-old struggle between ecclesiastical and astronomical, religion and science, the Church and Galileo, center of the universe yet still the damn thing moves) and the full moon (which would be tonight *the moon'll be out soon if this light doesn't change*) and a nineteen-year cycle (not a fifteen-minute increment) and there's some math involved, no complicated steps, really, just a bunch of steps, the long and short of it being that Easter could be as early as March 22 or as late as April 25 (someone explained it to me once, and I seem to sort of remember just that much) and it's best to just accept that it falls when it falls and it does 'cause it does and, if Easter falls on April 12 this year, then, fine, it does, but, if it fell on that same day, say seventy years ago, then fine, but, if it didn't, well, then that's fine too, 'cause I wouldn't know or understand it either way, I just do what I'm told, it's Easter when it's Easter and the Christmas tree goes out when it goes out and the whys and wherefores don't really matter that much to someone like me, simple, traditional, quaint to some, archaic to some *wishing this light would change* change comes easier to some than to others, me, I tend to like the old a little better than the new, but I'm told you can't stand in the way of history, although maybe someone should every now and again on general principle 'cause there is such a thing as a change for the worse and what about the world today should lead us to believe that every alteration has been an improvement, every shift a sure sign of progress maybe just maybe the folks before us Moses Aristotle Jefferson those guys had some of it right to begin with but that's all passe not wrong necessarily just off the table pushed to the side-lines defeated discredited mocked marginalized made the province of religious fanatics and armed militias and unindicted criminals who somehow somewhere got the crazy notion that religion and guns and criminal rights deserved protecting (damn that Bill of Rights anyway for making people think this was a free country or something how are they ever going to be politically corrected culturally sensitized great leap forward new soviet manned—er, peopled personned humanned humankind humankindred humankindness humankindnessless whatever—if human nature and Constitutional liberty and free thought and self-defense and the protection of a benevolent God keep getting in the way) and force may crush truth to the earth, but, crushed or not, truth is still truth, I read that somewhere, so maybe somebody ought to stand in the way of history defiant determined defending something ancient outdated outmoded quaint archaic and right whose day has come 'round once more, resistant to the narcissistic nihilistic amoral libertarian casual campus communism communism red scare *I'm scared this red light is never going to change* change campus communism of overprivileged oversexed strung-out students of the '60's and their half-baked home -grown present-day postlude, receptive instead to the more radical righteous principled premises, venerable not vulnerable, aged not decrepit, solid not stagnant, historical not hysterical, wordlessly enunciated by that one bold student fighting not for free love nor legalized drugs nor the fall of all conventions social moral ethical and otherwise but rather for faded forgotten ideals from a faraway land as he stood there, just stood there on his own two feet, silently swearing to the driver of the tank rolling inexorably towards him *I will not be moved maybe mocked marginalizd misbegotten martyred maybe but not moved and I may be crushed into dust in Tianenmen Square but crushed or not truth is still truth and so I stand in your way blocking your path refusing to give in fighting against history and time may move ineluctably onward but as for me I will not be moved* and he was not moved but the whole world was and in the end it will be history, not him, which gives way and it will be he, not history, who holds sway and the unbeatable foe will be beaten at last all our fallen virtues values verities ideas ideals time-tested truths will arise anew refreshed renewed revitalized resurrected *Easter Sunday tomorrow is Easter Sunday* funny how it fell that way why it did when it did and that's not the only one, either, 'cause the Martin Luther King holiday fell on January 19 this year, which just happened to have been Robert E. Lee's birthday, as well, and, although I'm sure you couldn't've found both men being celebrated on the same platform, what with the folks celebrating the one calling the other side racists and the folks celebrating the other calling the other side worse than that, I'm not so certain the two men couldn't've been shouldn't've been honored at the same time in the same place by the same people at the same podium, if only they could—we could—all see that they may have lived a century apart and fought for different causes, but they might've been saying the same thing after all, the general and the preacher, the white and the black, the Confederate commander and the civil rights leader, the noble southern Christian as they wrote said proclaimed with one pen voice, conviction *the march of Providence is so slow and our desires so impatient that one day on the red hills of Georgia the sons of former slaves and the sons of former*

292

slaveowners will be able to sit down together at the table of brother-hood the work of progress is so immense and our means of aiding it so feeble that my four little children will one day live in a nation where they will not be judged by the color of their skin but by the content of their character the life of humanity is so long and that of the individual so brief I've looked over and I've seen the Promised Land that we often see only the ebb of the advancing wave and are thus discouraged I may not get there with you but I want you to know tonight it is history that teaches us to hope that we as a people will get to the Promised Land and tomorrow is Easter Sunday day of resurrection redemption and hope but first there are Christmas trees to dispose of lifeless things long dead and not evergreen and then the light turns green and so I move forward and...

O, Georgia!

Professor Pepper's Byline
by Jim Allyn

He was a round man, a cuddly little fellow with soft fuzzy hair around the edges of his balding noggin, respected by his peers some years ago but by now long forgotten and relegated to a cluttered cubicle at a small Southeastern college.

And his problem was, he simply could not manage to get published any more.

Now, he had a vitae a mile long, mind you; yet its edges were yellowed, its listings merged or folded or shut down, and the last addition was in fact now more than a dozen years old. Like Hemingway's Santiago, who had gone eighty-four days without taking a fish, Professor Gerald McNay Pepper had hit a dry spell of epic proportions. He had in fact not been published since January of 1981, three days before that movie actor became president and, somehow, cannily changed the face of all scholarly journals so that they would not, could not, publish any of his essays.

Professor Pepper, whose presence amused each fall's new crop of freshmen upon their discovery that they could call him Dr. Pepper, taught Dead Language Literature at Pinkney State, a microscopic liberal arts school whose mascot was the Canaries. His tenure was secure, but his ego was not — at least any more — for it was eroded further with each day he went unpublished. He remained chipper in the classroom, or at least as chipper as a man could be in attempting to glamourize the writings of the great Chaldean poets and the Sumerian Book of the Dead, but inwardly he was sinking into a state of mild defeat, so that he no longer even wrote but now merely re-submitted manuscripts which had already been rejected a dozen times or more.

He owned three suits, which he wore in precisely the same rotation each week: the brown herringbone on Monday, the gray herringbone on Wednesday, and the brown polyester on Friday. For Tuesday-Thursday classes, he would repeat the first two, and catch up with the third on Sunday morning at the Methodist church. And he was equally precise with his lunch routine: a watercress sandwich, with the crusts trimmed off, on white bread, toasted

295

lightly...two ounces of almonds...a six-and-a-half-ounce Coca-Cola, in the genuine contour bottle...and a Hershey bar. Caffeine bounced off his phlegmatic system, even as the years advanced.

One gray October afternoon, Professor Pepper was sitting amid the books and the boxes and the papers that shared his office, pulling his once-again-rejected 42-page treatise from a large manilla envelope. It was entitled, "The Juxtaposed Roles of Honor, Fear, and Romantic Love as Expounded in Precursors to The Rubaiyat of Omar Khayyam: A Critical View," and this time the editor of "The Spire" had marked "deceased" through his own name in a bright red marker before mailing the tome back.

"Poor fellow," thought Professor Pepper, wondering why they didn't pass it on to the new editor instead. He made a note to have his assistant call the publication, and gently find the name of the new editor, so he could submit the piece again.

"Surely," he thought hopefully, "the new editor will be a man of singularly good taste — the way they used to run 'The Spire' in her heyday." A knock at the door startled him, just a bit, and he looked up to see Miss Pembody, who assisted the Dean.

"Ah, Miss Pembody, do come in," he said, attempting to stand but instead stumbling between two stacks of books which dustily covered the floor.

"Dean Whitley would like you to stop by his office, when you have a moment," she said, somewhat concerned at his stumbling but not wanting to embarrass him by calling attention to it.

"Thank you," he replied, steadying himself on a bookshelf that didn't look all that stable itself.

He walked the gothic winding stairway to the Dean's office, one story up, wondering what the meeting was all about. Perhaps one of the journals had decided to pick up one of his submissions, and they had notified the Dean first. That must have been it — good news from up above. He reached the third story and strode down the hall with a renewed bit of vigor in his step.

But the Dean burst his bubble. "Gerald, I'm getting pressure about your lack of publications from the administration. The alumni club is getting restless with the lack of publicity generated for the school lately, and they're tightening the screws. I'm afraid the concept of 'publish or perish' is rearing its ugly head at us all, Gerald."

Poor Gerald, stunned, sat still and clutched the arms of the hard wooden chair as though he were embarking on a roller coaster ride.

"The bottom line is this," Dean Whitley continued, toying with a knick-knack on the mantel above the fireplace that dominated his office and not making eye contact. "If you haven't been published by the end of this school year, we're either going to have to ask you to change your status to 'Emeritus' or part time."

Professor Pepper tuned out after that, not particularly hearing the rest, before returning to his office to prepare for his afternoon class. Fortunately, there was little preparation required that day; the class session was scheduled to be a pop quiz, which was already set to go. Before leaving his office, he grabbed an out-of-print text he had authored in 1959, so he could spend the hour scouring the volume in hopes of finding some ideas on new articles he would have to write.

The hour dragged, though, as did the next several days and weeks, during which the sun seemed to hide. Professor Pepper pored over every scrap of literature that littered his office, but to little avail; there simply were no new topics to cull from a subject which died twenty centuries ago. He did manage to pull together two papers, but his heart wasn't in either. He preferred "Primitive Pre-Celtic Feast Preparations: The Roles of the Hunter, the Fire Steward, and the Serving Class" to "Contrasts in Herding Signals, viz. the Nomads which Populated Siberia Before Crossing into America and the Barbarians of the Himalayas (Their Distant Cousins)," but the editors preferred neither, once again dashing his hopes with cold photocopied form letters and returned manuscripts, still paper-clipped in the same spot as though not even glanced through.

Mrs. Pepper believed in him, though, which meant a world of difference, and her encouragement helped as winter turned as harsh as the journal editors. The winds howled and the icy rain-drops flew as he sat for hours in his study at home, a pencil

297

sharpened in anticipation resting atop a steno notebook which bore no ideas, only blankness staring back at the man whose ideas were once esteemed.

The winter term came and went, yet the spring thaw missed Professor Pepper. He remained frozen in his now familiar hunched-over pose, whether in his study at home or his office on campus, searching for the point of interest which would end his slump. It wasn't as though he was expecting it to fall out of the sky for him — he genuinely was working as hard as he could to unearth fresh angles and write new articles — his flame just seemed to have burned out.

And then, it happened.

It was a Tuesday, the last Tuesday in April, and quite an unseasonably warm one at that, so he and Mrs. Pepper were sitting on the front porch before dinner, relaxing and chatting about the day, when a faint whistling sound became a roaring sound and the next thing they knew, there was a bright flash and something of an explosion right before their eyes and the front yard was filled with smoke.

Their jaws dropped, and their eyes opened wide, and they took turns staring at each other and at the dissipating smoke, their heads alternating back and forth as though watching a tennis match, and when the smoke finally cleared a bit they stood up and slowly walked to the edge of the porch.

Their gazes rested on the object which now occupied their expansive front yard — they lived on three acres in the country — and Mrs. Pepper spoke first.

"Is that a meteor?" she gasped.

"I believe it may well indeed be a meteor," he said, squinting to try and get a clearer view of the object.

The object had dug itself into the ground a little, scattering soil and displacing some sod, and was still smoking from its surface, the way a road might steam after a brief rain on a hot summer day. It looked very much like a chunk of granite, a big boring black boulder that hardly looked exotic, as a piece of asteroid or a wayward piece of another planet should appear — but that must have been what it was, because it certainly couldn't have been anything else.

"Better get the camera," Mrs. Pepper suggested, and Professor Pepper disappeared indoors and reappeared minutes later with a small Brownie box camera they had used to capture every photograph of their life together since Harry Truman was in the hot seat. He snapped four pictures, and then a fifth, before reaching the end of the roll — a strip of film which contained images of tiny grandchildren baking cookies as well as a fallen star from another galaxy.

"Should we telephone anyone?" Mrs. Pepper wondered.

"Such as?"

"I suppose the Sheriff, or the fire department, or...I don't know, perhaps the government?"

Professor Pepper paused to mull the options. "Perhaps later," he said. "I'm not so sure I want to have dozens of agencies and reporters camping out on our front yard just now," he said. She gazed into his eyes, still the same deep gray they were when she fell in love with them nearly five decades ago, and understood his need for stability and security just then, so she did not argue the point and they left it at that — a smoldering asteroid in their front yard as they passed the rolls and the vegetables at dinner that evening.

He dreamed about a dream that night — the dream Hemingway wrote for Santiago to enjoy most every night, where lions roamed the beaches — before awakening in a cold sweat and crawling out of bed to peek through the curtains to see that the meteor was indeed reality, with a full moon glistening off its edges. Sleep did not return easily that night, so he made himself a cup of tea and sat in his favorite chair in the living room, without a light on, thinking about his life and his career and wondering if it wasn't perhaps time to skip the 'Emeritus' step and retire altogether, and take the trip he had been promising Mrs. Pepper for some time.

Two o'clock. His thoughts wandered back to the meteor sprinkle of that evening, and all of a sudden he straightened up and heard himself saying, "That's it!"

He put down the tea, pulled the string from the small lamp

on the end table, reached into the drawer for a pad and pencil, and scribbled a note to himself. He had found the subject for the article that would finally be published, and all of a sudden he now felt free to be tired, so he slipped back into bed without disturbing Mrs. Pepper from her slumber.

The next morning, he practically ran from his 8:30 class back to his office: there was work to do. He eagerly sifted through his ancient volumes, searching for the accounts he needed so desperately to find. And find them he did; by early afternoon, he had assembled a stack of books and papers that would serve as the source material for his latest article, an article that was sure to be in hot demand by every scholarly journal in the field.

It took him nearly a week to write the article and tighten it up to the point where he felt it was right. The subject was how the ancients described their encounters with the heavens — shooting stars, meteor showers, eclipses of the sun, earthquakes, and other such phenomena which are now easily explained by modern science but, in primitive times, were mystifying and frightening.

He chose to introduce his topic with a rather stoic description of the event he and Mrs. Pepper had witnessed a few nights earlier, to set the stage for the contrast between modern interpretation and less sophisticated reactions. This factual account filled three pages, while the scholarly study took seventeen more.

His hurry in finishing was not simply renewed youthful enthusiasm, however. He finished just one day before having to leave town for a three-day conference, during which he undoubtedly would have no time to work on this new epic. So, he had to get his submission in the mail before he took off.

He made a copy of the manuscript — he still used an old Corona typewriter, refusing to have anything to do with computers — and left it resting inside a manilla envelope on the corner of his desk, with the photos inside, too. He pulled out the latest edition of "The Spire," the literary journal which had last published one of his works so many years ago, as the publication of choice (and vindication) for this new work, and laid the periodical next to the envelope. Not knowing how much postage to use and finding that the post office had already closed for the day, he planned to call his assistant the next morning and have her send it in.

He was off bright and early for the state capitol, where the conference was being held. It did not cross his mind that he had not been invited to speak that year, as he had not been invited to speak for more than a decade now, for he was bubbling over with excitement that he had written the paper of the century, certainly his best work, an article that would bring him adulation and recognition and would undoubtedly secure his position as *the* authority of dead languages in the region — if not the entire United States!

He registered at the conference before checking in to the hotel, and once he had settled in his room and called Mrs. Pepper to let her know he had arrived safe and sound, he phoned his office. He instructed his assistant to address the envelope to the editor of the publication which was sitting on the desk, and drop it in the mail. Which she did. The only problem was, a student who had come by the office that morning had put her books down on the desk for a moment and upon picking them up, did not notice she had left her copy of the National Enquirer (which was being used as a journalism class assignment, of course) right smack on top of Professor Pepper's copy of "The Spire." His able assistant thought it odd that he was sending something to the Enquirer, but she had no way to reach him and she was not exactly the most valuable assistant a professor could ask for, so the story on the meteor went off to the National Enquirer.

The conference went well, although with each passing year Professor Pepper noticed fewer and fewer faces seemed familiar, and after the three days he returned home.

It is worth noting that Professor Pepper had never in his entire life set foot in a convenience store, and that Mrs. Pepper dutifully did the grocery shopping so he seldom walked into a grocery store either, and that PBS was virtually the entire extent of his television viewing habit — so in other words, he was altogether unfamiliar with the National Enquirer, and had only heard the name but had no real sense of its literary value. If asked, he might have likened it to USA Today, as a national newspaper that delved into

301

investigative journalism.

So it surprised him a bit when he received a congratulatory note from the Enquirer, alerting him that they planned to publish his article the very next week. He reasoned that the new editor of "The Spire," not up to snuff with the way things used to be, must have passed the piece onto them. No matter; he was about to be published again. Such a sweet word — *published* — and he sat back in his chair to gaze out the window and enjoy a lovely sunny afternoon.

A few days later, he received another letter from the Enquirer, containing the front page of the current issue and a check for $350! He unfolded the story and read the headline:

RUNAWAY COMET
LANDS ON
DR. PEPPER'S
FRONT LAWN!

They used one of the photos, and he thought it odd how a smudge of ink looked quite like a little cherub with long antennae standing atop the boulder. He also thought it odd that they only ran the first part of the story, describing the background information on the meteor and not the most important part — its relevance to ancient languages. "Oh," he realized, "that part was continued inside the paper," yet he was still somewhat disappointed that they had mistakenly forgotten to include the inside pages, as well.

But no matter. He was not only published, he had been granted a byline, as well. He quickly typed the updated listing for his vitae, and made a copy of the front page of the Enquirer, and scurried off to the Dean's office, to show him that all it takes is a little patience, a little perseverance, to be published in a scholarly journal with an article of great importance.

Father of the Year
(an excerpt)

by Rosemary Colangelo Stewart

Eve fell in love with Billy McCabe the day he walked into school with a black eye.

When Sister Mary Veronica asked him what happened, Billy told her that his father beat him up the night before. Sister said that she doubted that very much, and suggested that Billy had been fighting.

Billy shrugged. "If that's what you want to believe."

"I'm sure your father had every good reason in the world to hit you—"

"He didn't just hit me. He beat the crap out of me."

At that, Sister Veronica slapped Billy in just about the same spot his father had left his mark the night before. Eve's hand went to the side of her face, as if she could feel the sting on her own cheek.

Billy looked up at the tall, stern nun, his face knotted in defiance, and started to lift up his shirt. "Wanna see the rest of my bruises?"

Sister Veronica grabbed him by the collar of his uniform blazer and shoved him toward the door. "We will go right down to the principal's office, young man, and we will see what she thinks of children who lie and swear and are defiant." She opened the door and turned back to the class. "I don't want to hear a sound from any of you."

Billy glanced around at his eighth grade classmates. His eyes met Eve's for a breath of a second. They grew wide in a silent plea, as if willing her to believe him. She gave him a weak smile and nodded her head. Then he was gone, dragged away by Sister Veronica to another beating at the hands of Sister Terese, the principal.

The Compassionate Sisters of the Sacred Heart of Jesus. Eve wondered if any of her classmates ever thought about the irony of that name.

As soon as the door shut, Anthony Manto slapped his desk. "Hoo, boy. That crazy son of a bitch."

"Who'd he get in a fight with?" Brian Kelly asked.

"I didn't hear about any fight," Gina Carucci said.

"There was no fight. Billy doesn't fight." Anthony leaned forward in his seat next to Eve. "He'll blab you to death with some baloney he picked up from somewhere, but he'll never fight you back."

"Then who gave him the black eye?" Eve asked.

Anthony shrugged. "Probably his old man, just like he said."

"Get out of town," Brian shouted.

Anthony turned and grinned. "What, Brian? You trying to tell me your old man never gave you a shot in the chops?"

"Yeah, but Mr. McCabe wouldn't do something like that," Brian said.

"Why the hell not?"

"Christ, he's practically a saint, from what my mother says. Head of the ushers' society, treasurer for the Knights of Columbus—"

"Hey, wasn't he Catholic Father of the Year last year?" Gina asked.

"Yeah. So what?" Anthony said.

"I don't think they make you Catholic Father of the Year if you beat up your kids," Gina said.

"You are so naive," Anthony said. "They just gave him that award because he's got seven kids and still has enough energy to show up for church on Sunday."

The class exploded in laughter. Gina's face grew scarlet. "Go blow, Manto."

"Let me put it to you this way," Anthony said to Gina. "If Billy McCabe was your kid, wouldn't you want to beat the hell out of him at least once a week, just for being who he is?"

Gina nodded. "Yeah, I guess you're right."

"I sure would," someone shouted from the back of the room.

"Yeah, I'd work him over at least *twice* a week," someone else said.

Eve's head whirled from one classmate to another as they snarled their condemnations of Billy. She'd heard stories about him

304

throughout grammar school, about how he talked back to the nuns and asked weird questions nobody could answer, but she'd never been in his class. Sure, he was different from everybody else, maybe a little crazy, even. But why were they all so damn thrilled that Billy's father had given him a black eye? Maybe it was because misery loved company, as she'd often heard the grown-ups say. The sad truth of the matter was that most parents she knew cuffed their kids about pretty good. Why should Billy be any different?

But Billy's beatings were different. They were a lot worse. Eve found this out for certain when Billy showed her his bruises after school.

Eve stepped into the sunshine and headed down the street toward home. Younger kids raced by in a rumble of noise, like a crowd of inmates just released from prison. By the time she reached the length of wooden row houses cramped together along the street, her schoolmates had left her to her own thoughts. She remained stuck on the two character play between Sister Veronica and Billy earlier that day. She couldn't shake the sickening sensation of being stuck in her seat, unable to move to his defense. Not that there was anything she could have done if she wanted to. It had been drilled into her from birth — you don't talk back to an adult, especially a nun.

Eve heard footsteps and flashed a look over her shoulder to find Billy coming up behind her.

"Hey, where you going, Eve?"

"Oh, Billy. I didn't see you."

"Did I scare you?"

"It's not like I'm gonna have a heart attack or something."

Billy nodded and gave her a look like he thought that was a real solid answer.

They continued walking, and after a moment he repeated in his soft mumble-whisper, "So where are you going, Eve?"

"Where do you think I'm going? I'm going home."

"What do you want to go home for?"

"Where else would I go?"

"You could go to the park with me."

He said it flat out, like he assumed that there was nothing in the world she'd rather do. His eyes were wide and expectant, just like that morning when they'd exchanged glances on his way to the principal's office. Deep inside her a silent moan went off, because Eve knew that, no matter what, she was going to go to the park with Billy McCabe.

She stalled for time anyway.

"Why are you going to the park?"

"I like going to the park. Besides, where else would I go?"

"You could go home."

"Oh yeah, terrific idea."

Eve stopped walking and stared at him. She knew that the McCabes had a perfectly good home — a house, in fact. She was impressed with anyone who lived in a house, because it was something that was unattainable for her family. Mr. McCabe was an insurance salesman, while Eve's father drove a delivery truck for a living.

"What are you getting all snotty about?" she asked.

Billy looked down at the ground, a sheepish smile on his face. "I'm sorry. I was just trying to be funny." He tilted his head sideways and peered up at her. "Come on, Eve. You should come to the park with me."

Eve looked around and tried to figure out what to do. If she turned right and up the hill, she would be home. If they continued straight, they'd eventually end up at the park. She spotted Bobby Booker riding his bike.

"Hey, Booker," she shouted.

"Yeah?"

"Do me a favor and tell my brother I stayed after school to help Sister Veronica."

Bobby eyed the two of them with curiosity. He looked like he questioned the sanity of wasting a good lie on Billy.

"Why should I?" he finally said.

"Cause if you don't, I'll tell your father you didn't win those

306

baseball cards in a spelling bee. That you shoplifted them from Leo's."

Bobby rode his bike around them in a tight circle and eyed her as if he were trying to figure out if she would really do it. He soon gave a slight nod of his head and sped up the hill toward their apartment house.

Billy squinted his eyes and gave Eve the once-over like he was impressed. Eve smiled at the road straight ahead, and continued walking alongside Billy toward the park.

It came into sight just over the hill. Eve turned to Billy and said, "Race you." She took off before he could respond.

Eve ran through the park to the tiny bungalow at the far end. She clambered up the stairs, pounded across the wooden porch, and tagged the front door just as Billy reached the bottom step.

"Come on, slow poke," she said, and stepped inside the entrance of Edgar Allan Poe's cottage, a local landmark.

Billy plodded in after her, holding a hand to his side.

"Damn, you're fast," he huffed.

Eve put a finger to her lips and hushed him. "Listen. Do you hear something?"

Billy cocked his head to the side. "I don't hear noth—"

"Shh. What's that?"

Billy stared at her.

"It sounds like a heartbeat," Eve whispered.

Billy lowered himself to his knees and felt around the floor.

"Come here. Feel this. There's a warm spot right here," he said.

Eve knelt down next to him and lay her hands flat on the wood floor. She looked at him sideways and shook her head. "Nah, I don't think so. The story says he buried him behind a wall."

The Telltale Heart was her favorite Poe story. She thought it was even scarier than *The Twilight Zone* on T.V.

Billy got to his feet and looked around. "If you were gonna murder somebody, where would you stash the body?"

Eve stood up and walked through the dim living room. The chairs and table in the roped off area looked like ghost furniture in the shadows. A heavy, damp scent hung in the air, as though some-thing alive really was rotting behind the walls. She gestured to Billy to follow her, then crossed to the wall that divided the rooms.

"Gina says she found it along this wall the last time she was here."

Billy placed his ear against the wall. He pulled back, his eyes wide with terror. Eve widened her own eyes, and he started to laugh.

"Gotcha!" he said.

"You jerk." She hit him lightly on the shoulder, and he re-coiled.

"Are you okay?" she asked.

He shook his head and walked away, rubbing at the spot where she'd hit him.

She walked up beside him and tried to look into his eyes, but he stared straight ahead at Mr. Poe's writing desk. Eve peered out of the corner of her eye at the dark replica of the raven perched on the living room door.

"People around here say that he wrote 'The Bells' because he used to hear the Fordham University carillon chime," she said. "I always thought that was what drove him crazy, those bells going off every fifteen minutes." She glanced over her shoulder at the raven and back again. "I can hear those bells from my house, too. I was always scared that they'd make me as crazy as he was. Then my father told me it wasn't possible, that he died before they even built the university."

"It figures that the only guy from this neighborhood who ever got at all famous was a loony writer," Billy said. He leaned real close and whispered in her ear, "That raven is watching you." He ran a spidery flow of fingers up her back, and Eve shivered.

"I hate that bird," she said, as if she could dispel some of its dark power by referring to it as a simple bird.

Billy and Eve leaned on the half-door looking into the bed-room. "There's something about this room that always makes me sad," she said. "I think it's his bed. It's so small, like a child's bed. Like he was just this pathetic, little man."

She was surprised as soon as she said it. She never told anyone she felt like that. She usually kept what she considered her own crazy, Poe-like thoughts to herself. But there was something about Billy McCabe that snatched the words from her heart.

They exited the cottage and blinked in the sunshine on the front porch. Eve pointed up the street and across the wide avenue that separated them from a long row of apartment buildings.

"This house used to be over there," she said. "There's a sign on one of those buildings that says so."

"Yeah, I heard that," Billy replied. "I always felt like they were cheating me by doing that. Like it makes this place less real."

"I know. I always thought it was neat to be in the place where he really wrote all those stories and poems. Then I find out that this isn't the actual place."

"It's like the time my parents took me to Plymouth Rock. You get there and you see this big, old rock in a cage. 'Here it is, the rock they landed on. Maybe.' " A flicker of anger lit his pale eyes. "You'd think they'd be more definite about something like that. They're so definite about everything else."

Eve just nodded. She wondered at the anger in his words as she followed him down the front steps of Mr. Poe's cottage.

Billy and Eve sat in a grassy area hidden behind a clump of bushes. The smell of fresh cut grass tickled her nose. She heard the hum of lawn mowers in the distance. A slight breeze rippled through the leaves above them. Shadows danced on the side of Billy's face, making it look like the bruise was magically disappearing and re-appearing within seconds. He watched her watching him, but she felt no embarrassment at getting caught looking.

"Does it hurt?" she asked.

"What? My eye? Nah, but I'm pretty sore around here." He gestured down at his torso.

"He hit you there, too?"

"Yeah, he hit me there. This is nothing," he said, pointing toward his eye. He looked at her as if he were trying to assess her

309

value in case someone were to suddenly ask him exactly how much she might cost. "You want to see?"

Of course she wanted to see. She'd wanted to see since he'd tossed it off to Sister Veronica that morning — 'Wanna see the rest of my bruises?' — even as she didn't want to see. She nodded her head.

Billy leaned forward, peeled off his green uniform blazer, and started to unbutton his shirt. Eve felt like she wanted to run back home, far away from him and his bruises. He hesitated at the bottom button, all the while watching her. As he pulled his shirt back from his skin, she noticed that his hands trembled ever so slightly.

There were swatches of an angry, purplish color all across his chest. They looked to Eve like demonic tattoos, stained glass drawings on his skin. She didn't recoil in horror as she'd expected she would. She had to make a conscious effort not to reach out and touch them.

Billy started talking fast in his hissing whisper-mumble. "My back is worse. It's all over, 'cause I rolled up into a ball on the floor trying to protect myself, and he just kept whaling at me."

"What did he hit you with?"

"The old broom handle, his favorite weapon."

"So he has done this to you before."

"Yeah, all the time." He made a face like this was common knowledge, and she should know better.

Eve stared at his bruises and tried to imprint them on her memory, as though this was something she needed to learn. Billy stared at her face just as intently. She looked up into his eyes and he whispered, "Go ahead. You can touch them."

She hesitated. He took her hand and laid it on a bruise that was over his heart. She felt its heat and wanted to cry. She moved her hand down his chest to his side, towards another large, purple welt, then back to his chest to a third bruise. Billy closed his eyes and rocked back and forth.

"Why'd he hit you like this?" she asked.

Billy opened his eyes and held out his hand. There was a

faded, bluish ink stain, a skull and crossbones, which, a day after he'd drawn it, looked like the ghost of another tattoo.

"He got ticked off because I drew this on my hand. He told me it was a symbol of the devil and to go wash it off. I told him I'd wash it off if I felt like it. So he punched me in the eye." He gave a quick laugh. "Then I told him he was some kind of dictator, that he ran the house like Hitler. That's when he really had a fit."

Eve's eyes widened at the idea of Billy talking to his father that way. Billy squirmed at her reaction.

"Still, that's no reason to do this," she said.

She reached out and passed a feathery touch over his bruised eye.

"Sometimes he's so mad he just can't deal with me any-more, so he ties me up in the basement." He rolled up his sleeves to show her his wrists. They were bruised and scalded a violent red.

"Jesus, Billy."

"He ties me to a chair and leaves me there. Sometimes all night."

Eve touched the rope burns on his wrists without looking. She stared into his eyes and tried to imagine what it would be like to see your father so enraged he'd do something like this to you. She let out a long breath of air.

"I can't believe your father's Catholic Father of the Year."

Billy smiled. "Yeah, maybe that's why nobody believes me."

They walked back toward Eve's apartment in silence. The late afternoon sun colored the buildings around them with a rosy glow. Billy dragged behind at times, so that Eve had to slow her pace. She wondered if it was because of his bruises, or if he was simply dreading going home, knowing his father would be waiting for him with the broom handle after he'd spoken to Sister Veronica the way he had.

When they got to the courtyard in front of Eve's apartment building, Billy said, "I know what you mean about that poem, 'The Bells.' Sometimes it makes me feel like maybe I'm a little bit nuts."

"You worry about going crazy, too?"

"Oh, yeah. All the time." Billy smiled and tapped her on

311

the shoulder in a gesture of farewell, and ran off.

Eve watched him run down the block and noticed that he was holding his side, where the worst of his bruises were. She thought about what he'd said about the bells. What it meant was that she was probably as crazy as he was. And that was either very good or very bad.

The following Sunday in church, Eve couldn't take her eyes off Mr. McCabe. He was serving as head usher at the children's mass, so it was easy for Eve to observe him unnoticed. He was a tall, slender, friendly looking man who wore a good suit and an insurance salesman's smile. He looked like he was born to be Catholic Father of the Year. Eve would've voted for him herself, if she didn't know what she knew now.

Billy was a miniature of his father with his pale skin, wiry body, and dusty blonde crew cut. She wondered if this was what Billy was going to look like when he got older, like a good-looking astronaut in a business suit.

Except Billy's eyes, however, were nothing like his father's cold blue eyes. She'd never seen anything like Billy's eyes. They were a greenish gray, a haunting color, that bored deep into the object of their attention, like eyes that had seen too much. Eve knew what they'd seen. It was the other face of Mr. McCabe that gave them a ghostly glow.

She twisted in her seat and peered over the heads of her classmates, until she found Billy, two pews behind her. He was staring up at the ceiling, not paying any more attention than she was to the service up on the altar. She could just make out the bruise by his eye. It had faded over the past few days to a bluish green. It clashed with the dull red and purple pattern formed on the side of his face by the sun streaming through the stained glass windows.

She turned back to watch Mr. McCabe going about the church with a self-contained authority. A simmering rage grew inside her, hatred so deep she felt like she was going to choke on it. The leftover smell of incense from an earlier high mass made her feel light-headed. The church grew darker around her. She lost all peripheral vision as her anger centered itself on the head usher— the Catholic Father of the Year.

When it came time to receive communion, Eve stayed in her seat. She knew that the murderous rage she was feeling was a sin in the eyes of the Lord. She was so overcome with sinister thoughts, surely God would strike her dead if she were to dare take the host into her mouth.

The line of children flowed past her toward the altar. She continued to sit rigid in her seat. Her classmates eyed her with suspicion as they squeezed past her to get out of the pew. She felt like God's special spotlight, reserved for the most heinous of mortal sinners, was shining on her, the only one left in the row.

Billy approached her pew while on the communion line and squinted at her. Eve shook her head and turned away. Billy left the line and sat down right next to her. She knew then how the whore who was about to get stoned felt when Jesus shamed her attackers into putting down their rocks.

"What are you doing?" she hissed. "Get back in line."

"What'd you do?" Billy whispered.

"Billy, get out of here." She glanced up at the front of the church toward Mr. McCabe. "He'll kill you if you don't go to communion."

"What did you do?" he repeated.

She looked into his face. His jaw was firmly set. There was no way she could persuade him to leave her now.

"Bad thoughts," she said.

"Oh, yeah?" Billy looked at her with a new appreciation. She knew what he was thinking. Having impure thoughts was about the worst thing you could do when you were thirteen years old.

"I want to kill your father," she said.

Billy's eyes grew wide. This was apparently even better than if she'd confessed to some wild sexual fantasy.

"Cool," he said. "Very cool."

They stared at each other as their classmates floated toward the altar rail. The nuns frowned at them from the end of the row,

313

and Mr. McCabe glowered from the front of the church where he was directing the flow of communicants. Eve knew that Billy was going to get a hell of a beating for this. He turned and looked directly at his father, a slight smile lifting the corners of his mouth. Eve held her missal in front of her face to hide her own secret smile.

Little Women

by Jennifer Gammage

Straight boyish hips.
Babies propped to mold them
into a curve to fit the
desires of poverty
and men.

My sisters.
Too young
to understand the
burden you carry.

Your faces seem so wise.
How old are you?
Ten
Eleven
Nine?

Scars
of poverty
are carved into
your swaying hips
and womanly carriage.

I want to hold you.
to cradle your
head and tell you
bedtime stories of
puppies and kittens.

But you have your own stories.
Gleaned
from the parties and
the men,
and the thin walls.

I hope you will remember
when you are older
to act like a child.
Catch the toddling
child that you lost
and hold her.

Let people laugh.
Become the child
you had a chance to be.

O, Georgia!

Jesus and Elvis and Pop and the Bear
by Regina U. Galloway

Sitting on a hillside among heaven's cloud
They're chuckling and talking away from the crowd
Back there in the Black Belt, no money to spare,
We had Jesus and Elvis and Pop and the Bear.
They're talking 'bout big deer and fast running backs
and cotton field blues and black panther tracks
We learned to be natural; their sins were our songs
They weren't ever loud; they were raised to be strong
No headlines, no CD's, no therapy sessions
no strategies, flowcharts, or rite-bound confessions
We were back on the farm roads, learning to share
from Jesus and Elvis and Pop and the Bear.
He'd stand at the back door on his way to the woods
He told us, "Be decent," and true if we could
He's leaning on the goal post in his houndstooth hat
Our Tide played their hearts out when he stood like that
He sings in black leather, a poor boy's blues
He won worlds from nothing, a part of our truth
He's sitting with children, creekside in a book,
We learned to be kind sometimes from that look
They worked hard and sang hard and played hard to win
They gloried in whippoorwills and they understood sin
our art was their living. It was fourth down and two
It was simple and forthright - "to thine own self be true."
They were "nothing but winners." They left us to care.
We had Jesus and Elvis and Pop and the Bear.

O, Georgia!

And The Dish Ran Away With The Spoon

by Dagmar Marshall

My back ached from sitting hunched over too long on the old cement bench. The final marker had been installed on Momma and Daddy's gravesite. Fiddle and Moon were coming to meet me to make sure everything was all right with it.

I got here early on purpose. Nothing settles me better than mountain gazing, and my Blue Ridge mountains surround the old cemetery like a mother's arms around a baby. They foam and smoke and carry a sense of peace and solidarity to my mind and soul.

Funny thing is, some people think markers and flowers and visits to the cemetery are to keep your grief pounding away in your mind and body. I find only comfort in feeling Momma and Daddy's spirits here in the countryside they loved so deeply and where I was raised.

I've seen the mountains out West and they are beautiful but they are not "done yet" in my opinion. They are full of tempest winds, sharp, cutting edges, and cold ice-caps. They aren't smooth and sleepy and foggy and soft like my Blue Ridge's. I can name every peak, ridge and gap as far as the eye can see, and some beyond that. But they are mountains for sure and they don't take easily to being dug and grazed. As hard as life was growing up in these mountains, Fiddle and Moon and I were happy kids and we thought of ourselves as rich blue-bloods. This was strictly a state of mind brought on by Momma and Daddy. Why the very air we breathed was clean, fresh Blue Ridge air, they would say, and so blue must be the color of our blood.

My Momma and Daddy loved nonsense. They were, without exception, the most quick-minded and joyous people I have ever known. Scratching out a living raising cattle and crops in the Blue Ridge mountains of Georgia is definitely not anything to laugh about and can put a marriage and a family to the test. But Momma and Daddy loved each other and us—and the land. They were so clever, they had Fiddle and Moon and me believing chores were fun and life fulfilling. Their philosophy ran something like this, and I quote, "Chores around a farm are as much a part of life as breathin'. And,

319

by gosh, if you can breathe, you can work your chores and if you work your chores, you'll be a happy person and deserve to be breathin'."

Nursery rhymes were their specialty with "Namings" a close second. We had all grown up under the spell of strange characters who lived in shoes or sat in a corner eating pie or fell off walls to a shattering end. When we had to work in the garden, they had us chanting "Mary, Mary, quite contrary, how does your garden grow?" When it was our turn to milk the cow, complaints were disguised as the chosen milker mumbled "The farmer in the dell" over and over again. Jack and Jill, under the guise of Fiddle and I, went up the hill millions of times to fetch a pail of water from the well.

My eyes were drawn to the new marker. Underneath the chiseled names and dates there was another inscription which read, "...And The Dish Ran Away With The Spoon" just like Momma had written. But just a minute, I'm getting to the end before the beginning and the middle.

But most important of all were the "Namings."

I was the first-born and because of the natural order of things I was first to receive my Name. Namings could happen any time from the day of your birth but Momma and Daddy declared no one could do anything worthy of a true Naming at least until they could walk.

I was baptized Cathleen Jane and was called that until several weeks after my fourth birthday. When you got to be around four, Momma and Daddy figured you could handle feeding the chickens. We had a mean and colorful rooster by the name of "Mister." You did not mess with Mister. He was the self-designated and nearly always, Boss of the Yard. I say nearly always because the only living thing that could aggravate that nasty rooster was our large yellow cat, named Cat. That feline loved to tease Mister. We had two other cats, a black and a calico. They would not go near Mister.

Cat loved to crouch down and give old Mister her mesmerizing, yellow-eyed stare. She'd growl way down low and swish her beautiful long, fluffy tail and oh, that made Mister mad. That rooster would fluff up his feathers, lower his neck and go after Cat at a dead run, beak wide open and screaming. She would freeze, tail sticking straight up in the air. She'd wait until Mister's beak was fractions away from her fiery gaze and then she would dance off quick and soft.

Then she'd turn, arch her back and meow at Mister, sometimes punctuated with a menacing hiss. Made him crazy. He'd try again but Cat always eluded him.

I had watched this show many times. I loved Cat, so swift, so sure. I loved her defiance. Mister was big, a lot bigger than she was, especially when he fluffed up, but she never showed fear. I was going to be just like Cat.

My day finally came. I was scattering that feed and I saw Mister just strutting around the yard. I started dancing softly and meowing like Cat. Mister ignored me for awhile, but I wouldn't give up. True, I had no fluffy tail but I did have a yellow pony tail and was sure I could fool him. Mister got tired of me or so I thought. I turned away and heard him scream. I turned and saw that mean rooster coming at me with his head lowered and his beak wide open. Loudly I said "No way bad Mister" and faced him. He stopped. I glared and he glared back. He screamed again and came after me and that's when I side-stepped that demon rooster, so fast, so quick, just like Cat. My Naming took place that day. My Daddy saw the whole thing and was rolling on the ground with laughter. "My Cat," he howled, "my little Cat!" And, that is how Cathleen Jane became forever "Cat."

Most people thought my little brother, Philip James, got his Naming because he started playing Daddy's fiddle when he was barely three. That's true—we had some neighbors who were so astounded by his abilities, they called him a "fiddlin' fool." Well, Momma and Daddy put that mantle on him in the name of Fiddle, real quick. They thought it was so cute. I could have shaken every one of those neighbors for giving that boy a cute name but it was done. I had to live with it so I gave Philip James my interpretation of his Naming. I named him Fiddle because he was always fiddlin' in my business and exasperating me to death.

Fiddle could get Moon and me fussin' so bad, blamin' each other for things he had done to aggravate us, Momma would finally pop our little behinds with her spatula and send us to our beds. We'd really be furious when we'd then hear that rascal fiddlin' away for Momma and Daddy while they clapped and sang. We sat on our beds snivelin' and swearing revenge on Fiddle.

I look back to the mountains, thinking now what untroubled and happy times those were. Moon and I would try to stay mad at Fiddle but of course it never lasted. He could always say or do something to make us laugh with him again. And, let no man, woman, or child, ever say anything against me or Moon. Fiddle was our protector and he finally got so big, no one would ever challenge him.

I heard cattle lowing and looked up to see a small herd grazing just beyond the fence surrounding the cemetery. Just hearing cows will always bring back Moon's scary and unexpected Naming day.

We were all out in the pasture helping Daddy move the cattle to another area of the farm. Maureen Elizabeth was just about four and wasn't much help but she was learning. The best teacher we had out there was our Australian Shepherd, Little Dog. That dog was the smartest animal I have ever seen or met to this day. Herding was born into him and he could instinctively anticipate every move of those cattle. Cattle are not too smart, and Little Dog knew that. He protected them from harm but he got them to do just what Daddy wanted and all Daddy had to do was whistle and point a finger.

My mind is filled with the images of that marvelous creature, darting, cutting and moving those cows. He would work until his pads were bleeding, but still keep going until the job was done.

Maureen Elizabeth got busy looking up at the rising moon. It was that time when the sun and moon can be seen at the same time and the moon was deep red from the sun's light. Maureen Elizabeth was just standing there pointing up and did not see one of the cattle spooking right at her. Little Dog saw what was happening and he jumped on the back of that old cow and sunk his teeth into his flank. Now cattle do not jump things, they go through things, but this day that cow was so surprised and hurting, it jumped smack over Maureen, with Little dog hanging on. It was a sight.

We were all so shocked and scared and Maureen Elizabeth just stood there, still as can be, pointing at the red moon. Little Dog came to her side, tongue hanging out, panting. Maureen Elizabeth turned and said, "Daddy, don't you think Little Dog looks like he's laughin'?"

Daddy went over and snatched her up and headed for the house. Little dog followed until Daddy told him to get back to business and drive those cattle. Maureen Elizabeth just cuddled up to Daddy and talked about the red moon. " I believe we have just had a Naming," I heard him say as he brought her to Momma.

We all sat at the table that evening and waited until Momma and Daddy spoke first. Even Fiddle was quiet for a change but I could feel his feet swinging under the table. The silence was unbearable. We were not a quiet family, ever. Finally, we saw Daddy reach out and take Momma's hand. We followed and were a circle, ready for the blessing. Daddy boomed our thanks to God for our food and we all said "Amen."

I looked up at my parents and saw little grins appearing on their faces. They began in unison, "Hey Diddle Diddle, The Cat And The Fiddle, The Cow Jumped Over The Moon!"

Fiddle and I pointed at Maureen Elizabeth chanting Moon, Moon, Moon! She giggled and chattered, "Me, Moon, Me, Moon." We got so loud Little Dog started barking which made us all laugh even harder. And that is how Namings happened.

Now, about the part that goes with the Dish and the Spoon? That's the most important. And the hardest to tell about.

Around my twelfth birthday, I started feeling very self-conscious about being called Cat. Up until then no one said anything about my name or Fiddle's or Moon's but one day it started. My friends started walking by me and would make meow sounds and hiss between their teeth. I started noticing smirky smiles when they did it, too. Momma and Daddy always called us our special names in front of everyone and we'd been called those names for so long, no one seemed to know we had <u>real</u> names.

I started in on Momma and Daddy about it and begged them to please start calling me Cathleen Jane now. I told them I even asked my teacher to call me Cathleen Jane and she said she would try to remember. I was just sure that if people heard our real names enough, they'd forget the Naming ones. Momma and Daddy just laughed and promised and promptly forgot. Fiddle and Moon thought I was being uppity.

But one day Fiddle had a girl come by and he was all feet and talky tongue. She was brand new in town and Moon and I heard her call him Philip. He tried so hard to act manly and grown but then Momma came in and called him <u>Fiddle</u> right in front of the girl. I saw his face turn crimson but he held his tongue. Then, sure enough, after the girl left, he started begging Momma to stop calling him Fiddle and to please tell Daddy, too.

"It's getting stupid. Cat and Moon don't like it any more, either. Cat already <u>told</u> you. And Moon told me something really dumb happened to her today."

Moon spoke up and said someone in her class asked her if her brains were made of cheese, like the moon in the sky. "It isn't fair!" she howled.

We brought it up every night at dinner until Daddy finally set down the law. "You can call yourselves anything you want but you are our Cat, Fiddle and Moon."

We knew that the fortress gates of decision were closed. Momma and Daddy never made a split judgement. They were so close you could never tell who actually made the final decisions. Then Daddy took Momma's hand and they looked hard at us and gave a slight nod. Case closed.

Fiddle, as usual, started thinking and as usual, we knew it would mean trouble. He came into my room pulling Moon with him one night and declared that it was <u>our turn</u>. We were going to give Momma and Daddy <u>their</u> Namings and he already knew exactly what they would be.

I warned him I wanted no part of such a plan. Momma and

Daddy might get hurt feelings and we might get hurt behinds.

He insisted it would be all right. We'd just not ever tell them. We would eat cooked red cabbage before we'd ever tell. We all hated cooked red cabbage. It would be our secret. We hung on edge waiting to hear what he had dreamed up for Namings. He stood pompously in the middle of my room, hands on hips, feet just a fiddling and dancing and wearing a super smirky grin.

"Now, you know very well, Momma is round and you know very well, Daddy is like a long stick and I declare they be named, the Dish and the Spoon, now and forever! Time they became part of the nursery rhyme, just like us."

Moon and I started laughing so hard, Fiddle threatened to smother us with our pillows.

I announced that I would slip up, I just knew it and Moon could never keep a secret, not ever. Besides I thought it was no good if it was just us who knew. Maybe if they knew, they would see how much we couldn't stand our Namings anymore.

But Fiddle was adamant and not so brave as he pretended. He declared it would just be fun if it was just us who knew. "Besides," he proclaimed, "soon as we are grown up and out of here, we don't have to use those names."

Moon declared she couldn't call Momma, Dish, and couldn't call Daddy, Spoon. "sounds like we're making fun of them," she said. Moon was always the most tender-hearted of all of us. To hurt someone's feelings was unthinkable to her.

"But Moon," Fiddle looked deep into her eyes, "we all know how much we love Momma and Daddy. It's just for fun. We won't hurt their feelings because they will never know. We got the best Momma and Daddy of anyone in the whole world and we know it." Oh, that Fiddle!, I thought. Slick as grease on a brass door knob he is.

We got in the habit of talking about Momma and Daddy as Dish and Spoon but never to their faces. We just accepted being Cat, Fiddle and Moon to everyone and made a pact that we would not try to change anything until Momma and Daddy were gone. That made Moon weep hard tears. "I'd rather be called Moon until

325

I die than lose Momma and Daddy. I hope I die first!" she had sobbed.

The solemnity of that thought ended all further conversation on the subject of our Namings.

The day came for all of us when we left for college, jobs and to begin our own families. Fiddle was the one who decided to carry on with farming and went to Agriculture College. He married a pretty college classmate who studied animal husbandry and partnered with the local veterinarian. Moon and I were carried off by our husbands, she to Virginia, I to Colorado. We both traveled home as often as possible and were still Cat, Fiddle and Moon to everyone we knew, our spouse's included. Momma and Daddy were still our secret Dish and Spoon.

Fiddle was there when Daddy collapsed and nearly died of a heart attack. The doctor said he had to stay very quiet for awhile, just sit around. The doctor told him he could be up and walking soon but could not do any strenuous farming again. Well, that killed his spirit quicker than any heart attack could. He simply wasted away. He and Momma would sit together on the porch just holding hands and rocking. Fiddle said they chattered constantly about "Namings" and named everything in sight and out of sight using their nursery rhyme sense of humor. Fiddle said it seemed to be the only time Daddy would act as though he was happy. Fiddle said he had to have help because Momma would rarely move from Daddy's side and he was afraid to leave them alone while he tended to the farm.

One day, the call came. Fiddle was broken and sobbing on the phone and I knew right away Daddy had passed.

He told me Moon was on her way. I told him I'd be home quick as I could get there.

When I arrived at the farm, Fiddle and Moon were sitting on the front porch in Momma and Daddy's rockers. Little Dog, the Third, sat with them.

"Where's Momma?" My blood felt frozen in my body. "Why isn't she here to meet me, too?"

"Moon and I went into the room last night to bring Momma

something to eat. She had just been sitting there holding Daddy's hand since he passed. We let her be. Daddy was all dressed for the viewing and looked so fine. When we went in, Momma had laid down beside him, still holding on to his hand. In her other hand, this note. She was gone, Cat."

Fiddle handed me a scrap of paper. My eyes did not want to focus on the familiar scratchy handwriting. It was Momma's hand. It said, "Dearest Cat, Fiddle and Moon. The Dish Ran Away With The Spoon! Love, Momma and Daddy."

I just stood rock still staring at the words. Momma and Daddy knew. They had known all along.

The next day, after the service and interment, the three of us stood by the fresh grave after everyone went home, holding hands and grieving.

I don't know how long we had been there when Fiddle broke away and stood before us. He positioned his arms as though to play the fiddle and began to tap and shuffle his feet. "Ah one, ah two, ah three."

We joined in the familiar chant. "Hey Diddle Diddle, The Cat And The Fiddle, The Cow Jumped Over The Moon, The Little Dog Laughed To See Such Sport And The Dish Ran Away With The Spoon."

Moon and I hugged and rocked, sniffled and laughed softly. I felt Momma and Daddy's spirits here, but we still had something we had to do.

"You know what time this is, Maureen Elizabeth?" I asked loud so Fiddle would hear.

"Why yes, Catherine Jane, I do. It is pact time." We looked at each other and grinned.

Fiddle strode to us with a scowling face. "I heard every word. Shame on you."

"But Philip James," we chorused.

"Fiddle's the name."

He came close and drew our eyes to his face with a mesmerizing gaze. "You think you can muddy up Momma and Daddy's memories by not using your Naming Names? No pacts, no secrets anymore. I say, 'Momma and Daddy are forever inscribed for all to see as "Dish and Spoon" and we are forever known and someday will be inscribed as, Cat, Fiddle and Moon.' Forever!"

"Fiddle," I said, "You didn't think for one second that..."

He tossed his smirky grin at us. "Not for one second."

As I waited, I looked up in the sky and knew Momma and Daddy's beautiful love was spreading all over Heaven. But the best part is I know exactly what Momma and Daddy are doing. Naming Angels, of course.

Insanity
by Jennifer Gammage

She sat patiently in the chair, her eyes downcast, gazing at her hands clasped in her lap. She smiled faintly as if at some inner joke.

"Mrs. Johnson? How much do you take home monthly, weekly, or biweekly after taxes?"

She looked up at me slowly, as if she were moving in a dream. The soft smile and placid expression didn't waver as she answered, "I don't work. I get Social Security." she looked back down at her lap. I waited for a moment. She continued to stare at her hands. Disconcerted, I gazed at her. She was a tall black woman, but her slumped shoulders and demure posture gave the impression of one much smaller. Her eyes were a soft, dark brown that seemed to be looking just beyond you. Twice, I had to keep myself from looking over my shoulder to see if someone was standing there. Her hair was short, just above her ears and hadn't seen a relaxer in a while. Tight beads of hair rimmed her neck and the straight part down the middle of her unkempt hair. She wore an old faded shirt, and a long, khaki skirt. She was heavy for her height, her curves rounded in odd places, making her overweight body look misshapen. She smelled overpoweringly of baby powder and…something else, something that frightened me and made me uncomfortable. If insanity had a smell, I'd call it that. Yes, she smelled of baby powder and something off color, something stinking and rotting inside a cellar, like a fungus.

"Mrs. Johnson? How much is your SSI?"

Again the slow look. In soft measured tones, she told me, "Seven-fifty."

"And does that include AFDC?"

She continued to smile faintly at her lap. Flustered, I looked to the other woman in the room. She sat next to Mrs. Johnson. She was smiling like a proud parent at the older woman. Her face was encouraging and excited. Of course, she was the one really getting furniture, not Mrs. Johnson, so she had every right to look pleased.

Mrs. Johnson still hadn't looked up from her lap, so I asked again, "Is that including AFDC, Mrs. Johnson?"

The woman next to Mrs. Johnson spoke up quickly, "Yes."

My cynical mind, accustomed to this procedure, prayed that Mrs. Johnson wouldn't get approved. I'd seen this so many times. People came in here with their handicapped and elderly relatives, got credit, charged it up and then never paid for it. The bill isn't in their names, so they don't worry about it.

"Honey, I bought that furniture for my daughter. She da one who pay on it. God, I wish I'd never done it now, da way you folks' worryin' me."

"Well, Mrs. So-and-So, the credit is in your name and it's your credit rating that is going down and the company is about to file legals on this account."

"Lawd have mercy, Jesus! And I don' know where dat gul is! Can you give me to next week? I'll get the money somehow. I done got my check for dis month. It's been and gone, but I'll get the money up somehow."

I hate those calls. I hate putting the squeeze on nice people. I hate to have to tell people that they're going to court because they're kind people who love their daughters and sons and nieces and nephews. I harden my heart to them, though. They have to learn the hard way, the way I did. Never loan family money because they'll throw it all at you—all the times they took you to Sunday School when you were three years old and anything else they can think of rather than give it back. Never let family borrow anything that you want back or want back in the condition it was sent. And never get anything in your name, or on your credit, for your family members. I learned that with my credit cards, and I learned it from working in a furniture company and watching innocent people go to court.

My head swam slightly. The cloying scent of baby powder and adult body odor assailed my nostrils. The stillness about the strange woman and within her eyes made me more and more nervous. Something about this woman set me on edge. I wanted her out of my office. Now. I quickly ran through the forms, not bothering to white-out my many mistakes. A sense of urgency ran through me. I don't know if somewhere in my mind I felt, primitively, that her obvious insanity was contagious, but I knew that I was in a hurry to get her out of there. Her stillness, her placid smile, reminded me too sharply of my own frenetic, fanatic energy that past week, my own closeness to a breakdown.

Some strange, compulsive part of me kept seeing myself reaching out to that woman and touching the stillness about her. It felt cool, embracing, soothing. I could see myself wrapping up in that stillness and becoming that woman. The urge to lose touch with everything around me, to be that free to smile softly at some inner something that no one can understand but me, was powerful.

I wanted that woman out of my office.

When she was turned down, I ran to the bathroom and stood with my head pressed to the mirror. Sweat beaded my brow and I felt bile rise in my throat. I fought it down. Panic attack. That's what Dr. Miller told me they were. I took deep calming breaths, as I had been taught, and tried to think of something soothing…besides the strangely compelling stillness about that woman.

O, Georgia!

Etowah
by David Schmidt

At the river's edge,
high in a sparsely-needled pine,
a hawk stares steadily at the sunlight-dappled water below,
the surface of the water a shiny liquid mirror reflecting
the porcelain blues and milky whites of the ever-changing sky,
the bright greens and rusty browns of the river's wooded shores,
and the broad, dark shadow of the bridge on which I stand —
I, too, gazing at the river, on whose surface I see
the hawk's shuddering reflection intermingled
with a confusion of other images and designs.
Nearby, a strong, insistent wind animates a tree-lined riverbank,
causing the trees to tremble and shimmer and sway
with vibrant and manifest life. They almost dance
with rapturous abandon in celebration of the day.
But the wind quickly dies away,
and the trees become still once more...
Far above, the hawk suddenly leaps from his perch
into the warm, heavy air, free-falling only briefly
before laboring slowly upward with long, stiff wings,
his small black silhouette rising higher and higher
until it finally disintegrates in the brilliant yellow light
of the dazzling summer sun.

Without thought, I throw a stone from the bridge.
It shatters the many reflections on the water's glassy surface.

The reflections, broken now, drift in multicolored fragments
with the slow, soft current, until, like bits of tumbling debris,
they disappear into the dark depths of the cold and inexorable
river.

O, Georgia!

Basketball
by Meryl L. Martin

If I could be a boy again
I would put these reading glasses aside
And close this worn leather briefcase.
I would shut my office door behind me
And slip on a pair of high top sneakers
Black canvas that smell of dirty socks
Not white leather smelling of success.

We would run out on that court and hear
The squeaking of our soles against
The waxed wood and feel the warmth
Of the rigid leather in our hands.
I would feel the air rush past my face
As you came driving, blocking, running
Past me.
When you jumped and stretched
Your lean body taut and straight
My fingers would be next to yours
And we would tip the ball into
That orange metal hoop together.
The walls of the gymnasium would echo
With cries of victory, and
The shouts and cheering for you
Would be for me too,
And I would be your friend.

If I could be a boy again
And not your father.

O, Georgia!

Secret of the Cohullasee
by Walton Young

"Yeah. This is where I hid. Behind these bushes."

Shook went on to explain that the bushes were smaller then. But, of course, so was he; hiding was no problem.

I stepped carefully through the knee-high weeds—I didn't want to disturb the afternoon slumber of a rattlesnake—past the bushes to the edge of a steep bluff, which dropped forty feet or so to the rocky bank of the Cohullasee. The river was about fifty yards wide at this point as it continued its downward spiral from the Blue Ridge to the Piedmont. The clear water tumbled around dark gray granite boulders, worn smooth by the constant assault of the water, and swirled violently into a series of rapid plunges, which the white water adventurers called Murderers Row. Few, if any of the rafters who challenged these icy rapids knew what happened here thirty years ago. In fact, I didn't know either, until Shook invaded my office two nights previously and proceeded to tell me what he thought I should know.

"So, this is where it happened?" I called out above the roar of the water.

Shook nodded his head. He seemed unwilling to venture to the edge of the bluff, as if the gravity of his memory would pull him down to the rapids. After looking again at the froth, I walked back toward Shook.

"What were you doing here?"

"Smokin'. I was just twelve. If my old man caught me smokin', he'd blister my rump. So I'd come here to smoke; it was a good hidin' place."

As I stood in the sweltering heat of a late August afternoon, I didn't know what to think. I stared at Shook's deeply lined face, gaunt and strangely pale in the shadow of his baseball cap. He never smiled; he never raised his voice above a hoarse whisper. And in the heat and the humidity I detected the stale smell of liquor, which called to mind the stories I had heard about Rafe Shook, a dependable mason when he was sober, which wasn't too often. I had heard Shook was one of only a few people left in the mountains who knew how to build a masonry fireplace that didn't smoke.

"I know you've told me before," I said, "but I want to hear it again, here where it happened. Tell me what you saw."

Shook breathed deeply and stared at the ground.

" I was sittin' at the edge of that there bluff smokin' when I heard this car pull up. At first I thought it might be Pa out lookin' for me, so I scampered into the bushes. Then I saw it was George Cable; I recognized his black Chevy Impala. He got out and Deedra Sams got out with him. She was gigglin'. I had no idea what was goin' on. They went down the hill right to the edge of the water and spread out a blanket. I thought maybe they was goin' to have themselves a picnic, but I remember thinkin' it was kinda strange 'cause Deedra was married to Hank Sams. Well, they wasn't havin' no picnic, or maybe they was, dependin' on how you looked at it. Next thing I knew they pulled off every stitch of clothin' and started doin' it right there in the shade of that there water oak. It was quite a show for a twelve-year-old kid. My eyes almost popped out. Well, after they finished, they just sat there on the blanket, butt naked, smokin' and talkin' and laughin'. I reckon 'cause of the loud noise the river makes they didn't hear a car pull up, but I did. I shifted position so I could see who it was. Well, it was Hank Sams, Deedra's husband; he had a friend, Pete Wells, with him."

"Are you absolutely sure it was Hank Sams?"

"Positive. I've known Hank all my life. It was him."

Before resuming his narrative, Shook lit a cigarette. The smoke drifted upward, quickly lost in the summer haze.

"Hank and Pete didn't look none too happy. They walked right past me, so close I figured they could hear me breathin', but they didn't notice; they had other things on their minds. Hank carried a pistol, a big pistol. I mean to tell you George and Deedra had quite a surprise. They jumped to their feet, still butt naked, cryin' and hollerin'. I couldn't hear what they was sayin', but I heard the first shot. Hank slowly raised the pistol, and George backed into the river and dropped to his knees, his arms wavin' above his head. He was either beggin' for mercy or tryin' to fly. No matter. Hank shot him right between the eyes. I can still see the dazed look on

George's face and then the blood. There was a lot of blood in the water. He fell over and the river swept him two miles downstream. A coupla fishermen found him the next day. Well, Deedra was screamin' somethin' terrible, and for a long time nothin' happened. Hank just stood there, listenin' to her, and I thought he was goin' to let her go. He even smiled at her. It was one of those don't-worry-honey-it's-going-to-be-all-right kind of smiles. But hell, he shot her, too, right in the stomach—I think just to watch her suffer a bit. She rolled around on the blanket, then off the blanket. He watched her for a while; then he walked over to her and shot her in the head. He picked her up, real careful like, which was kinda odd, threw her over his shoulder, and carried her to his car. Pete fetched her clothes and the blanket. Before leavin', they stood outside the car and looked around, just to make sure nobody was watchin', I reckon. I lay low in the bushes, not darin' to move a muscle. They drove off. I was so sick from the sight of all that blood I started pukin' my guts out."

When he finished the narrative in his usual monotone, he discarded the remains of the cigarette and immediately lit another. Meanwhile, I wiped the sweat from my face with a handkerchief. I had heard Shook's story twice and the details had not varied. Of course, he could've rehearsed it countless times. Beneath the scorching sun I wrestled with the question—was Shook a credible source? Most of the townspeople, if not all, would say absolutely not. Shook was a drunk; he'd say most anything for a buck. However, I had not offered him money, more importantly, he had not asked for any. So, why was he revealing this story to me?

Shook seemed sure of himself, nervous but sure, just as he had two nights ago. Nevertheless, I remained incredulous. I had gone to the library and researched the rest of the story. Newspaper articles on microfilm recounted that Deedra's fully clothed body was found behind the cash register of the grocery store where she worked. Cable's body, as Shook said, was found two miles downstream. Hank Sams was described as a hard-working, grieving husband who faced the daunting task of rearing his four children alone. The portrait of Hank Sams was not the portrait of a murderer.

"Shook, what you're telling me happened thirty years ago. Pete Wells died in 1974, so he sure can't defend himself. Why have you waited all these years to come forward?"

"I reckon I was afraid—afraid Hank or one of his friends would kill me. I saw what he did to George Cable and to his own wife. I figured it sure wouldn't bother him none to put a bullet hole in me."

"All right. Thirty years ago—twenty years ago—ten years ago—you were afraid. But today you're not. I've got a problem with that."

"Mr. McClanahan, it don't matter no more."

"What do you mean?"

"I'm dyin'. I got lung cancer. Doc Gibson says it's spread, so it's too late to do much. Of course, if'n I had the kind of money somebody like Hank Sams had, I'm sure Doc would find somethin' to do for me. Mr. McClanahan, I've carried this secret with me for thirty years. I ain't carryin' it to my grave."

"Why don't you go to the police?" I don't understand why you're talking to me."

"Do you really think the police would believe me? I'm Rafe Shook, a drunk. I haven't held a steady job in years. The police wouldn't give me the time of day. But you, Mr. McClanahan, you're an outsider. You ain't from here. Nobody in this town is goin' to believe me. Hell, I wouldn't believe me, either. But you ain't one of us. I figure you'll listen. You may not believe me but at least you'll listen. Somethin' real bad happened here, and the wrong man is still payin' the price."

Shook began coughing and he tossed the cigarette to the ground. Without saying another word, he headed to the car.

As the afternoon faded into evening, I sat before the computer in my office and recorded my notes. Occasionally I'd sit back and stare at the screen, not really reading the words. The story was a bomb set to go off the moment it appeared in print. Printing the story, however, was out of the question. I needed more information, obtaining it would be difficult. If I were to start asking questions, folks would become suspicious.

I hardly noticed that darkness was sliding across the town square; I hadn't even bothered to turn on the lights. Running my fingers through my hair, I wished that Shook had remained a figure I had only heard about it. I wished he'd never crossed the threshold of my office. But he had. This sort of thing was not what I had bargained for when I decided to move to this valley tucked quietly among the forested slopes of the Blue Ridge. I recalled the conversation I had had with Cranston, my managing editior at the newspaper in Atlanta.

A former Marine, Cranston was a large, imposing task master, who rightfully believed his readers should get the best from his reporters, and he made sure his reporters delivered. We sat in his glass-walled office, which gave him a commanding view of the entire newsroom, and he held the letter of resignation firmly in two monstrous hands. An inscrutable smile crossed his thin lips.

"I make it part of my job to know my people," he sad. "Generally I do a damn good job. But not in your case. I've got to hand it to you, Trey. You've surprised me. You've lived in a city all your life. What the hell do you know about living in a small town?"

"My grandparents lived in a small town."

"They aren't the ones who are going to publish this newspaper you've bought. You're the one who's going to publish it."

"What's the point, Cranston?"

"Trey, you know as well as I do that running a small town weekly is a little different from running a metro daily. And I'm not talking about circulation numbers. Here, if you write an article that exposes a little corruption at city hall, readers are going to appreciate it. Now, if you do the same thing in a small town, a lot of feathers are going to get ruffled. Everygody knows everybody. Suddenly your new neighbors are going to look at you askance and wonder what you're trying to prove. If this scenario plays all the way out, things can get a little nasty."

"I'm not moving to Mount Holly to start a war with city hall. Besides, they don't have a city hall. They have a courthouse."

341

"That's even worse. Trey, what are you going to write about—quilting parties and weddings? Of course, when Farmer Jones's cow has a calf, that's front page news. Is that what you're going to cover? Hell, no. You're a newspaperman, and a damn good one. You've got this uncanny knack of digging up juicy little stories that the bad guys thought they had buried for good. But hey—go ahead. Publish this thing. Get it out of your system. I figure it'll take two years. Then you'll be back."

Three months had elapsed since I walked out the doors of the Atlanta newspaper. If Cranston could see me sitting in front of the computer screen, pondering my notes on a crime that occurred thirty years ago, a big, I-told-you-so smile would sprint across his face. Then he would hand me an employment application.

But I wouldn't sign it.

No, even if Cranston were standing in my office, placing the application on my desk, exhorting me to return, promising me that I would not lose my tenure, I wouldn't sign. There was a story in my notes. I had to determine how to handle it.

I hardly knew Hank Sams. Working at the paper in Atlanta, I had heard of him. He wielded considerable political clout not just in Mount Holly but throughout the state. Though he had never held office, he influenced those who did. Candidates sought his support. Hank Sams could deliver the mountain vote. I had talked with him briefly at several civic events, and I came away with a favorable impression. The irony of it all, I suppose, was that Hank Sams was indirectly responsible for my even being in Mount Holly. Hank's eldest son, Clifford, was my best friend. We first met in Vietnam in a makeshift NCO club. We were surprised to find we were both from Georgia—and yet worlds apart. I was from Atlanta and he was from Mount Holly, a small town in the mountains of northeast Georgia.

Clifford was in another platoon. I suppose it was luck he was in the sector close to the one we were patrolling. When the booby traps exploded, shattering the tranquillity of the impenetrable jungle, he and his men came running to lend assistance. He found me bleeding to death. I barely remember his face hovering above me, his hands pressing the bandage against the wound, but I do remember his words: "You're going to make it." I'm still not sure how I did. Because of Clifford Sams, one more Georgia boy was able to return home alive. He came often to the hospital. We'd sit and talk about our past and plans for the future—he'd always try to impress me with the virtues of Mount Holly.

"I don't get it," I confessed. "I know a lot of guys from small towns and they're eager as hell to get away to see the bright lights of the city."

"They haven't lived in Mount Holly. It's a special place, Trey. Believe me—man was not created to live in a city. You come for a visit, and you'll want to stay."

I accepted the invitation. As the road climbed into northeast Georgia, with the blue-veiled slopes of the mountains rising to greet me, I felt an exhilaration never experienced among the glass towers of the city. When I saw the vacant office in the century-old, red brick two-story building opposite the courthouse, the office with the faded, clipped words *Mount Holly Gazette* spread across the window, I knew I'd end up here.

But I didn't know I'd end up staring at the notes related to an implausible story concocted by a dying alcoholic.

When the glass door rattled open, I strained in the darkness to see a large figure shuffling toward me.

"Can I help you?"

"It's me Trey. Hope I didn't startle you. Damn, you like working in the dark, or what?"

By this time the screen saver was on, which was good because I didn't want Fred Kines to see my notes. Fred turned on a desk lamp and collapsed into a chair next to my desk. Even in the shadows I could see that his round face was flushed.

"Man, it's hot," he said. "I think I'll retire and move to Maine."

"Fred, you are retired."

"Well, I think I'll still move to Maine. It's gotta be cooler

343

up there. By the way, here's the info on the golf tournament. We need all the publicity you can give us."

After handing me a manila envelope, he continued to sit and it was obvious he was observing me. His words came in short, breathy bursts.

"I understand you had a meeting with Rafe Shook."

"So?"

"In a small town it's hard to do things without everybody seeing, and it's hard to say things without everybody hearing. I suppose Shook shared with you his little fable."

"What little fable?"

Fred laughed.

"Of course he did. He's been telling that story for years to anyone who'd listen."

"Fred, what can you add to his story?"

Fred's laughter subsided and again he studied me.

"From the moment you moved here, I've tried to be your friend. But, Trey, that question sounds like it's coming from an Atlanta newspaper reporter, not from a Mount Holly friend."

"I no longer work for an Atlanta newspaper. I've got my own paper right here. But I'd still like to hear what you know about Shook's story. I'm not recording. I'm not writing anything down."

Any semblance of mirth on Fred's face was gone, replaced by a cold and hard expression.

"Hank Sams is one of the finest fellows I've ever know, a true credit to his community and to his state."

"I'm not asking for a profile that's handed out to the press."

"Hank Sams would have never done anything to harm his wife. Is that what you're wanting to hear? I shouldn't have to say it, but I will. It's the truth, Trey. And something else is the truth—we got the man who did harm his wife. We tried him and we convicted him and we sent his sorry ass to prison. My only regret is that he didn't fry in the chair. But a slick lawyer—from Atlanta, by the way—got him a life sentence. Every time his petition for parole comes up, the board denies it. That ought to tell you something."

"Did you know the man who was convicted?"

"I know everybody in this town and in this county. I especially knew him. From the day he was born Jarod Miles was nothing but trouble. He was kicked out of high school'cause he was always picking fights. He even got into a fight with a teacher, threatened to kill him if he didn't get a passing grade in math. That's the kind of person Jarrod Miles was and is. He resented Hank because Hank was successful. Hank had a lot of money but it wasn't handed to him, he worked for it. George Cable was also a hard worker. Both George and Jarrod worked at Hank's manufacturing plant. I remember warning Hank not to hire Jarrod, but Hank insisted on giving the poor boy a chance. 'A chance is all he needs,' Hank told me. Well, Jarrod needed more than a chance. He needed a desire to make something of himself, a quality that George had. As a result, George got promoted. Jarrod got angry. He accused Hank of playing favorites. He stormed out of the plant, swearing he'd get even with both Hank and George. He found George down at the river fishing, and he killed him."

"How do you explain—"

"George not having any clothes on" Maybe the fish weren't biting. It was a hot day, so he decided to go skinny-dipping. After killing George, Jarrod went to the grocery store, where Hank always picked Deedra up at the end of the day. But Hank had a meeting that afternoon at the plant—verified in court, by the way. Deedra was by herself. I reckon Jarrod figured killing Deedra would just have to do. Trey, I don't like reliving what happened. Goodness know, Hank's family doesn't want to relive it. Clifford doesn't want to relive it."

"I'm just looking for answers."

"The questions have all been answered. Trey, we proved in court, beyond a show of a doubt, that Jarrod Miles committed those murders. He had even hid the pistol under the mattress in his mobile home. During the trial, Shook could have testified, but he didn't. I know—he was afraid. I hope you don't believe that. He didn't say anything back then because he had nothing to say. All the liquor he's consumed over the years must have thrown his imagination into overdrive. What his motives are baffles me. But, Trey, I'm ask-

345

ing you not to listen to him. I know you're a good newspaperman, but there's no story here. None. Hank is a friend to everybody in this town. Hank is also the father of the man who saved your life in Vietnam."

Fred rose unsteadily and disappeared into the darkness. i tapped the space bar on the keyboard and the notes returned to the screen. Again the words became a blur. The telephone rang.

"Honey, the kids and I are starving, why don't you come on home? What could be so important that you can't leave the office?"

"Karla, I can tell from the sound of your voice that you've cooked something new and you can't wait to try it on me."

"Trey, dear, it's food, not a scientific experiment. There's no need to pick up antacid at the pharmacy. I promise you you're safe. Do you remember when we lived in Atlanta, we never had time to cook? It was always fast food. This town has changed our lives, for the better, I might add. What are you working on—a story that's going to cause the old courthouse to crumble?"

"Yeah. You know me. If there's a story, I'm going to find it. I'll be home in fifteen minutes."

With the tap of a key, I sent the notes fleeing to a disk, where they were safe.

Armor
by Linda S. Kirkland

My armored heart

stays closed to you

can't feel your pain

won't let it through

can't hear your cries

inside your heart

stay walled away

stay locked apart

My armored heart

can't feel your pain

until your heart

can beat again

until you heal

from inside out

my armored heart

can do without

O, Georgia!

Mother & Daddy in Sepia
by Anne Webster

Like his Rebel grandfather, he stands
brass buttoned on the roof
of Georgia Military College.
In his hands a saxophone gleams
dully in the after-Taps dusk.
He points the wide mouth at a flush
of lights icing the nearby College
for Women. One yellow pane hides
a girl so close that Sweet William
is her perfume, and the pulse of her
throat is just beyond his touch.
He pushes out with the horn, a long
honeyed sound. In her room the girl
sits writing in her small neat hand.
Her eyes mirror the desk lamp
as she dreams of the Dean's list
and Sunday's parlor visit. Again,
she sees his muscles moving beneath
sharp creases as he sits the hard chair.
The blaze of his smile and his crackling
black eyes touch her through woolly
uniform folds. Her breath comes short
and her writing slows. She leans
ruddy curls against a white arm,
caught in a gilt frame of sound.

O, Georgia!

Dream Passin' By

by John Neal Bagwell

There are nights here with the moonlight cold and
ghastly; and the whippoorwills; and the screech owls
alone disturbing the silence, when I could tear my hair
and cry alone for all that is past and gone.

Mary Chestnut

He lay motionless between the cloud and the town.

He had spent the better part of the last four years out-of-doors, and had never noticed how beautiful, and untouchable, a cloud could be. The cloud seemed so close that it was almost as though he could reach and grab it; reshape it with his hands; keep it for himself. But, no, it was beyond his reach; beyond his control. He lay there and wondered where the cloud would end up on its journey through God's heaven, wishing he could go with it.

A few minutes earlier, he had realized that the cloud was moving almost due east.

West to east. North and south were not part of the cloud's world. This pleased him, since everything in *his* world had, of late, revolved completely around the question of north and south.

He reluctantly turned away from the cloud for a moment and looked at the town, afforded a good view of it from his perch on the hillside on which he lay. It seemed to him that he had last seen the town about ten thousand years ago

But, he didn't want to see the town, didn't want to face the town. That is, he didn't want to face his family, the acquaintances, his friends (those who were still around, anyway). For almost four years, he had dreamed of this moment; longed for the time when he would once again view the only home he had ever known from this hill. And, now that he was here, it didn't seem real, didn't seem right. So, he again lifted his eyes to the cloud.

Being the simple man that he was, he didn't know that the cloud that commanded his attention was called a cumulous cloud; couldn't perceive that its zenith was as high as 25,000 feet above the earth. All he knew was that the cloud was the most beautiful, most captivating thing he had ever seen. But his common sense, which his lack of formal education did not diminish, told him why the cloud was so captivating. Watching the cloud prolonged the time when he would have to face reality.

Not that he wasn't glad to be home. His brass bed would certainly beat out the ground he had been sleeping on for so long. There would be no more drill, no more sergeants. From now on, if it were raining, he would simply step under an eve, or even indoors, by God. And, his mother's bread certainly would not be moldy, nor would he have to share her stews or grits with boweevuls.

No more midnight picket duty. No more packs to tote, or rifles to clean. He wouldn't even have to clean a hunting rifle, for since that night when he got cut off from his lines while scouting in the wilderness and was hunted like a rabbit by a Yankee patrol for four hours, he had vowed ne'er to hunt another animal again.

And then, of course, there was now to be the absence of death, or death in vast numbers anyway. From now on, anyone that he knew would be taken out by God, not some bluejacketed sharpshooter.

But, in a strange sort of way, he knew that he would somehow miss all these things which he had considered evils. After all, it was the life he had grown accustomed to over the years; the life he had resigned himself to live. Lord knows, after Pennsylvania, it seemed it would never end, 'least not till all of them were dead.

But, during the worst battles, when he was in the tightest spots, it was then that he felt most alive. Reflecting on them now, he did not see how he was able to perform some of the feats that saw him through. He just couldn't fathom how he, or anyone, survived that whole catastrophic business. But, whatever the reason, he knew that a man is the most alive when death is just a step behind him.

And that was part of the reason he did not move from his cloud vigil. It wasn't, he knew, his nostalgia over his now-former life that kept him on that hill. It's just that it seemed he had borne witness to too many things to now return to his father's store. How could he sell feed to farmers when only a month ago he was killing farmers sons? And, how could he expect his father to understand that, least of all his mother? They wouldn't be able to understand, couldn't understand. The war had mercifully left Jackson County untouched, except for some little skirmish below Jefferson he had heard about. Aside from what they had probably read in the papers, his folks would have no idea...none at all.

So, what will they say, he wondered. Will they see it in his eyes? In his walk? If they do, will they forgive him for it? Questions without answers that kept him on the hill.

At some time in their lives, everyone wishes for a chance to turn back the clock, a time machine to transport them back to some ancient fork in the road, so that maybe they can remember which fork they originally took and then take the other one, no matter where it leads. Well, that's what he wished for, too...summer of '61...he and Elander Mize walking out the road toward Gainesville...27th Georgia Infantry...train station...ladies waving their handkerchiefs, more girls than he had ever seen at one place in his life...crowded rail cars...Cornelia and Toccoa and still more stops with more ladies...the Carolinas...never been more than six miles from home, and now look...finest set of clothes he had ever seen, butternut with blue trim just like everyone else.

And the pervading theme everywhere he went: whip the hell out of the Yankees. He had never been too sure of the why, but he knew they could do it just the same. One Southern boy was worth ten Yankees, everybody knew. And now they had their own country, and were out to prove the theory.

But it wasn't until that first battle, and probably the second, that the seriousness of the affair settled in on him. The train station orators were conspicuously absent from the battlefield, as were some of his friends after the battle.... Where had his country gone? And what inestimable price had his country paid to try to be its own country?

No! This wasn't good enough, not far enough. Turn it back farther, before the war. School days...church homecomings ...dances.... Impossible, even in thought. The boy was buried too deep, and the man that took his place could not let go of the last four years to allow his host a remembrance of time before the war.

And so he lay there, killing no one and nothing, but time. He studied the cloud more closely, and saw the boy and the war and the cause tucked into its clefs and ridges. The folds and the rounded edges housed the South as he had known it, and envisioned it to be. And as he watched it, the cloud, influenced by wind and temperature, slowly changed shape and form right before his eyes. And as it did, he too changed, influenced by the transition into this, his third life. The changes, both of them, were barely perceptible to him. But he could see the changes occurring, both of them.

For four years, his mother and father had looked for the boy who had walked down that road to come walking back up the road. But, he knew, they would never see the boy again. The man that had replaced the creature who had replaced the boy was who they would have to learn to live with. He just hoped he would be able to live with him also.

Gradually, the cloud, and the boy, and the South continued their eastward trek, there was no stopping them. He pulled himself up and, before starting down the hill, took one last fleeting look over his shoulder.

Then, purposefully, and with measured tread, he began his descent toward home, as the cloud disappeared over the horizon forever.

Summertime

(an excerpt)

by Sheri Layne Smith

The best time to live in Athens is the summertime, Leanne thought as she walked from the Legal Aid office down nearly-deserted Washington Street. Only a few stray students left in town, no traffic, no crowds. And at 6:30 on a Friday evening there were empty parking spaces on the street in front of the bar where she was headed. Amazing.

Sam, her ex-husband, had taken their two daughters to the lake for a week and Leanne had a delicious taste of what her life might have been like if she'd made different choices. At 42, as a single mother and criminal defense attorney, Leanne's life was ruled by other people's demands: her clients, her children, judges. She missed her daughters while they were away, but, oh, the luxury of time that was hers alone. Of course, only the weekend was Leanne's alone; she had a murder trial beginning in two weeks so she had lots of work to do come Monday.

So what was Leanne going to do on this weekend of all weekends? So many possibilities. Inside the Uptown Lounge, Cammy, her Legal Aid student and friend, was full of ideas. "You could go to the Bulldog Inn and try to pick up a traveling salesman in the lounge." Cammy struggled not to smile while making this suggestion. Leanne had sworn off men entirely after her long combative marriage finally unraveled.

"I wouldn't set foot in that dump. Do people still pick people up these days with AIDS and all?" Leanne poured herself a beer from the pitcher on the counter.

"I don't know," Cammy said. "I'm just trying to think of things you'd never do with the girls here. You need some adventure in your life, Leanne. You may as well be ninety years old the way you act, I swear to God." She swallowed the last sip of her beer and thumped the mug down on the table for emphasis. Cammy was dark-haired and petite and she always got asked for an i.d. at bars, even though she was three months away from her thirtieth birthday.

Leanne looked at Cammy, smirking, "Well, I feel ninety

355

years old, does that count?" Leanne was forty-two, with dirty blonde hair, hazel eyes framed by smile wrinkles, and a long, lean frame.

"Hello! You feel that old because you act that old," Cammy said. "If you'd just forget yourself for a few hours and do something fun for a change, you'd feel a whole lot younger, I guarantee you."

Leanne crossed her legs and swung a loafer back and forth, balancing it on her big toe. "Assuming without deciding that what you say is true, exactly what kind of stuff do you do for fun?"

"You know, go to the movies, go shopping, get dressed up and go out to dinner somewhere nice in Atlanta. Lots of things."

"I could go to the grocery store. That might be kind of fun to do without the girls whining for every piece of junk food in Bi-Lo."

"Leanne, I swear. You wouldn't know fun if it bit you on the butt. Trust me, the grocery store does not qualify under anyone's definition." Cammy shook her head in disgust.

"Well, I don't like movies since'The Sound of Music', I don't like to go shopping. And I'm not driving all the way to Atlanta just to eat."

"I know!" Cammy grabbed Leanne's arm in excitement. "The law school is having a cocktail party tomorrow night to celebrate the opening of the International Law Center. We could go to that. You got an invitation, I saw it in your in-box."

"The law school! Why on earth would I want to go over there?" Leanne despised the law school and made no secret of it. She'd resented the professors and their ivory tower attitude ever since she was in law school herself.

"It's summertime, nobody's around so nobody annoying is going to show up. Come on, it'll be fun!"

"You know how I feel about the law school. Surely there's something better we can find to do."

"This will be great. Free food and drinks, a jazz quartet. When was the last time you went to a cocktail party? We can just hang out with Todd and Marilyn, they're going to be there." Todd and Marilyn worked at Legal Aid, too, and made a habit of hitting any place in town where there were free beverages.

"What can we wear? What do people wear to cocktail parties? My parents weren't the cocktail party type and by the time Sam and I were married they were passé. You know what would be fun? We should go to the Salvation Army thrift shop and get real cocktail dresses like people wore on T.V. in the 70's."

"My parents went to a few cocktail parties." Cammy smiled, thinking back. "My mom had this silver Lurex dress she made and wore with silver high-heeled sandals. I thought she looked so mod. She always put her hair up in big sausage curls on top of her head, too, and wore dangly silver earrings."

"Hurry up and finish your beer. It's already seven o'clock and I think they close at eight. Let's run over there and see what we can find." Leanne put out her cigarette and picked up her purse from the cold cement floor.

"Okay, I'm finished." Cammy pulled out her wallet and put a five on the bar as she slid from the barstool.

The thrift shop had a large selection of cocktail dresses. No Lurex, to Cammy's dismay, but chiffon in every bright 70's shade you could think of. Leanne chose a sleeveless, high-necked, tent-style minidress in watermelon pink. Cammy found a chartreuse number with an empire waist and a plunging neckline. They hooted at each other in the dressing room, looking like refugees from Rowan and Martin's Laugh-In. Excited about their purchases, they discussed hairdos and jewelry all the way back to Leanne's house.

The next day, Leanne's head throbbed in the humid late afternoon air. Why did she let Cammy do her hair? It had always given her a headache to have her hair worked over and teased up. Inhaling the twenty-five coats of hair spray didn't help matters. Leanne was afraid to light a cigarette for hours. Maybe the headache was nicotine withdrawal. She rummaged through her purse mindlessly for her cigarettes. Why in the hell did she think going to this cocktail party would be a fun way to spend a Saturday night? She pulled at the hem of her ridiculous cocktail dress.

It's been a long time since I wore a skirt this short, Leanne thought. This thing barely covers my butt. Where was Cammy, anyway? It was after seven and she was supposed to have met Leanne at the fountain in the President's Garden at ten 'til. Leanne smoked and swung her leg from the park bench where she sat. I'm giving her ten more minutes, then I'm going home to wash this crap out of my hair.

Cammy hurried up as Leanne stubbed out her cigarette. "I'm sorry, don't be mad, I couldn't find my car keys and the spares — You look great!"

"I feel like crap. What in the hell did you use on my hair? Super glue?"

"No, just Spraynet, you know that old timey junk."

"Well, you look cute."

"Thanks." Cammy turned a quick pirouette, the chartreuse crepe of her cocktail dress flowing in the breeze she made with the movement of her body.

"How did I let you talk me into this?" Leanne shook her head.

"Oh, now, it'll be fun. Let's go face the music."

"Let me smoke one more cigarette and then we can go."

"Why are you carrying that purse! It's all wrong for your look."

"This is the only purse I've got, so it's this or nothing." Leanne patted the hefty chunk of beige leather affectionately.

"Then it needs to be nothing. Give me your cigarettes and your car keys. You won't need money or anything else." Cammy jammed the cigarette pouch and keys into her tiny silver shoulder bag. "Here, you'd better carry it or you'll be looking for me every time you need a cigarette."

"I guess we may as well go on over there. I need something to drink, my head's splitting."

Leanne and Cammy stepped gingerly across the lawn to the tent set up in front of the Rusk Center. There were uniformed attendants passing through the sparse crowd with trays of hors d'oeuvres. Leanne quickly approached a bartender at a side table.

"Yes, ma'am."

What was it that her daddy always drank to get rid of a headache? Was it bourbon?

"I want two shots of Jack Daniels in a highball glass, no ice."

Leanne drank it as soon as it was handed to her, shuddering at the taste of the bourbon. "One more, please."

The bartender looked at her with concern, but brought her another drink. She took the second glass and walked slowly to the edge of the tent. Were people staring at her? Oh, yeah, the outfit and the hairdo. Leanne thought, I should probably feel ridiculous, but I don't give a damn what these shriveled up old coots think.

Leanne shook her head and stuck out her chin defiantly, then quickly drained her drink. Once more with feeling, she thought, as she headed back to the bar.

Cammy found Leanne a half hour later leaning against a tent pole for support. "Are you drunk? Come on, let's find you somewhere to sit down. You're going to pull this tent down if you're not careful."

Leanne leaned heavily on the younger woman's arm as they looked for a place to sit. There was a jazz quartet and Leanne recognized the tune, "Satin Doll." The bourbon had done its trick. Leanne felt seductive and loose, like her backbone was made out of rubber. With no trace of a headache, she smiled broadly at complete strangers, even winked at a couple of old men. Cammy deposited her into a chair and said, "You need to eat something. Stay here and I'll be right back with some crackers or something."

Leanne looked for her purse, then vaguely remembered it slipping from her fingers as she leaned on the tent pole. She had to find it, it wasn't even hers! And it had her cigarettes in it! She really wanted a cigarette. She tried to remember which tent pole she'd been standing by, but they all looked the same. And everywhere were identical groups of white-haired preppies. She resolved to walk from pole to pole until she found the purse. On her second time around the tent, with eyes glued to the grass and concentrating on her search, Leanne bumped full force into a firm broad back wearing a black suit. The man whirled around and caught Leanne's arm.

"Hey!"

"Oh, 'scuse me, I'm jus' lookin' for—Walker!" Leanne beamed delightedly at Walker Burton, the young judge who was to preside over her client's murder trial that month. "What are you doin' here?"

Walker looked her up and down, taking in the watermelon minidress, the big hair and the retro makeup. "Did I miss something? Is this a costume party, counselor?" As usual, Walker's grin undermined the serious tone of his voice.

Leanne batted her false eyelashes at him and tucked his arm into hers. "Now, you can't mean that, Judge! Do I look like Halloween or something?"

"No, but you don't look any way I've ever seen you look. Are you all right?"

"I had a headache when I first got here, but I had a couple of bourbons and I'm feeling good right now."

"Uh huh. Why don't we find somewhere to sit down? You seem a little tired." Walker had known Leanne since he was a newlywed and in law school, and she and her husband were in practice together. Walker was widowed just after he began practicing and spent a lot of bitter years trying to deal with the loss of his wife. Family and political connections meant he was appointed to the bench in his late thirties, just a few years before.

"I'm not tired, but everybody keeps making me sit down and then they leave me by myself. I'll sit down if you'll stay with me," Leanne said.

"That's a deal. Hey, is that girl in the green dress looking for you?"

"Cammy!" Leanne shrieked. "Over here!" Cammy had her purse on her shoulder, Leanne noticed, and a plate full of snacks.

"Hey, Judge Burton, how are you doing this evening?" Cammy put down the plate at the table closest to her and thrust her hand forward to meet Walker's.

"I'm fine, thank you. Is this food for Leanne?"

"Yes, that's right. I thought it might pep her up a little if she'd eat something."

"Great idea. How about getting her a Co-Cola and I'll sit here with her while she eats."

"Be right back."

"Get her purse," Leanne said.

"We don't need that purse. You're going to eat some of this good stuff she picked out for you, right now. Looky here, there's some shrimp and little sausage balls and crab dip, just about anything you'd want. Try one of these little ham biscuits for me." Leanne tried to look up at Walker seductively from under her long, luxurious fake eyelashes. He was such a good looking devil, with that jet black hair and dark eyes. A kind mouth, Leanne thought. He's really a sweet man. She let him feed her tiny bites of biscuit and wipe her mouth for her.

"You eat some, too, Walker."

His lips twitched at her childish tone. "Okay, honey, I'll have this piece of pineapple. Now it's your turn to have a bite of chicken wing."

Cammy delivered the tall glass of Coke silently and melted back into the growing crowd. Slowly, patiently, Walker fed Leanne every last morsel on her plate. Minutes passed and they sat together in silence. The smell of the freshly cut lawn mingled with that of the women's perfumes and the smoke from the old men's cigars. Song gave way to song, and they sat together still.

The air grew cooler, though it was still quite heavy. Leanne had shaken loose some of her hair and it made her look younger and more vulnerable. The quartet played "Summertime," and Leanne leaned her head onto Walker's shoulder. He'd taken off his suit jacket at some point and rolled up the sleeves of his starched white oxford cloth shirt. Leanne sat up purposefully, reached for his hand, then traced her fingers slowly up his arm to the roll of cloth. She gently pulled the sleeve back down over Walker's forearm. With her right index finger, she traced the initials monogrammed on the cuff of his sleeve, WLB, then sighed and looked up into his eyes. "Wow, it's really you."

361

O, Georgia!

Atlanta
by Terry L. Hensel

We didn't have thirty-five dollars
to buy a brick for ourselves.
We did buy a brick for Joan's parents,
her father would have been pleased.
They were of the old tradition-filled Atlanta.
Rich's tree lighting, then rides on the pink pig.
Suits from Muse's and personal greetings
at Maier & Berkele as the door chimed behind you.
There were Eastlake summers of tennis and swim.
Sweet Auburn didn't see Eastlake, but she had life
and dignity as business thrived
and families ate together. Years later,
Atlanta is a pinwheel with telescoping spokes.
Her growth has everyone out and away.
Malls and country clubs follow the spokes
to an ever widening perimeter.
New traditions are made in suburban pockets.
Sweet Auburn received an Olympic face-lift,
but she dozes
like an old lady on social security.
Even so, tradition sits along the roadside
eating one of Thelma's rib sandwiches.

O, Georgia!

Breast Cancer
by Leila Weisberg

There is no gentle way to say it. The diagnosis was Breast Cancer.

Hospital Admissions 101

Some things need to be written down and remembered. The trauma of being scheduled for surgery cries out for comic relief. Because my mammogram showed some irregularities, I was scheduled for a biopsy and then a lumpectomy. I was to check into the hospital on Monday, September 14, 1992, and was given the standard instructions—have nothing to eat or drink after midnight Sunday; arrive at the hospital at 7:00 a.m.; surgery scheduled for 10:00 a.m.. Working on the theory that cooperation makes things easier, I didn't have anything to eat or drink after 8:00 p.m. Sunday evening just to make sure.

I arrived at the hospital at 7:00 a.m. and was immediately taken to my room. The hospital has a pre-admissions procedure, so all of the paper work had been completed the week before. My "hospital kit: water jug, glass, Kleenex box, slippers, and carrying case emblazoned with the name of the hospital, was waiting for me. And of course, the HOSPITAL GOWN, the symbol of the loss of authority. Having been told to take off my clothes, I was left with no alternative but to put it on and surrender to the powers that be.

Time to rest! Oh no. Enter Nurse #1 with a specimen bottle. "Mrs. Weisberg, can you give us a urine sample?"

"I'll try." I trotted off to the bathroom trying to hold my gown closed to preserve some degree of modesty. Now if you recall, I had had nothing to eat or drink since 8:00 p.m. Sunday. I was really hard pressed to come up with a tinkle. "Oh God," I thought, "what are my children going to think? I'm going to fail Hospital Admissions 101." Minutes passed like hours. At last success. Just then the nurse knocked at the door.

"Is everything alright in there?"

Joyfully I answered, "My cup runneth over."

Back to bed, perchance to rest. Enter Nurse #2 to set up the

IV. To get my mind off the procedure he started to make small talk. "What kind of work do you do?"

"I'm retired."

"What kind of work did you do?"

"I worked for the Easter Seal Society..."

"Oh, you're the one who licked all those little stamps."

In a matter of seconds, my career was reduced to licking stamps.

He departed. Rest? No, not yet. Enter Nurse #3. "Just a shot to help you relax. It won't hurt a bit. Just a little prick." Who is she trying to kid? It hurt. At last, rest.

Enter nurse #4 with the Operating Room gurney. "Just slide over...." I'm half asleep....couldn't I just float over?

We rode the elevator to the O.R. where I was greeted by the doctor. "And how are <u>we</u> this morning?"

Is that a rhetorical question? He should know how <u>he</u> is, I thought, and he's supposed to know how <u>I</u> am. But instead of telling him this, I just managed a weak, "O.K."

Into the O.R., slide onto the operating table, people hovering all around, things very hazy. Then suddenly I hear a voice, "Mrs. Ellison...." My mind quickly snapped to attention. "No, no wait. I'm not Mrs. Ellison, I'm Mrs. Weisberg!"

A kindly reassuring face came close to mine. "I know dear. I was just telling you that <u>I'm</u> Mrs. Ellison.

The blissful oblivion. I woke up in the recovery room with blood pressure, respiration, temperature, pulse, heart all working. "O.K. to move her back to her room."

There are probably rules about which way your head and feet should point as they wheel you back, but it seemed to me that the gurney kept changing direction at a dizzying pace. I, who had survived whale watching in Boston Harbor during a storm, got very sick and up-chucked what little was left in me.

Then I slept until the next morning although I do vaguely remember my daughter and then the doctor poking their heads into my room.

I woke up feeling really good and when I finally convinced

them to detach me from the IV, I had a good breakfast, washed and dressed and was ready to leave by 10:30 a.m.

A nurse from the O.R. came to check on the patient. She thought that I was visiting...so I exited laughing.

Radiation Treatments

If they are looking for buried treasure, I can tell them right now that they are looking in the wrong place! They measured me and marked me with X's and arrows as they decided where they would aim the x-rays. They never tell you everything beforehand, but some of those spots are now permanently tattooed on my chest...I would have preferred a rose.

And so I started my thirty treatments. It's so strange because you don't feel anything. When you take a pill, you swallow; when you get a shot, you feel the prick; you feel the cooling or warmth of salve; but only the buzz of the machine lets you know that you have been irradiated.

The machine is formidable. It moves around until it locks onto those six tattoos on my chest. Then they tell me to lie still. The door closes. I am alone with the machine. I think, 'Beam me up, Scotty."

I'm in and out of the Radiation Center in fifteen minutes most of the time. I wear clothes that button, hook, snap or zip in front to save time. Occasionally there are glitches in the machine. Can you imagine lying flat on an x-ray table with your chest bare while all those technicians scurry around trying to set things right?

Wouldn't you know it, in the midst of all of that, I was called for Jury Duty. I couldn't report because I had to go for therapy every day. I called and explained and they sent me an affidavit for the doctor to complete. You can only be excused if you are permanently disabled or mentally retarded so I will be called back at a later date because I am not in those categories yet.

The treatments have made me tired, but I still manage to drive, clean, wash, iron, etc. I have to admit to sometimes using it as an excuse to get out of things I don't want to do.

367

I seem to dream a lot. For those of you who are old enough, you will remember the ads, "I dreamed I went out (walking, driving, dancing, etc.) in my Maidenform Brassiere." If you follow local grocery store ads you will also appreciate the dream I had in which I had a conversation with my surgeon who explained that he could do two for the price of one.

I'm counting down treatments, 30—29—28—27—. When they get down to three, they let you rest for a few days and then give you three super zaps.

By Thanksgiving I should be discharged. The prognosis is good. MAY THE FORCE BE WITH ME.

Denoument

The day of the 26th treatment was a Monday. Monday is the day you see the doctor. It's a time when you can voice your complaints; tell about the aches and pains and the terrible tiredness you feel. It's the day you get the proverbial pat on the back and are told that what you're experiencing is not unusual.

But this Monday was different. Again flat on my back, the doctor drew new diagrams on my chest, admonished me not to wash them off and described the last three treatments as super doses directed at the incision.

Did you ever try to take a one-sided shower? It's tricky but can be done. And so I appeared the next day for my first super dose. The machine was set up differently and a lead plate with a cut out that seemed to match the oval that had been drawn on my breast was lowered. It was closer than anything I had had before. Again, the admonition to hold still—the door closed——and then the buzz.

I had gotten into the habit of counting during the buzz. I usually got to thirty something. This time I was past fifty when it stopped.

The new treatments have been no better or worse than the ones that came before.

The last day has finally come. I brought a canister of Hershey Kisses to give to the technicians. They have been very supportive.

So now what? Check ups and more checkups. Even though the prognosis is good, there is still an element of uncertainty.

It's hard to believe that this has happened within the space of three months. I should be rid of all the effects of the therapy in four weeks.

So today I left the Radiation Center for the last time, a little asymmetrical but optimistic.

As I drove into my driveway, I was followed by a truck from Balloons Atlanta. They delivered a beautiful bouquet of balloons. The card, which said "Congratulations, you did it!" was tied to a champagne bottle full of jelly beans.

September 14, 1997

It's Saturday and I'm waiting for my family to come over for brunch. The table has been set with care and my centerpiece is a champagne bottle, decorated with ribbons and bows. The jelly beans are gone, but the card is still attached.

Five years have gone by without incident. Mammograms have all been O.K. We're celebrating.

I AM A SURVIVOR!

O, Georgia!

The Yamacraw Construct

(an excerpt)

by Sam Isaac Edwards

CHAPTER ONE

The cold October rain splattered across the long hood of my old Austin Healey as I cut through the three a.m. darkness of Peachtree Street, trying to get home after a thirteen hour day. A half a block in front of me I saw a black and white Atlanta Police Department cruiser parked at an angle to the curb. A skinny patrolman in his twenties was kneeling by a pajama clad body lying face down, the upper half of him in the street. Who the hell would be out in this mess wearing only his PJ's , I wondered. Some old drunk no doubt. I drove slowly by the scene trying to make myself go home, I was damned tired, but for some reason, for some really dumb reason, I eased up beside the cruiser and stopped. As I stepped out of the Healey, a handful of raindrops temporarily washed the weariness from my head before I could yank up the hood of the faded blue parka I'd had since college. I walked up to the young officer still kneeling by the elderly body.

"Helluva place to take a nap, huh?"

His unlined face looked up at me and was but a second away from giving me the third shift salute-a snarl and a piss off-when I pointed to the Lieutenant's shield hanging on my belt. He stood, but without the crispness of a daytimer. He left large pauses between some of his words. "I don't know sir, he's..." his fair complexion paled even more, "he's..., shit, I think he's dead, sir."

I squatted down and laid my fingers across the old neck to check for a pulse. His throat was icy but I couldn't tell if it was a death cold. There was no pulse that I could feel. I stood and cinched my parka back around my waist to fend off the chill. "Go ahead and call the paramedics, tell them what we got-old, cold and no pulse," I said to the young officer. He stopped me as I started to walk away.

"Sir, the call I got from dispatch didn't have anything to do with this, I was up there at the light and just happened to see...I

371

stopped here because this was the address they gave me...somebody reported a man with a gun running across the road here, from that big house over there across the street."

I knew it; I should've kept right on going. I looked through the rain across Peachtree and in a semi-circular drive, a couple of hundred feet away, saw a white Lincoln. The vapor near the rear told me the engine was running. The interior light was on and I could see at least one back door open. Great. Motor going, back door open in the pouring rain, no sign of activity anywhere around and three o'clock in the morning, all the elements necessary to keep me from getting home any time before dawn.

" What's your name?" I asked the young officer.

"Jenkins, sir." he replied.

"Well, Jenkins," I said, as I yanked at the snap of the holster I wore on my belt, "get us some back up, and I'll ease on over and see what's shaking."

I trotted across the road, still yanking at the holster's strap. I hadn't had the Walther PPK out since last year's qualifying at the range and the metal snap had rusted shut. I stopped on the sidewalk and scanned the well-kept yard around the idling Lincoln, and let my eyes stop on the large front door of the Victorian style mansion. There seemed to be a dark pile of something at the base of the door. With a hard tug I finally freed the weapon from its leather holder. I checked the clip for rounds and then began to walk slowly toward the Lincoln.

Twenty feet away I stepped around a hedge and what I saw made me chamber a round into the German automatic. Sitting on the ground with his legs splayed out like a child in a sandbox was a large black man. His back was against the door jam of the Lincoln and he was slumped over, his head turned slightly toward me. There was a hole where his left eye used to be and a rivulet of blood ran steadily down across his nose and onto a fine white shirt. He'd just become a panelist on the 'Newly-Dead Game.' That fresh hole in his head made me freeze by the short hedge and lower my profile to a half crouch. I could feel my heart; it was like a baseball bat crashing against the inside of my rib cage. I wasn't this kind of cop; I'd

372

made my rank through politics not with this kind of street shoot-em-up shit.

After a couple of deep breaths, I eased my finger inside the trigger housing of the Walther. I didn't know why, the warden at the pistol range was a buddy of mine; he always signed off on my paperwork, because he knew that I couldn't hit the side of a Marta bus with this friggin' thing. I'd been a pretty good pitcher in college, and I would have felt a lot more comfortable in this situation with a handful of good-sized rocks.

I gave the grounds another 180-degree look and still saw no motion from anything alive. I began to take baby steps toward the body. His suit coat was curled outward, and against the white shirt I saw the straps of a shoulder holster, but his hands were empty. I stopped beside the rear wheel well, leaned down and looked into the back seat.

"JESUS!" I reeled back against the hedge. Another black man was lying on his side and also had a hole where his left eye used to be. His blood rivulet ran down the side of his nose and into an open mouth. I looked past him and on the ground beside the other open back door was a third body. I stood to get a better look and as I did I noticed again the dark clump near the front door of the house. To my dismay I discovered it was companion to the rest. I walked around the car and up to the stoop. This one had three tiny holes in his cheek, in a group no bigger than a quarter. I felt like just easing away from this scene. With my shooting talent the guy who made these shots was the last dude I wanted to do battle with.

I walked back across Peachtree, fear fueling my steps, eager to put some distance between me and the carnage, to where Jenkins was placing a small piece of blue tarp over the body. Before I could say anything the officer looked up at me. The steady rain forced us to speak louder than usual.

"Lieutenant, you know what I think?"

"No, Jenkins, what do you think?"

"I think this old guy was a jumper. Look up there."

I looked to where he was pointing, to the tenth floor penthouse of the 1600 building, where a dim light shown from the balcony. It was the only light on in the upper floors. Then one went on inside my head. 1600 Peachtree, the Connor Foundation, the old guy in the nice pajamas-I dropped to my knees beside the body, the running water from the gutter splashing over me, and jerked back the tarp. I pushed away the gray hair that covered the profile and gasped. "JESUS MARY AND MOSES!"

"What is it Lieutenant, you all right?" Jenkins spat frightened.

"My God...do you know who this is?" I said, staring disbelievingly at the body.

"No sir, I don't think so," he replied with some hesitation.

"It's John Connor."

"You mean—President John Connor?"

"Yeah." I stared at the body of the former President. Then something else hit me—I hadn't seen a driver in the Lincoln. I stood up quickly. "Jenkins, call everybody, we've got four fresh kills across the street and the shooter may still be around here. Seal off both ends of the block and reroute the traffic, everything around here is to be considered inside the yellow tape, code three. You got it?"

"Yes sir," he snapped enthusiastically.

"And seal the building as soon as you get some more help, I've gotta check the Lincoln again."

"Right, Lieutenant."

I could hear him barking into the radio as I jogged away, back to a scene I didn't care to revisit. I wasn't gone long. I found the driver, lying across the front seat with a small caliber entry wound at the base of his skull. That made five. And I noticed something else. The Lincoln had Diplomatic plates.

Two other units arrived during my short absence and began sealing the block. I walked up to the locked glass doors of the 1600 building and looked in. There was a security desk just inside but no attendant. I gave the glass a couple of raps. A few seconds later a young hispanic-looking man in a neat uniform came walking toward me from a hallway. He looked past me at all the activity before his eyes returned to the shield I held against the glass. After giving it a cursory glance, he opened the doors.

"What's going on, sir?"

"Anyone entered the building in the last half hour?"

"No sir, not a soul," he replied, in perfect unaccented English.

"I'm gonna need to get up to the Penthouse. Where's the Secret Service station?"

"It's on the same floor, across the hall from the President's quarters."

"How do I get up there?"

"I'll have to call them to send the elevator down." His attention drifted by me once again to the activity outside and to the body on the sidewalk.

"Then let's do that," I said with some firmness.

"Yes sir, yes sir, come on in," he replied leading me to his station.

He picked up a small radio from his desk and just before keying the mike, pointed toward the hallway to my right. "Down there sir, it'll open down there."

His curiosity finally got to him as I walked away. "What's going on outside, sir, has it got anything to do with President Connor?"

The single door to the elevator had a bullet proof glass panel about a foot square at eye level. I saw an unlikely face inside and held up my badge. There were cameras visible everywhere, and probably microphones as well. I was sure the Agents had already checked me out. A young woman opened the door and addressed me with a crispness I had not heard since Army boot camp.

"Lieutenant Garcia," she said, extending her hand from inside the small elevator, "I'm Agent Gallaway, how may I help you?"

I liked the way she looked but her smug self-importance was off putting. "Yes, hello, I uh," I decided to cut to the chase, "Agent Gallaway, I need to go up to the quarters."

"That's really not possible, Lieutenant, unless of course you have a compelling reason for disturbing the Connors at this time of morning."

I'd forgotten the former President lived here with his daughter although I knew that his wife had died some years ago. I decided not to be too gentle with the young Agent. "Ms. Gallaway, your protectee has just pulled a Superman off the balcony, he's lying out there on the sidewalk. Ms. Gallaway, President Connor is dead."

She looked at my chest and then toward the front entrance of the building, barely visible from where we stood. "That can't be," she said, shaking her head.

"I'm sorry, Agent, but it is. Now I'm sure you have superiors to contact, please do that and let me go about my job. I need to go into the quarters."

She motioned me into the elevator but remained in something of a fog. She set the box in motion by placing her hand in a palm scanner and entering a set of coded digits. We stepped out into a short hallway a half minute later. Directly in front of me was the Agents station, an alcove about the size of a mid-size sedan. The Agent seated behind a desk in the alcove stood as we exited the elevator and walked toward us.

"My God Jerry," Agent Gallaway finally gasped, "he's dead, the President's dead, he fell off the balcony-"

The male Agent straightened his six foot plus form, "What do you mean, Jenny, what?" He then looked directly at me.

I nodded my head. "My name's Garcia, APD. I need to look inside, see if I can find out what happened."

Agent Jerry was as stunned as Agent Jenny for a few seconds, then moved past me back into the elevator and keyed the doors on the other side. They opened into the penthouse.

"Agent, uh, do you have a handkerchief, I don't have..."

He pulled one from the inside of his jacket pocket without moving more than was necessary and handed it to me robotically. Suddenly the weight of the pronouncement hit him, "You call this in Jenny, I'm going down." The female Agent picked up a blue phone from the desk in the alcove, the secure line to a command post, I assumed.

I stepped into the residence and the doors closed behind me. The whine of the elevator motor was the only sound I could hear. There was a large open space, at least a thousand feet square, between me and the balcony. There was a lot of leather, old, rich, naturally-hued leather covering sofas, chairs and love seats, none from the same family. A smaller room to my left was encircled with floor to ceiling walnut bookshelves, an entertainment center and two very comfortable looking overstuffed chairs in one corner. A large brass table with a tall black reading lamp in the middle emitted just the least bit of light, reminding me of either a funeral home or a bar.

Between the two rooms was a long hallway, and from dimmed recessed lighting I could see three doors equally spaced. I was just about to move toward the balcony when the middle of those doors opened. A woman in her late twenties to early thirties stepped out, drying her hair with a towel. The long black robe she was wearing was open at the front and I saw two shocks of matching red hair against an almost paper white background. She had a sinewy, athletic body, with the long thigh muscles and muscular calves of a sprinter. I was staring at her small breasts when she saw me. I would have turned as red as her hair had I not been thinking of how I was going to tell this pretty, young, beautifully proportioned woman that her famous father, a man revered even by his enemies, was no longer living.

I dropped my gaze to the carpet immediately and was stunned when she did not react with some hostility. "A little off your beat, aren't you?" This woman had no fear.

"No, I'm..." I waited for something proper to come out, but nothing did, so I lifted my eyes from the carpet and was shoved into even more mental suspension when I saw that she still had not closed her robe and was continuing to dry her hair with the towel.

"I'm waiting officer, and your explanation better fit into the doozy category, or I'm going to be one angry redhead."

My senses finally returned. "You're Ms. Connor, right?"

"No, my father keeps a thirty-year-old concubine whom he often passes off as his daughter."

She then pulled her robe closed with no particular haste.

"Uh, ma'am, my name is Garcia, I'm with the Atlanta Police Department and uh..."

"I've already got that figured out, except for the Garcia part, you don't look Hispanic."

"Yes ma'am"

"And can we dispense with the ma'am, business. You don't have that many years on me."

"Yes ma-..., Ms. Connor, I have to, uh," I dropped my chin to my chest and mumbled, "I'm not gonna be able to get through this, I shouldn't be the one having-."

Her voice then became a bit testy. "Mr. Garcia, is this going to take long, because if it is, I probably need to get dressed, but before I do could you give me the slightest hint as to why you're prowling around in our house at this hour?"

I said it much quicker than I wanted to, and with much less consolation. "Ms. Connor, the President fell off the balcony. I'm sorry, I'm afraid your father's dead."

She hit the floor before I could move, like she'd been shot in the head. I ran to her, picked her up and opened the door to what I assumed was her bedroom, walked in and laid her gently down on a shiny black comforter which covered the bed. Her face, the face I had thought so pretty, was suddenly oozing the ugliness of pain. I dialed 911 on the phone next to the bed, ID'd myself and ordered a psychological trauma team. I then called my Captain, something I should have done earlier, but didn't, and got a cold compress for her forehead while I waited for them to arrive. I stared at her for a long while. This was going to hurt her for the rest of her life; I'd remembered from news reports that she had never married and after her mother had died she had become a surrogate, traveling the globe furthering her father's many ambitions. They were inseparable, the newsies said.

My captain and the psych/trauma team arrived within minutes of each other. I recounted the events to him as we surveyed the penthouse; trodding gingerly about what might be a crime scene. Five dead diplomats and a dead former President did not add up to coincidence.

I woke up on the sofa in my office a little after two in the afternoon. I felt how ugly looked. After giving my face a splash of water from the john, I settled in behind the desk to finish the preliminary report I'd fallen asleep on a few hours earlier. My Captain, Pete Tomason, dragged his caramel-colored, middle-aged form across the fake Persian rug that covered most of my office floor, and flopped down on the couch.

"Abby, we've got one hell of a mess on our hands, and none of it makes the least bit of sense." There was a heavy note of exasperation in his voice.

I propped my chin on the backs of my crossed fingers and looked across the desk at him. "So, did he jump or didn't he?"

"Can't tell, least not yet."

"Who's the basketball team in the Lincoln."

"The main man, the one in the back seat, is-was, the President of Congola, President Connor's chief partner in this African peace business he's been working on for the past six or seven years. They'd just signed a treaty or something last year, I think. Anyhow, the other three were bodyguards, but not very good ones, I guess. And the poor bastard at the house was just a butler or something."

"Well, the cat who scratched this set was a champeen shooter."

"No shit. Forensics said he probably made the hits in sequence. The driver, soon after the back door opened, then the one on the left, then the right-he was probably in profile, maybe turning toward the pop. He took it in the ear, then President Nobila in the back seat.The domestic comes out on the stoop for a look see and takes three in the cheek. Jesus Christ, from a hundred feet away on a rainy night, three rounds in an inch and a quarter grouping. Abby, this son of a bitch is a .22 caliber surgeon."

"So it was a .22?"

"Yep, ain't gonna be much left of a slug that small after it cue balls around inside the skull."

379

"Probably not." I looked him in the eye. "So, what about the Connor thing? He's not exactly jumper material."

The Captain pawed at the back of his neck and snickered, "and wait till ya hear this, he was the one who reported the shooting!"

"He reported it?!" I sat straight up in my chair. "Damn...that's...well, for a former President he sure keeps some strange hours. And his daughter was up too...gotta be something genetic."

"You know why he was up at three in the morning?"

"No, why?" I mumbled.

"Because he was taking a call from his dear friend, the Prime Minister of Great Britain, who was telling him that he had just won the Nobel Peace Prize."

And so began, the best, and the worst year of my life.

Point of Surrender
by Kimberly C. Fears

Trapped in darkness
In the depth of despair
No one could help me
I could not even care.

Prisoner of a worldly mind
A heart bound with anger and fears
A mouth that opened with curses and screams
Eyes constantly clouded by tears.

Life was unbearable
I wanted to be free
Finally, on my knees I prayed,
"Lord, please help me."

Suddenly a light engulfed me with love
It cut through the darkness
I knew it was from Above.

My mind opened up
Chains on my heart set free
My mouth opened with praise
As He said "Have faith in Me."

Now my heart brims with love
My mind is absorbed in His light
My mouth offers prayer
Both day and night.

O, Georgia!

One question, however,
remained deep in my heart
I had to ask
"Lord, why did you leave me so long in the dark?"

He embraced me close
Smiled, and answered so tender
"Child, I could only bring you in the light,
at your point of surrender."

Old Friends
by Edith Harper Pinson

It's time to reminisce,
of days so long ago,
And of the carefree friends,
who I used to know.
We talked; we laughed;
and we had so much fun,
as we ran and we played,
in the rain and the sun.
Then we all grew up,
and went our separate ways,
to experience life,
in a different phase.
And now we meet again,
after years have passed,
to renew old friendships,
that continue to last.
And the smiles on our faces,
show the marks that we bear;
For wrinkles on our brows,
are adorned with silver hair.
But beneath those aged marks,
are still the same old friends,
with the same personalities,
and the same mischievous grins.
So by far the richest treasures,
that memories can unfold,
are of old friends and classmates,
as precious as pure gold.

O, Georgia!

Of Signs and Wonders
by Farrar M. Atkinson

Nathan Bone disappeared two months ago. He's my cousin Carlotta's thirty-year-old boyfriend. That caused a lot of gossip in our little Georgia town, but I never heard anybody say they blamed my cousin for it.

If Carlotta doubted he would return, she never let on. All conversations revolved around him, the latest being at my house one hot July afternoon. The chain of our front porch swing screeched as we swung back and forth while she talked.

"I can see him now in that Christmas sweater I knitted to match his blue eyes. His thick blonde hair and his sweet smile, almost as broad as his shoulders. When he got miffed with me, that stubborn jaw set," she said with a wistful smile, "but, we really never had spats like most couples. I...I know he loves me Evie." She almost choked on the words.

Then, she leaned nearer and whispered confidingly. "You know, I have a feeling that we'll hear some news today. There's gonna be a sign—something to let me know he's okay."

Carlotta was almost thirty herself. She and Nathan Bone had dated fourteen years until one day he just up and left without saying a word to anybody. Not a note nor a phone call. Nothing.

"Evie, don't ever give up when you want something. I want Nathan. That's why I know he's coming back. My wanting is like a magnet and even if he's hundreds of miles away, it's pulling at him, just like static electricity pulls your petticoat around your legs."

"But Carlotta, he left the end of May and you haven't heard a word since."

"Hush! I know how long it's been. I've marked a red 'x' on my calendar every day. Sixty-two it'll be, this Saturday."

"Todd Martin told Mama he'd like to go out with you. Said he could make you forget Nathan if you were so minded."

"Well, I'm not so minded. Todd is puny looking compared to my Nathan's muscular physique. Nope, Nathan Bone is my man and I'm not settling for any other. Of course, I don't expect a girl of fifteen to understand that. You lack the experience to fathom what

I'm saying."

Carlotta reads a lot and uses words most folks don't say around here. "I know 'fathom', Carlotta, and...for your information, I've had a crush or two myself, thank you."

She gave me a look of exasperation and kept on swinging. Carlotta is pretty, with long, black wavy hair and gray onyx eyes, which slant ever so slightly with the help of Maybelline. She still gets wolf whistles when we walk to the Dairy Queen, even if she has put on five or six pounds since Nathan left. I wish I looked as good as she did in her high school pictures when she was a cheerleader and on the homecoming court.

I gathered she wasn't one of the most popular girls, due to her high standards. Singing in the church choir and going to the Baptist Training Union on Sunday nights kept her and Mama out of the back seats of boyfriends' cars at the drive-in movies. Mama said she wanted me to follow in their footsteps. Well, I'm too skinny and have mousy brown hair and I can't even sing. The old drive-in movie closed years ago. Besides that, I don't even have a boyfriend—which is another story.

Anyway, I'm sure she and Nathan hadn't dated fourteen years without doing more than hand holding, but I never would've said that to her face nor to Mama's. I did say, "What does Francine say about his leaving?"

Carlotta tossed her black hair over her left shoulder. "I'm not about to give that sister of his the satisfaction of asking. She was always a little jealous of the attention Nathan gave me. I know he practically raised her, what with their poor mother being so sickly for the last ten years, but...well, we both know Nathan was good to his mama."

"Yeah, you said he waited on her hand and foot."

"And toward the end, he even slept in a chair by her bed in case she called out for him. You know what? I think that responsibility and pain was too much for Nathan—too hard on him and he just had to get away from there. That's why he left less than two weeks after she died," she said, as if I hadn't heard it all umpteen times before.

She gazed into the distance beaming her love and desires across the miles like she was some antenna or radio tower. I could almost see the rays emanating from her bedroom eyes. Maybe I've read too many 'true romances' or just have a vivid imagination, but I couldn't help noticing her heaving bosom. Poor Carlotta. I imagined her lying awake at night with unfulfilled passion, worrying where he was—who he was with. I wondered how she faced people at work in the bank each day.

Mama told me that talking about things probably helped Carlotta, so I said "I think you are holding up so well. How do you do it?"

"Why, each morning I get up and say, 'This is the day he's coming back,' and I do my hair and make-up and dress just like we're going on a date."

She stopped the swing a minute. "Evie, maybe you could phone Francine—now, don't you dare say I asked you to—just casually say something like what's the latest from your big brother?' or 'Nathan not homesick for Buford yet?'"

"Aw, Carlotta, you call her. She's gonna wonder why on earth I would be asking unless you put me up to it."

"Yeah, I guess you're right. She must miss him as much as I do." Quickly, she sat upright and pointed. "Look! There. That's it—the sign I've been waiting for. I just know it."

She was staring at an old crow that had flown down and perched on the porch railing. "Don't move, Evie. See how he's cocking his head and looking at me. He's a harbinger of good news, as sure as I'm sitting here."

It was bizarre—one of Carlotta's favorite words. That old crow hopped closer, turned his head and stared at her. Carlotta and I sat staring back. It was hard to say who was mesmerizing who.

"Don't you believe in signs, Evie? Nathan and I both do. Did I tell you about the day his Mama died?" She whispered. "The grandfather clock that sat in the foyer stopped at ten-fifteen that morning. Later, when we checked the death certificate, it said she'd passed away at ten-seventeen. Now, if that wasn't an omen, what was it?"

Her voice had grown huskier and she stared at that old crow like he was Nathan himself. There was something about the whole thing that made shivers slither across my bare thighs. I turned sideways to see better and more goose flesh rose on my arms. I held my breath as they watched each other.

"Nathan used to look at me that same way. He'd cock his head and stare as if he could see right into my very soul."

Her voice was so soft, I strained to hear because Mr. Pop's ice cream truck rattled by just then with music jangling. All that noise should've made that old crow fly the coop, but he just hopped a little closer like he was trying to hear what Carlotta said, too.

Talk about strange. At that moment I also heard the squeak of the mailbox hinge next door and craned my neck to see Mr. Laughlin poke some mail in Gertrude Wiley's bird-house mail box. I saw her creepy cat, Crissy, wrap herself around the mailman's legs. He leaned over and petted her. Then, Mr. Laughlin ambled over to our walkway.

"Hello, ladies. I got some special mail today, Carlotta. Seeing you're here, I'll give it to you rather than drop it off at your house." Shuffling through the batch, he pulled out a thick letter. "Mr. Bone wrote to you from St. Louis, according to the postmark," he said, stepping up to the porch.

That crow cawed once, flapped his wings and flew off.

Without a word, Carlotta sprang from the swing like a jack-in-the-box and snatched that letter right out of Mr. Laughlin's hand. Her face turned white as buttermilk and she ran into the house.

Mr. Laughlin and I stood looking after her. "Hot today, ain't it?" I said, trying to make conversation.

"The hottest this summer," he replied, wiping his sweaty brow on his blue shirt sleeve. "Sure could do with a cool glass of water, Evie, if you'd be so kind as to oblige.'

"Sure thing, Mr. Laughlin." I hurried inside, glad of an excuse to see how Carlotta was doing. I passed through the hall and glanced into the den. She stood frozen at the window, shoulders hunched, as she read Nathan's letter.

After running the water into a plastic tumbler, I came back

up the hall and looked in again. I heard an unmistakable sob and almost went to her, but decided to finish my errand.

"Here Mr. Laughlin. Fresh from the well," I said, repeating my father's standing line whenever he gave someone a drink of tap water.

"Sure hope Carlotta got good news. I know she's been waiting quite a spell for some word from Nathan."

"Yes, sir," I said, shifting from one foot to the other, anxious to get back inside.

"Well, thank you, Miss Evie. Guess I'd better move on."

"Bye, Mr. Laughlin."

When I went back to the den, Carlotta wasn't there. I ran upstairs to my room. Even through the closed door, I heard her crying. Not sure if I should intrude, I stood at the open hall window.

"Lord, have mercy!" I exclaimed, nearly falling over backwards. That stupid crow flew straight at me, smacked into the glass of the upper half of the window and plunked down on the front porch roof, stone dead. I stared at it, wondering what the heck that could be a sign of.

Knocking on the door, I said, "Hey, Carlotta. Guess what. That crow of yours just broke his neck flying against the hall window."

In a minute, Carlotta opened the door. No doubt about it. Her red swollen eyes were a sure sign of misery. "Bad news?" I asked.

She nodded. "Come on in." Crossing to a rocking chair in the corner, she sat down and I sat on my bed.

Starting to rock, she said, "You know, I imagined all sorts of reasons for Nathan's leaving, but I wasn't even close. I wondered if there was another woman, or if he was tired of me after all these years." Her chin quivered, but she went on. " I wondered if maybe he wanted a bit of freedom after being tied down so long with Francine and with his mama's illness."

Wiping her eyes and blowing her nose, she said, "Oh, I wish it was any one of those reasons instead of what he wrote!"

"What is it, Carlotta? It can't be that bad."

"Oh, it is. The worst thing of all. He's got cancer, Evie. Like his mother, but his is of the larynx." She stood up and for a minute I thought she looked a little angry. "You know, he never could throw away those stupid cigarettes. Said he had to have them to cope with all he had on his plate. Well, they operated and now he can't talk. His pretty blonde hair has all fallen out from the treatments."

Crying harder, she turned from me. "He...said he would never put me and Francine through the agony he'd suffered watching his mother die."

"Does he say how long he's got?"

"Maybe six months. He's in one of those cancer research institutes. Said he might as well do something for mankind, seeing as how his life hadn't amounted to much—and his mother's hospital and funeral bills had taken all the money they had."

"Are you going to see him?"

Dazedly, she shook her head. "He asked me not to. He did ask that I write him, though. But he wants me to remember him as he was. Oh, Evie! I can't stand this! I thought not knowing was bad, that nothing could be worse, but this is." She buried her face in her hands and cried louder.

I felt as useless in trying to help her as she probably felt about helping poor Nathan. "I'll get us some iced tea. Why don't you come down to the porch for some fresh air?"

She nodded. I went to the hall phone and called my aunt Dora's house. "Hey. This is Evie. Carlotta just got a letter from Nathan. I think you and Mama better come over here."

When she said they'd come right away, I hung up and went down to the kitchen. After filling two tumblers with tea, I took them to the porch.

"Here, Carlotta." She sipped, then stared just beyond me. A bewildered look was on her face, so I turned to see what she was staring at.

"I thought you said my crow flew against the upstairs window and broke its neck."

"Yeah, I thought it did. Maybe there's two, " I said, seeing

390

that a crow was again perched on the rail.

"No. See how he's cocking his head. It must be the same one that was here earlier. Can't be two that tame."

"I'm going to see." I ran upstairs to look on the porch roof. It was hard to believe, but that bird was gone!

Running back to the porch, I said "maybe it was just stunned. There's no dead bird on the roof now."

"Oh, Evie! That's the sign! Don't you see? Nathan may be down now, but he's going to make it. When that poor crow recovered, it was to show me that Nathan will, too."

Her radiant smile was convincing. If she found hope in the visit of a crow, I wasn't about to tell her otherwise.

"Sure looks like it, Carlotta. That's a sign if there ever was one."

I moved in front of her and crossed my fingers, hoping she wouldn't look behind me. It wouldn't help her a bit to see Mrs. Wiley's cat squatting under our gardenia bush with what looked like black feathers sticking out of her mouth.

Crissy loved catching birds.

O, Georgia!

Ponderings
by Lisa Haman

When I was younger,
I used to ponder—
Think about things,
And really wonder—
How trees grew
To be so straight and tall.
I used to sit—
And ponder is all.

How zebras got so many stripes,
Why ducks waddled
And windshields wiped.
Why winter's snow
All feathery and light,
Melted in my hand
Right before my sight.

As I grew older,
My ponderings grew.
The world around me
Was so bright and new.
There were many things
I wanted to know.
I had questions to ask
And oats to sow.

I'm older now,
But I still ponder—
Think about things,
And really wonder—
How trees grow
To be so straight and tall
I just sit—
And ponder is all.

O, Georgia!

Hair Therapy
by April S. Fields

Just when you think things can't possibly change, the roof caves in. Keeps you humble, you know?

Today, for example. First, I open up early because Sylvia McAllister has this noon wedding and needs her roots done. I do these extras for my good customers, keeps them that way. She comes in moaning about her son's speeding tickets and how it'll send his already high insurance into orbit. She fusses and fumes the whole two hours about irresponsible teenagers. I smile and sympathize giving her an extra dose while I'm massaging her head, really working in the Lipisome Hair Restorer. She's a good tipper.

I'm great with hair, a natural talent since I was thirteen when I used my older sister and mother as guinea pigs. They were good sports. Mom used to say, "Don't worry, dear, it'll grow back." Now I run my own shop, Lana's Style Emporium and Nails. I rent out space to two other gals, another stylist, Louise Seymour and a nail technician, Delia Jasper. They're okay. Sometimes I have to remind Delia when the rent is due, but nail customers usually turn into hair customers and that's what I'm about.

After Sylvia leaves, this great looking guy walks in and wants to know if I do men. I think, loaded question, honey, and tell him sure darling, what can I do for you?

"Little off the sides and clean up the back?" he asks. That's when he flashes a smile that would melt your toe nail polish and I have to take off my glasses so I can see. Feeling a bit flushed I excuse myself to the back room. I stand behind the door looking through the crack so I can take a harder look at this piece of work. He's about fiftyish, a couple years older than I am. No ring. Good. Maybe. Some guys don't wear rings, cramps their style. I could write a book about this subject. Anyway, he's tall, thinnish, not too muscular but healthy looking. He's got great hair, thick and just touched with a little silver. I'm in love. I straighten my smock and wish I'd worn my new one. Then I blow it. I look in the mirror. No matter how I squint I can't make the crepey neck tighten up or disguise those not so funny laugh lines. I think about slapping on another quick layer of base all over but figure looking like a clown had to be worse. Disgusted by the ugly truth at hand, I go back to work.

I'm so nervous, when I fit the cape around him, I make it too tight but he slips a finger up discreetly to loosen it so I won't be embarrassed. What style. I'm really hacked to see my hand shaking. I'm thinking, what's the matter with me? Good looking guys come in every day. I'm no teenager, I've been cruising down the road long enough to know how to play it cool. But I feel sweat forming on my upper lip and then I really know I'm in trouble.

I decide to distract him with small talk and the first thing pops out of my mouth is, "So, you married?" I want to take my sharpest scissors and stab myself right there.

"Divorced two years. You?" He says in a smooth radio announcer's voice.

"Divorced, too," I say, "isn't everyone?" I'm losing ground fast. He acts like he doesn't notice and says, "I just moved here last week. I still don't know my way around very well. People warned me Atlanta is a hard town to learn. I can find my office, this shopping center and the cleaners. I'm terrible with directions."

He's so at ease with himself, I can't stay nervous anymore. We start talking like we're old buddies. He tells me he's a psychologist and recently opened a new office here in Buckhead so he can be near his daughter and grandson. He's got an apartment but wants to start looking for a house to buy.

Then I tell him I put my life savings into this place and how I'm a sort of lay psychologist for my customers who tell me everything that's wrong in their lives. And then, like I'm lying on his couch or something, I start telling him how my ex-husband dumped me for his young, bimbo-brained secretary and my only daughter can't get her life together. I guess I take advantage.

But you know he listens and never offers anything but sympathy. And I have to tell you, now I know how others feel when they leave my shop, renewed inside and out.

I finish up and when he asks how much, I say, no charge, professional courtesy.

His laugh is pure twenty-four carat. He says then maybe I would "allow him the honor" of taking me to dinner sometime. I'm grinning like a fool when he walks out. I watch him saunter over to his white 'Beemer' and drive off. Next thing I know, Mary Lou Dobson is in my face asking if she's next. I have to shake my head to remember next for what.

As usual she's full of rotten news. Her sister's seriously sick and she's afraid she'll end up with her three wild nephews. My ears are still ringing when she leaves and Carlene Popivich takes her place in the chair. Her dad died yesterday and she's got to catch a flight out. Now she doesn't know what she'll do about her mom living alone. Her brothers won't help and her house is too small to take on the poor old thing.

By the time five o'clock rolls around, I'm drained. All these folks and their troubles have sucked the juice right out of me. When Darcy Morehead finally leaves with a new perm and a suggestion from me on how to get her husband to make love more often, I'm ready to sit down and cry. Who do these people think I am anyway?

Louise and Delia both leave early, so naturally I'm left with the mess. I look around. Saturday from Hell. Hair clippings of every known color piled in layers around the chairs. I consider leaving it, coming back tomorrow to clean up, but I know I can't do it. I get the broom. Somehow, the day and the mess and my aching feet finally get the best of me and I'm standing there, leaning on my broom, sobbing my fool head off. It feels like everything I have ever done has ended up a big zero. I look up and see my pitiful self in the glass and realize how dumb I am. I know the only thing left to do - I get out my scissors...and start cutting my hair.

When I'm dragging, my best therapy has always been a new haircut. My hair's about four inches from my scalp right now, which is a good indication of how depressed I've been lately. There's not a lot I can take off but when I need to, somehow I can always get it shorter. So, there I am cutting away, looking like a cross between the Wicked Witch of the West and Night of The Living Dead with my mascara smudged under my eyes when I look over and see Mr. Perfect waving in the front window. I'm frozen. I wonder if he sees

397

me. Yeah, right. I'm such a dork.

When my neurons kick in again, I wave back silly-like and he motions to the door like he wants me to open it. I know I'm having a bad dream and promise myself to lay off the extra chili peppers for lunch. But he keeps smiling and pointing to the door. I'm thinking this day has been the story of my life, long on potential, short on luck. I open the door and say, trick or treat, ha ha. He laughs that expensive laugh again, tells me he knows how to get to this great restaurant, and wonders if I might be willing to join him.

What can I do but stand there with this ridiculous look on my face waiting for the punch line? Finally I say something like, well, I'm right in the middle of cutting my hair, could you wait a few minutes? And then he says, and I'm quoting exactly here, "I've waited this long, a few minutes more won't matter."

I pretend I didn't hear that and rush over to my chair and finish up my cut. I do a quick fix because now I don't really need to do it anymore.

"Do you mind if we stop by my apartment so I can change?" I ask.

Then Tall, Cool and Wonderful says, "Tonight is your night, we can go wherever you choose so long as you know how to get there."

Now, I'm thinking, if I wake up suddenly, and this is just a dream, I guess I'll have no choice but to shave my head.

More Than Just Your Arms

by Jim Connor

Nick Castle didn't start the Grandpa Program right after his retirement. He had fulfilled life's responsibilities by working at unremarkable jobs from the time he was eighteen until his sixty-fifth birthday. They paid well and kept his family warm and safe and provided most of the children's tuition payments, and now he found himself free to accept only the demands he placed on himself.

Christine, his wife, had passed on some ten years ago; he had lost one son in Viet Nam in 1969; his two daughters turned out loving and protective, but both lived a day's journey away. He was making room in his life for silence.

He had tried the "gardener phase" of retirement, but he was not a born putterer. He had brought home crates of flower bulbs, sprigs and seeds. "I'll make a rainbow swath in the back yard," he'd said, and rented a roto-tiller which would have plowed away New York's Central Park. He cut a six foot arc across his backyard through whatever got in his way. He turned the red dirt over and over until all roots had become mulch; he fertilized, and began to sow.

He planted a wide variety of flowers: cosmos, promised by their envelope to reach five feet in height, zinnias, dahlias, gladioli by the cartons full, phlox around the edges, marigolds for scent, cedar chips for relief and a bird feeder in the center of it all. The flowers either died or remained stubble without blooms. He had watered to supply life; he had weeded in order to give the plants room and freedom to grow unmolested; he aereated to give them air to breathe; he mulched rich potting soil into Georgia's cruel red clay; to encourage the soil he bought a time-release fertilizer, but the weeds proved to be a formidable enemy. They continued to surround and choke the plants until both he and the new growth lost heart.

He nurtured an irrational hatred of the weeds, regarding their growth as a personal attack, so in Fall, after the growing season, he went to the nursery and bought a gallon of Afton's Soil Sterilizer, attached the bottle to the water hose, and soaked the entire garden area.

The flowers disintegrated, but the following spring a half-dozen dandelion heads poked through the weed killer residue and transformed themselves into fertile thistles, blowing with a care-free, mocking tilt on the wafting breeze to the center of his lawn.

"I'll repair things instead," he said, and removed the hinges from the cellar door which had humbugged him for a lifetime by not closing properly. He laid the door on a saw horse he bought at the hardware store for $59.95 and began to plane the door's top with a new tool which cost $24.95. He slid it about awkwardly for he had never used a plane before.

His knuckle skinned twice, once against its knob, and once against the split corner when the tool slipped. The plane skimmed the edge of the hollow door where the top met the sides, caught on a protruding corner, and all four edges splintered and spread apart like the Blue Angels smoke trails as they performed their final Fleur de Lis. He put the tools away, leaned the splintered door against the rear cellar wall and nailed a heavy drape-like material ($14.50) to the top of the door frame. He decided instead to resurface the back patio.

He brought in fourteen bags of all-purpose concrete mix ($89.90) and two heavy duty trowels ($21.65), mixed the concrete in a serviceable wheel barrow (bought used for $25.00). He mixed thoroughly and trawled surprisingly skillfully over the old crack-ing surface and beamed at his finished product. Four days later the concrete surface puffed up a dusty film, and soon pieces of cement as round as dinner plates separated from each other. He spent two weeks sweeping away powder and chunks of all-purpose concrete.

That was when, at his daughter Winnie's suggestion, he joined the Grandpa Program at the community hospital. "No tools Dad, nothing to break, all you need is you."

"It's a great help to us," Nurse Kate Kavanaugh said. She was a handsome woman, almost six feet tall Nick would have judged, and slightly square. Her striped Registered Nurse cap sat back on her head a fraction more than the other nurses', and whether she intended it or not there was a hint of John Wayne about her. Only when she spoke of the babies did her voice lose its trail-boss tone and the compassion filter through. Nick liked her.

"All babies are not born to loving families, you know, some are simply abandoned—you read about those. Some are born already addicted to drugs through their mothers. The mothers sign a few forms, promise to attend some drug classes, and leave the hospital without ever peeking into the maternity ward. There are so many reasons we have them here.

"For your part, you scrub up, put on a hospital gown, and sit in the "Grandpa Ward" with other Grandpa volunteers in very comfortable rocking chairs. You simply hold them and pet them and talk to them while you rock."

"This does what?"

"It does whatever the human touch does. It conveys another's presence, another's concern. The most destructive thing for a baby is a sense of isolation. Getting their diapers changed is sometimes the only human contact some of these babies have. The nurses try to get in to rub backs and massage them when they can, but time is their enemy."

"AIDS babies?"

"Some."

"Is..."

"Every precaution is taken. Is there a problem?"

"I guess not. It's a question I wouldn't have had a problem answering in theory, but when you say "Here, hold this AIDS baby,' all kinds of fears pop up."

"Mr. Castle..."

"It's all right, I'll be glad to be of help to any of them."

So Nick filled out the application form, revealing more of himself than he ever dreamed he would have to, and five days later, checked and cleared of all perverse leanings, he found himself back in the pediatric ward, dressed in hospital green, and feeling very self-conscious.

"We call this the 'Rockin' Room,'" said a different, younger

401

nurse. She was short and plump, with a fresh scrubbed look and peach colored hair that seemed to be its natural color. She smiled as she ushered him into a large, square room with highly polished, off-white vinyl floors. "Please take a seat, I'll be right back."

Hospital rooms seemed to him, to sprout from one great design head and this one was no different. It lacked the pervasive antiseptic smell, but the germ-free attitude emanated from every square inch. The room held four well-spaced rocking chairs topped with inch thick seating pads. Two of the chairs were already occupied with voluntary "Grandpas" rocking gently with tiny babies lying hunched upon their laps or supported up on their shoulders. They were gently rubbing the small backs. Both men nodded to him, but continued to speak to their tiny charges in a monotone coo.

The same young nurse, wearing the name tag "Donna Millette," returned with a swarm of blankets. She unrolled them to reveal a baby perhaps a month old. "Sit down, Mr. Castle. Let me introduce Carl to you. You and he will get along just fine, I'm sure, but if you need help each rocker has a 'panic button' built into the arm. Just press it if you need something." She smiled as she left. "Don't worry, you'll be great."

The tiny body had practically no weight to it, and that surprised him. He'd forgotten his own Mary Lou and Winnie at this age—and even the grandchildren seemed so long ago. He cradled the baby as he watched the other Grandpas for hints. They rocked easily and talked soft nonsense to the little ones. He began his own tempo and tried to talk to this little stranger.

"Hi Carl, how'ya doing? I'm kind of new at all this. I guess you figured that out eh? Not that I haven't done it before. No, I've got kids of my own—grandkids too—just that I haven't done it lately. Well I'll do the best I can. What songs do you like? I'll start with a couple from my days, they're the only ones I know the words to. Now here's an oldie, but goodie:

Hush little baby don't say a word
Papa's gonna buy you a mockingbird.
And if..."

402

The baby wailed. He waved his small arms frantically without rhythm as only a month old child can do. He gave a hiccup and something white escaped from the corner of his mouth. There was only a moment of panic as his mind raced. "What am I doing here?" But his memory and instinct kicked in and he wiped the baby's mouth clean. He continued his patter.

"Don't like my singing eh? Probably an octave high for you. I'll just tell you about my day, okay?" And as Castle's voice returned from the higher register to the deep baritone of Grandpa babble, the child quieted again. Castle rubbed his small back in circles, then moved his hand to the back of the tiny neck. He shifted the child up to his shoulder as he confided to him his problems with the flower bed and the weeds, and the disappointing careers he had endured. "Worked from high school graduation until I was sixty-five, and as Don Cornell once said in a song, "All I got to show for it is the muscle in my arm.' "

Thirty minutes passed and Donna Millette returned. "He's a quiet one, isn't he?" Doctors are concerned about that. They're keeping an eye on him. Well, Mr. Castle, you've earned your ten minute break. You can use the lounge around that corner or the balcony through that sliding glass door. There's a hard chair out there—hospital issue." She indicated both choices as she picked up the infant in that competent, seemingly careless manner that the true expert has. "I'll be bringing you Lucy in ten minutes. She's a little fussy one." Nick stood and found himself wanting a cigarette, a habit he'd given up over sixteen years ago.

"Well, at least Carl is still alive. I didn't break him."

Lucy came and was, as promised, fussy. The deep baritone failed to quiet the incessant squeaks and moans. Each change of position seemed only to feed the baby's high pitched complaints. He tried lullabies; old Sinatra songs; Como's croonings; even Christmas carols. Nothing worked. He looked down with some dismay at the red, crinkly little thing in his arms and began in a semi-gutteral voice:

> You ain't nothin' but a hound dog.
> Just a-barkin' all the time,

You ain't never caught a rabbit
And you ain't...
It was like shutting off a faucet. The tiny eyes dried and grew wide at him. He laughed, and his chest shook where her small head lay. He pressed his cheek against hers and she gave a sound Nick interpreted as contentment. "They don't call him 'The King' for nothin' Lucy" It was with regret, thirty minutes later that he had to release her to Nurse Millette.

"She give you a bad time, Mr. Castle?"

"Piece of cake, Miss Donna." She smirked at him and he blushed. "Can I have her again tomorrow?"

"They'll be regulars, Mr. Castle, at least as long as we have them here. Four babies a day, thirty minutes each, two hours a day. We don't want to wear out our volunteers—or our children. Eventually they go to foster homes, or for the lucky ones, immediate adoption."

The third baby jerked in his arms in something resembling minor convulsions as quickly as he was handed over to him, "We call him 'Billy' for no real reason—at least none known to me—his mother was severely addicted to crack. The baby has it in his system too. He's better than he was when he first came to us, and the doctors are treating it just like an adult addiction, but don't expect too much from him yet."

After fifteen minutes Castle had to push the chair's button for help. "He gasps for air all the time like he can't get his breath. Is he okay" Am I doing something wrong? Am I hurting him?"

"He was hurt long before you signed on, Mr. Castle. Here, I'll take him. We'll try again tomorrow. It's a getting to know each other process. Maybe we can help him, maybe not. Time will tell."

Kenny, the final baby, hardly moved his head the entire thirty minute period. Loving words, soft musical tones, deep throat humming sounds. Nothing affected him. Only when Nick stroked behind the small shoulder blades did Kenny react, and then without a sound.

"We think there's some kind of hearing problem—maybe his voice box too. Doctors aren't sure yet. Well, that's your first day, Mr. Castle. What do you think?"

404

"No parents anywhere? Nowhere?"
"None we'll ever see. It's you and us, Mr. Castle. Tomorrow at two o'clock?"
"I'll be here. Good night."

Nick's first beer that evening slid down his throat, cool and soothing, filling every imaginary grid. Each second of his day crowded into his thoughts for first attention. Every feel of each child, every movement, every sound. Those small bodies, resting on his shoulder or hunched up like little rabbits on his lap, seemed suddenly to be of more value than any possession he'd ever had. He remembered holding his own children and the same loving, protective feeling swelled once more within him. Places in his heart which had grown dry and brittle from disuse felt a warm flow and began to soften. New wine restoring suppleness to old wineskin.

The following morning jarred Nick. On arrival at the employees' entrance he was forced to stand aside while three ambulances, sirens screaming, pulled down the emergency ramp from the nearby freeway, and in a frenzy of activity, the ambulance transferred accident victims onto waiting gurneys and into the hands of the ER personnel. Nick pinned himself against the inside wall as the bleeding and moaning victims rolled past. He was grateful, minutes later on the fourth floor, when Miss Millette's voice brought him back to his own work.

"You remember Carl, Mr. Castle, our contemplative?"
"Well, Carl hasn't been properly introduced to the finer things, yet. He's probably just very particular about what he listens to, you know. Today I'll find out if he likes Elvis, too."
The woman recognized the affection in his voice. She heard it often enough from the Grandpas as they grew more comfortable with their role and more competent in their abilities. She knew how difficult it was for them to remain "distantly efficient" with the babies who looked to them for warmth and care. She was aware of

405

the pangs they suffered when they handed over their heart to a child who was preordained to be taken from them in a short time.

Carl copied his first day—restless, frightened. Nick did "Hound Dog" as he had done for Lucy, but to no avail. He rubbed his cheek against the child's and placed the small hand against his lips and made a splashing sound. He slid the tiny fingers down his new growth of late afternoon beard, and allowed him to feel the gutteral vibrations of his throat. "How about this, Carl?" He let out a deep throated rattle mindful of an outboard motor starting.

It quickly got Carl's attention. "You like that eh?" Tough on the epiglottis though, kid," He repeated the sound against the small hand much to Carl's delight. Nick looked up, chagrined. He had been so completely absorbed in the child, he forgot that he wasn't alone in the room.

Two smiles from across the room. One of the men said in a stage whisper, "Anything that works, Grandpa." One could not miss the empathy. There was no self-consciousness in their cooing and mooing sounds, no humiliation when they couldn't still the small cries nor quiet the fears raised from the trauma of the previous nine months.

Carl had been taken back for a snack and Nick sang in delight to Lucy about Heartbreak Hotels and Hound Dogs and Blue Suede Shoes and wished his time with her had been much longer. But he failed in the following twenty minutes to comfort Billy, his "addict" and, as much as he regretted it, he again pressed the chair's relief button. Nick was apologizing to Nurse Millette about having to call her a second day, but she smiled a warm understanding smile as she lifted the convulsive child off Nick's shoulder.

As she did so, the thickly padded port-holed doors to the ward opened, and Nurse Kavanaugh came out smiling with an elderly priest who was winding his white stole around two fingers and slipping it under his greens and into a pants pocket. "Thanks for coming this afternoon, Father, his mother will be relieved. She was worried abut getting him baptized when he was so fragile."

"My pleasure, Kate, although I think the Lord would have taken care of things without us." She squeezed his arm and retreated back in the ward. The priest approached Nick. "Hello, I'm Father Jack Moore, chaplain here at Doubleday Community."

Nick shook the man's hand and looked up at Nurse Millette before she got away with Billy. "I'm sorry I had to call again, Miss Donna, the crying and jerking was starting to pull at my guts. Sorry."

She smiled a second time as she carried the child away from the discouraged man. "Twenty minutes today—only kept him fifteen yesterday," and he touched her arm in thanks. She pushed open the padded door with her hip and disappeared behind it.

He turned back to the priest. "Hello Father, my name is Nick Castle. I'm a Grandpa here."

"I can see that. Have a tough rocker?"

"Billy. He's got drugs in his system. Jumps and jerks all the time."

"Yeah, I know Billy." He watched Nick's eyes brim but not spill over.

"I'm just me, you know, I don't know what to do with him. I don't even know what I'm trying to do here. With him…"

"You're not a miracle man, Mr. Castle, you're not even a doctor. You're here to give thirty minutes a day of attention and human contact with him. You're not expected to cure anyone. You're not even expected to try. Don't take on an unbearable burden or you won't be of help to anyone."

Nick looked up at the priest. He was shorter than average, 5'7 perhaps, 5'8 at most. His hair had been a deep black at one time but gray was taking over. His eyes were at once calm and haunted by his chosen life. He was light, maybe 150 pounds, but not weak, wiry perhaps. There was a tiny vertical crease low on his forehead, nearly between his eyes, forever puzzling a question.

"You been chaplain here long, Father?"

"Most of my ordained life. I was a year at St. Robert's, practically around the corner, and when Fr. Beauclair was moved downtown they moved me here. Shortest distance for anybody, maybe."

"Looking forward to retirement, Father?"

He smiled. A private smile. "One day, I suppose. How old

do you think I am, Mr. Castle?"

Nick, in his life's mistakes, had learned the lesson of always shooting low in response to this question. "Sixty, maybe fifty-nine."

A gracious smile formed. "I'm forty-two."

Nick maintained a discreet silence. What had this man seen that would suck twenty years from his appearance? Before either man could fill the silence, Nurse Millette pushed through the heavy doors and dropped Kenny, the quiet one, into Nick's arms.

"I look forward to talking with you again, Mr. Castle."

"Nick."

"Nick. See you."

Nick welcomed the thirty minutes of silence from Kenny, offering the child a pensive, circular back rub, healing and comforting both man and child. The thirty minutes ended too quickly and Castle didn't remember the drive home.

The rest of the week was unchanging routine. Carl in his joy of touch, Lucy loving the gutteral sounds of rock and roll, Billy in his deep need, and Kenny in his solitude. Nick found himself eager to rise each morning, to make the drive to the hospital, and to feel the slight weight of the babies across his knees or against his shoulder. Why had he seen so little of his own grandchildren? He would soon correct that.

The following Monday Lucy was gone. Nick felt a mule kick in his chest.

"It had been in the works for some time, Mr. Castle. A perfect couple adopted her. Not too young, not too old, well positioned and stable. They had been waiting so long, and they wanted a little girl so badly. They were in tears when Catholic Services called and set up the formalities. They're everything we could have hoped for Lucy."

"Lucy's gone."

"Remember what I warned you about, Mr. Castle, the little ones are just passing through here."

"I know, but…"

"She's safe, Mr. Castle, and very much wanted. It's a good

thing."

"Of course. The placement people must know, don't they?"
"They're very careful."

Tears came anyway. They came without any sound at all. "I
hope someone told them that she likes Elvis." The woman waited.
She knew she should. Nick spoke into his laced fingers, "I was
never very good at things. You know, fixing, repairing, measuring.
Nobody in our family was. We worked all our lives and raised happy
families, but if you wanted a wall put up or a floor laid or a lamp
fixed, it wasn't something I could do. My idea of good measure-
ment is having the milk and cereal run out at the same time. Actually
I'm still not very good at things. I did okay with Lucy but then it's
no great talent to hold a baby. To give her your arms."

"You give them more than just your arms, Mr. Castle."

Carl, Kenny and Billy remained. Later that week Lucy's
replacement came. It was a premature baby left on the doorstep of
the Union Mission downtown, rags marked with blood stuffed in
around him. A ring of a doorbell and the retreat of running footsteps and here he was.

Standing on the inside of the padded doors, and in the midst
of a strong smell of disinfectant hand soap, Nick found himself
before an oversized hospital scrub sink and heeded Donna Millette's
instructions: "This is new for you, Mr. Castle, scrub hard and long.
He's very vulnerable." He scrubbed for what seemed like ten minutes before he was fitted in gown and surgical mask and let into a
separate section of the ward, silent and darkened.

"We keep the preemies, when we get them, here in warming units. Just put your hand through the hole in the unit and rub
gently with your finger. Like he was a new kitten." It was Nurse
Kavanaugh with him now.

"So tiny, small as my hand."

"Just three pounds and something. Came very early and with
very poor nutrition. A preemie. Just a few minutes, Mr. Castle, we'll
come back for you."

"So many tubes, so much tape, so much junk."

"The junk keeps him alive, Mr. Castle. You are the non-junk. Let him know he's a human being. Let him know you're here. Let him know we care."

It was like petting a little gray mouse. Everything was softness, no bones, no body skeleton, no firmness. Nick looked at the tiny body's veins showing through transparent skin, its eyes tightly closed. "Fight it, little one, fight it. You shouldn't have to learn to fight so soon but you're going to have to anyway. I'll help. I promise."

He was willing life into this small child, transferring his own pulse into this frail body, seeding it with his own strength, willing it to live through the touch of a single caressing finger.

Fr. Moore found Nick at 5:15 on the balcony outside the Rockin' Room. He was sitting in the hardback waiting-room chair, watching the early evening violet fade, and waiting for the diffusion of the orange colored parking lot lights to take effect.

"My favorite time of day."

"Hello, Father."

"Long day?"

"Longer than two hours."

"Yeah. It happens too often." The priest leaned against the balcony railing and put all his weight on both hands. He drew a deep breath, as though to get all the outdoors within him, and released it very slowly.

"You see it all don't you Father? I mean you see the results of all those accidents on I-75. All those torn up bodies. The illnesses that last too long. The diseases that decay healthy people. You see the old ones leave us and watch the young ones come in with their own kind of pain. The ones born too soon."

"I heard you had your first preemie today."

"He didn't even have a name. I call him Nathaniel. Remember what the Lord said about Nathaniel, Father?"

"Behold a man without guile."

"Yes. Without guile. Innocent."

"Not quite the same thing."

410

"Whatever. Don't you get angry, Father? Aren't you bitter about it? Why don't you hate it all?"

"Too hard."

"What?"

"Too hard to hate everything. It eats you up. Jerks you around like a puppet on a string."

"But you see all this every day. How can you ever smile or laugh or enjoy anything even when you're away from here, knowing all this is going on even after you leave the building? It's here every single day. Don't you get angry with Him?"

"Other people see lots worse than this. I don't know. I have some great memories to carry me through things. I guess my growing up was good. Happy things happened. I've had a share of love, and I guess I have a good reserve of memories to draw from. They help carry me through most of the days."

The priest watched a car pull out of its parking place and crawl down its aisle to the main exit. Was the driver going home happy after his visit? Was he filled with relief? Or was his day tragic? The car turned into the mainstream of traffic and was gone. He picked up his thread of thought. "Nick, I know what you're saying, but the ones I pity are those who have no memories—or those whose memories are so hurting that maybe no memory would be better than what they have. Oh, I'm no pollyanna. I know the shadow is always there. There is no day so right that the shadow doesn't fall somewhere into it. But, Nick, to reject the light when it comes simply because one day in the future it may not come is to reject God's respite, His gift of peace. And that's really what provides the strength for the times when we have to do without that light. Wherever the shadow comes from it falls on us because He permits it. He's promised that He will give us whatever we need to bear it.

Nick looked away refusing the answer. "Lucy may have those memories, those days of light you're talking about, but what about Billy, my addict or Nathaniel, my preemie. How do you explain their pain? How do they bear that? How do YOU bear that?"

"I don't always. Lots of times I can't. I certainly don't pretend to understand it all. If the shadow is too great for us, and the

411

pain truly unbearable, He asks for our patience and even our forgiveness until we come to understand."

Nick looked away again. "Pious piffle!"

"Probably. I'll let you alone now. Be careful driving home,
okay."

Nick waved him away, then called back to him, "Where do
you go to find peace? Do you have a place? What do you do to stay
in one piece?"

"Sometimes I ride my ten-speed into the hills until I'm exhausted. Until my legs scream. Sometimes I run the high school
track until my body won't go any more. I just drop down in the
infield. Sometimes I cry. And yes, I do have a place I go, although
I can't always find it."

The men reflected, separate yet together. Fr. Moore watched
a cloud turn from rose to gray while Nick watched the tops of parked
cars reflect the hospital lot's mercury lights "Well, I'd better be going too, Father, I've got kids tomorrow who'll want me at my best."
The men shook hands and departed.

For almost two weeks the pattern didn't vary. Carl was always brought first, and because of his hearing and speech
impediments, gave Nick a quiet, comfortable first thirty minute
period. Then on Monday Nick's fourth week, Nurse Millette brought
Carl in, smiling as only bearers of good news smile.

"The news is that they found a blockage in Carl's eardrum,
just a dab of flesh where it shouldn't have been. He had a minor
blockage on the other side. Only very low tones registered with
him. That's why he could enjoy your low speaking voice but why
your higher singing pitch sounded sharp to him. The doctors are
sure they'll be able to remove the blockage. He's going to have normal hearing, and there's no reason he won't be able to speak. He'll
be normal in every respect. They're going to do the operation tomorrow. I knew you'd be glad to know."

Nick eyes lit and his heart sang. Then after a moment: "He'll
be easy to adopt out then won't he? He's so bright otherwise and

412

lovable."

"They're waiting in line, Mr. Castle, he'll be gone as soon as he heals."

Billy came and squirreled about for his thirty minutes. Through the weeks Nick had been able to tame his own tensions with Billy and sometimes felt the child was calmer. In any event he was now always able to keep the child the entire period. After Billy he always went through the padded doors, scrubbed, masked and gowned to stroke Nathaniel's back with his forefinger. Four o'clock came, and Nick was glad for Kenny's silence to end the day. The man drew as much consolation from the child as the child did from the man, but this day a child's consolation was not enough to still his restless spirit. He left the hospital and walked across the quadrangle to the chaplain's quarters.

There was a pink post-it note on the door, signed with the housekeeper's scrawl. She had obviously gone for the day. "Father is in. Do not ring. Knock and come in." She had left the door ajar.

Castle pushed it with a tentative hand. "Father Moore?" He stepped quietly into the living room. "Father Moore?" He looked into the kitchen area, but it was empty, too. He turned and was about to leave rather than impose on the priest's privacy when he saw the door to the study standing half-open. He took a step toward it and cocked his head to look inside.

Father Moore was there on a kneeler before a crucifix, his eyes closed, his head bowed. Nick stepped quickly backwards intending to tip-toe away without disturbing the man when he saw the priest's limp arms grow slowly rigid and the slumping torso draw erect. His head rose gradually, his eyes still closed. Peace softened his features, and an aura of serenity formed, insulating him from the surrounding world. Nick withdrew quietly, frightened and humbled. Outside, he remembered his question to the priest: "Where do you find your answers? Where do you go? How do you stay in one piece?" He didn't remember walking to the parking lot nor finding his car.

On Monday, the following week, Nurse Donna Millette told Nick that his preemie was gaining weight. "Not a lot," she cau-

413

tioned, "but a gain is a gain and a positive sign of hope."

On Tuesday, she smiled again. Carl's operation had not been that complicated. It was swift and clean and completely successful. Only the healing inside the ear and getting accustomed to sound remained for him.

On Wednesday it was Kate Kavanaugh who brought Billy out to Nick, her face flushed, her swagger matching the tilted-back nurses's cap. Nick braced himself for the fitful child. He loosened the wrap at the wrinkly neck, adjusted the baby across his lap of swaddling clothes, and waited for the wail, for the anger, for the hurting cry of withdrawal symptoms. None came. Kate Kavanaugh stood watching. Nick lifted Billy up to his shoulder and waited for the wild puppet movements, the flailing arms striking at his ears. But all he felt was a tiny head roll gently onto his gowned shoulder. He turned a confused look up to the smiling nurse.

"We think he's clean, Mr. Castle." Her voice couldn't conceal her joy. "It looked like it might be coming for the past few days. You may have noticed it. The medication, the diet, its additives, the length of time we've had him and YOUR patience too, Mr. Castle, YOUR caring certainly helped detox procedures. The doctors all agree that he's 95 percent clear of the residual effects."

Castle looked down at the calm face, stroked the baby's crown, listened to the babble of contentment. Billy stretched himself out in full length luxury as a cat would before a fire. Nick held the small cheek up to his own and wet the baby's face with his tears. "Billy, I'm glad. I'm so glad."

On Thursday it was decided that Kenny's silence was a more serious problem than Doubleday Community was equipped to handle. The mother had taken a fall during the pregnancy, and the doctors thought there may be brain damage although no one would say that for the record. Not enough information. They all agreed that more could be done for him at St. Mary's than here. "He really should have progressed more than he has. We'll move him as soon as they have room. Probably Monday. He can get specialized treatment there." Kate Kavanaugh's explanation made perfect medical sense. That day Nick petted Kenny and sang to him, and lovingly caressed his back and neck, although his mind and heart were at

414

distinct odds.

On Friday Nathaniel die.

"You said he had gained weight," Nick protested to Donna Millette. "It looked promising you said."

"He had so little to work with. His respiratory system didn't have time to develop properly. His heart was so erratic. He just wasn't ready to be on his own. I'm sorry, Mr. Castle, we're all sorry. We had grown to love him too. We were all pulling for..."

Nick chest heaved and his body felt like stone.

The Rockin' Room was empty. Only the indirect lighting offered dim relief from the night and Castle welcomed the dark. He had been alone now for hours. The other Grandpas had gone home and the nurses gave him his privacy. One toe had absently rocked the chair. Then even that stopped.

"I don't understand," he spoke softly in his isolation, if You were going to take him why didn't You take him right away? Why put him through all this for so long? Why? Is suffering so important?"

He closed his eyes and thought of the failed flowers in his garden; of the door that he couldn't plane correctly; of the paint that he couldn't get to come out his sprayer; of the concrete that turned to powder. He thought of the fifty years of undistinguished work he'd performed. He thought of his wife gone these ten years; of his son lost in 'Nam; of Kenny's uncertain future. But his thoughts were guided elsewhere despite his darkness: to his daughters, grown and committed to families of their own, to Carl's successful operation and imminent adoption; to Billy's freedom; to Lucy, his dearest charge, who loved Elvis; to the other Grandpas' loving babble.

His head bowed, and a lifetime of supportive memories flooded in. "To those who have no memories—or whose memories are so hurting that maybe no memory would be better than what they have—YOU are one of their memories, Mr. Castle, a good memory—for all whom you have touched. You have given more than just your arms."

415

His hands, hanging limp against the sides of his rocker, rose lightly to rest on the arms of the chair. His bowed head rose, his face lifted, and a soft acceptance relaxed his features. "I suppose. So many attempts fail—but some of them succeed. So many dreams never come true—but every once in a while one does. Maybe that's all anyone can ever hope for." He looked across the room at the two empty rockers; he smelled the sweet disinfectant hand soap that had become part of his life; he heard the quiet hum of the hospital's internal systems keeping it all together; he tasted the salty remains of his tears, drying on his lips.

"This is a good place. Not like Father Moore's place, but good. I can find some answers here. Not all the answers, but enough to keep a man asking for a lifetime." His body, which had been motionless for such a long time, cracked at every joint when he pushed himself up to his feet. "Stiff, like some old man." And he smiled to himself. "Like a Grandpa."

Snow
by Beth Alphin

Snow arrives floating on darkened wings
Finely peppering over black landscape,
As though God has turned His shaker upside down.
Wind begins to whip the whiteness
Swirling frozen liquid into froth
As it dances across the backyard
Sparkling in the glow of porch light.
Strain with all ear senses to hear
As silent snow deepness surrounds.
Why is snow so quiet?
Spring rain bangs, beats,
Summer nights fill with humming,
Even fall leaves flutter, nestle.
Winter snow always arrives on soundless paws
Sneaking into the world as a crystal white tiger.

O, Georgia!

Maybe, Maybe Not
by Helen Freeman

SERENDIPITY CALLS FOR THE SIMPLICITY
OF YES OR NO.
UNCHARTED GROUND FOR ME, THIS AMBIGUITY
MAYBE, MAYBE NOT.
MY WORLD REVOLVES AROUND POLARITIES—NOT UNCERTAINTIES
MAYBE, MAYBE NOT, INDEED.
BEING IN THE MIDDLE
FEAR IMPALES MY HEART
AND FIXES MY BREATH IN SUSPENDED TIME.
HEART BEATS LOUDER
SOUL WANTS MORE PEACE
WITH THIS AMBIGUITY
OF MAYBE, MAYBE NOT.
"ACT AS IF" THE AUTHOR SAYS.
"THEN LATER REAL PEACE WILL COME."
IT'S PROCESS NOT ARRIVAL THAT GETS US THROUGH THIS RIDE.
BUT WHEN? ACCEPT SOME SWEET SURPRISE.
LIFE IS NOT ONLY CERTAINTY: SAVOR SERENDIPITY
FEEL ALIVE-
I'LL TRY;
WILL I SUCCEED?
MAYBE, MAYBE NOT INDEED.

O, Georgia!

Bag Tags
by Virginia M. McGuffey

Sandy. It had to be Sandy, of all people. She ran toward my car calling my name as I opened the door. Her green plaid tennis skirt swayed back and forth at the top of long white legs which were lightly freckled from decades in the sun.

"Hi, Sandy," I said.

I climbed from the car and wobbled on the heels I wore. My feet and ankles bore markings from the press of the hiking boots and socks I had taken off at McDonald's up the street. Thank goodness I had thrown a dress and heels into the trunk last Saturday as I left the office.

"Kelly! Where in the world have you been? You scared us to death!" Sandy was saying. "How could you do that to us—to disappear like that?"

"That certainly wasn't the point," I said.

She plucked a small leaf from my hair and held it up.

"The mountains?" she asked.

"Does that look like a sea shell?" I countered. I had considered the beach.

"So what were you doing?"

"Thinking." It was the only answer that came to mind. What was I doing? I had no idea. Then I added, "About the job. They want me to go full time."

"Oh. Well, it's nice to see you," she said finally and gave me a little hug. "Welcome back."

She sighed, then added, "I guess."

I shrugged and looked past her to the green funeral home tent flanked by flowers and slow-moving people. Rows of padded folding chairs faced a closed casket beside a mound of dirt. I supposed there was a hole there, rectangular and waiting, but I couldn't see it from where I stood.

"Have you been by your house?" Sandy asked.

"There wasn't time. I didn't know until. . . ." but that was none of her business.

"Jeff. Have you called Jeff?" she reached in her purse for a

421

cell phone but I stopped her hand.

"No. Not yet. Please."

"Jeez, Kelly. You gotta call him. Here, I will."

"No." What would I say?

"The man's worried sick over you."

"How do you know that?" I figured he'd be angry. Very angry. Jeff is intense.

"Every time I called your house, he answered."

"How many times did you call?"

"Well, a lot, I guess. I kept thinking you'd get back. Or maybe Jeff would leave or quit answering and I could leave you a message."

"Oh."

"I tried all day one day. Monday. He never went into the office. Kept picking up the phone."

"I see." Monday was the date of one of his biggest closings. He loved closings, the importance of the day, the catered luncheons, the drama of big money changing hands, the culmination of weeks of work. Monday, I figured, was the one day he would be too busy to miss me.

"You know how husbands are about tennis calls. I couldn't imagine leaving him a message about the lineup, with you being gone and all."

"You were calling about the lineup?" I asked.

"Our toughest match is tomorrow morning. And with Molly, well . . . " she nodded toward the casket, " . . . with Molly out of the lineup, we had to do *something*," she said.

I stared. "We could forfeit."

"Have you lost your mind? We've got a shot at city finals. We could win the division again, even up here at C-2."

ALTA, the Atlanta Lawn Tennis Association, had moved us from C-7 to C-2 because we kept winning our division. The fact that there were B and A and AA divisions, we pretty much ignored, proud to be big fish in our little pond.

After all, we each had five bag tags to show for it, round plastic circles that clattered on our tennis bags. One yellow, two gray, and two green. Now it was spring of another year and although we didn't know what color this season's bag tag would be, we knew it would be round and plastic and would clatter with the rest. We'd be winners, all of us mothers and wives would be winners. It felt good sometimes.

"And if we forfeit the One's, we forfeit all the way down the lineup. Five points lost. We can't do that."

"So?" I asked.

"So we need the lineup. We've been waiting for you to get back. We knew you'd be here in time," Sandy said.

"Okay. I'll move Ellen or Amy up to play at One with you. Which one do you want?"

"Neither. They've gotten too old. We don't need to split them."

I looked at the tennis shoes she wore and wished she would disappear, but she was right. Our Two's had played together since before we formed our current team, and they resisted being split about as much as the rest of the team resisted playing with them.

"They keep winning," I said absently. "What about Kim or Barbara?"

These were our regular alternates. I kept thinking the conversation was almost over, and I dreaded facing the rest of the team.

"Kim's subbing at the elementary school and Barbara's hurt her ankle," said Sandy.

Then it sank in. My face must have shown my sudden understanding.

"Right," said Sandy. "We've only got nine players available. Plus Lame."

"Lane," I corrected. Lane was Molly's cousin which was the only reason she was on the team. She should have been on a C-7 team, but Molly had insisted we take her.

"I guess I'll have to move the Two's up to play at One and the Three's to Two and put you to play at Three with a Four." This would work. Pairs could move up or down one position, single players, two.

"You can't do that!"

"Why not?"

"I've played at One for three seasons now. I can't play down at Three!"

Her voice almost cracked with frustration. "Especially with a Four," she added. "I'm better than that!"

"Then you should win. A point is a point," I said.

"Not with a Four," she pleaded.

"Then I'll put you with a Five," I said. "You can play with Ellen and we can put Lane with Sally."

"You're out of your mind!"

"Sandy," I said finally. "Can't this wait?"

Some of the people milling around had begun to find seats under the tent, though a few cars were still arriving. I looked for Jeff in the crowd. I did not know if I wanted to see him or not.

"He's not here," said Sandy.

"Who?" I asked. I did not want her to think she could read my thoughts. Of all people.

"Jeff," Sandy was blunt. "You're looking for Jeff, of course. Or you should be. I tell you, he's sitting by the phone. Call him!"

"I don't get why he's sitting by the phone. We have an answering machine," I said.

"He was afraid if you called you wouldn't leave a message."

He was right.

Lynn saw us and waved from the crowd. She grabbed Amy and Ellen and ran toward me. Suddenly I was surrounded by opinions.

"That is so cool," one of them said after Sandy explained my absence.

"I think about doing that sometimes. Getting away to think things out, but I never had the guts."

"So how was it?" one of them asked. "Did you find what you were looking for?"

"I don't know," I said. This was more complicated than I could answer right then. It was more than a career decision, it was burdened with way-of-life issues.

"Are you going back after the funeral, to, wherever you..."

That was a question I had not gotten to yet.

"Are you okay?" asked Lynn, my partner and probably my best friend, if adults have best friends. "We covered the school store for you this morning," she added.

School store. That's what I had forgotten. I had left clean clothes, a stocked refrigerator, a list of car pools and lessons and other things to remember. School store. That one I had forgotten.

"Thanks," I said.

"You look beat. Can I do anything for you?" asked Lynn.

I shook my head and ran my fingers through my short curly hair hoping not to feel any more leaves. Dressing in the bathroom at McDonald's had been awkward.

Then it dawned on me that Sandy wore a tennis skirt and shoes, which is all I had ever seen her in so it had seemed normal. I swear she can't read my mind, but she must have followed my glance at her skirt.

"It was in the instructions Molly left," Sandy explained.

"Instructions?"

"Yeah. The whole funeral was laid out in a five-page document. Frank found it on her computer in a directory called "Death." There were some poems there, too, that the preacher is going to read out loud."

It was too late to tell them about Molly's creative writing class and the assignments she typed on the computer at night when Frank thought she was practicing for the typing class he thought she was taking.

"The rest of us just *couldn't* wear the tennis uniform," explained Ellen. "Even in Dunwoody. Not to a funeral." Thank goodness.

"Well, I did," Sandy said sternly. "I know she's looking down and that she's glad that at least one of us did it. Some friends you are."

"Why was Frank looking through her computer?" I asked.

"She didn't leave a note."

"A note?" I asked.

"Well, it might have been, you know, not really an accident."

"A note?" I repeated. This wasn't making sense.

"People leave notes, sometimes, when they try to commit..."

Sandy was having trouble saying the word.

" . . . suicide." It finally came out in a whisper.

"Oh," I said.

"Oh, yeah. All those pills she takes for her tennis elbow. And she had a sinus infection," Ellen offered this.

"She took way too much," Sandy said. "She knew not to take that much."

"No she didn't. The prescriptions were stronger than usual, and they reacted with each other. It was an accident," said Ellen.

Amy grabbed Ellen's elbow. "Tell her about the dates."

"The dates?" I asked.

"On the pill bottles. The refills. . . . " Amy began.

" . . . were the same date you left," Ellen broke in. "But we called the pharmacy and it was late on Saturday. You left early that morning, we know from the message you left on your office voice mail about the Carly will, long distance from well north of here."

"Jeff recorded it on his dictating machine and played it over and over," added Amy.

"The pharmacy said the doctor called to increase the strengths on the refills. It was legit," said Ellen.

The dates? Me leaving?

"We figured you didn't have anything to do with it," Amy said.

An awkward silence followed. I looked at Sandy, then at Ellen and Amy, finally at Lynn.

"Oh, Kelly. We've missed you so much," Lynn said.

She gave me another hug, followed by hugs from Ellen and Amy. Sandy watched with her arms crossed, goosebumps on her legs. The sleeveless white top with the green plaid collar offered little protection against the cool afternoon breeze.

"So what are you going to do?" Sandy asked. She looked me square in the eyes and I turned aside. Surely she wasn't asking about the lineup again.

"We could ask Judy to play," she said finally. It didn't surprise me that she had worked out a solution to the lineup, although it had taken her longer than usual to get to the point.

"Judy's not on the team," was my immediate response.

"We can drop/add her until midnight tonight, by the telephone computer."

"So?"

"So we could drop Molly and add Judy," Sandy said. The others shuffled and exchanged looks.

"Molly won't get her bag tag if we drop her," said Amy. Ellen nodded. Were they defending Molly or barricading against Judy? It could have been either.

I said, "I don't think Molly would care about the bag tag."

"She might," said Lynn. She pointed at the casket. Five plastic circles hung from a handle on the side, one yellow, two gray, two green.

"Part of the funeral instructions," said Ellen.

The wind or a mourner knocked them together. They clunked with a dead plastic clatter.

"Oh," I said.

"Judy's available tomorrow and for the rest of the season. She's better than Molly was," Sandy argued.

"She didn't join another team this season?"

"No one would take her."

"Not surprising," said Ellen.

"How do you know she's available?" I asked.

"I called her," said Sandy.

"You called her?"

"We had to do something."

"If we add her, we're stuck with her for the rest of the season. Maybe forever. She's wanted to be on our team for years," I said.

"We could tell her 'no' after this season," Sandy suggested.

"Right," I said suppressing the sarcasm as much as possible. Sandy had wanted her on the team from the beginning. She was the only one who Judy got along with.

"Molly was much better than Judy." Amy seemed compelled to defend the dead.

"Whatever," said Sandy. "So, what do you think?"

I was the captain and under ALTA rules, I didn't have to take a vote. I could dictate the roster, the lineup and any other important decisions. But these were my friends.

"Amy?" I asked.

"She's a good player," was Amy's noncommittal response. I knew that for Amy, that was saying "no."

"Ellen?" I asked.

"Well. . . ."

About that time the preacher began the service, and that was fine with me. We hurried toward the tent and stood together at one side. The preacher began with a prayer, and I closed my eyes and was back on the trail.

The call had come at dawn on Wednesday. I had turned the cell phone on for the first time and then decided I wasn't ready to talk to anyone yet. What would I say? What could I say? What should I say, not that that mattered. What did I want to have said?

I left the phone on a rock near the fire and was rinsing my stainless coffee cup in the creek when it rang. After four days on the trail, my ears had grown used to forest sounds. The ring came from another world.

I stared at the phone and let it ring until it went silent. I had decided to move my campsite and had started to pack up. I went back to packing, wishing I knew who had called.

The phone rang again as I was fan-folding the internal poles that I had slid from the nylon dome tent's shell. The fabric lay wrinkled and thin on the ground, like a burst balloon. Strong and thin, it had provided adequate protection against the pouring rain that had come on Monday. It had not kept out the loneliness. It had not directed my thoughts. But it had kept me dry and it was light enough to carry on my back. That was all I had asked of it.

428

Again I let the phone ring itself out. I rolled up the nylon fabric and stuffed it with the poles into the tent bag. Then I moved on to the next item. Each part of my campsite had a specific place in my backpack, an orderly role to play.

As I packed, the area returned more and more to itself, pinestraw, trees, a creek, evergreen leaves on short plants, some buds on branches, a snail on a rock, one minnow darting in and around the rocks in the creek.

I was grateful for the solitude. I had picked an abandoned section of the Appalachian Trail, a segment taken out of use for rejuvenation, so I wouldn't run into other hikers. If Jeff had reported my absence, which I knew he wouldn't, I didn't want to be found.

At the beach there would have been no solitude. I would have seen groups with kids, teens sneaking beer, a woman in a maternity suit, a man with a laptop computer, four towels in a row and a bucket of shells. Footprints in the evening, gone by dawn. Lovers. I had not wanted to see lovers.

The phone rang again and this time I pulled it from my pack and answered.

"Mom! It's you."

"Hi, Meghan," I said. To my surprise it sounded good to hear her voice. Her pre-teen voice seemed almost pleasant, with an edge of stress. Her voice crackled over the cell phone. I must be near the edge of a cell or behind a mountain, I thought.

"Mom, please come home. I miss you," she said.

I was surprised at her frankness. This was the hardest part. And the easiest part. It was not her I was running from. I had come to the mountains to negotiate with myself. I weighed the as-yet unsacrificed years of my daughters' dwindling childhoods against ambitions that had grown stale. The wildcard, of course, was the family financial situation.

"I miss you too, baby," I said. She wasn't a baby, at 12, but she was younger than Christine and she'd always be my baby girl.

"Daddy misses you, too," she said.

"Is Daddy there?" I asked.

"No, I'm calling from the pay phone at school. We've been trying to call since you left, but especially since. . . ."

"Since what?" I asked. There was something in her voice.

"They tried to save her. . . ."

"Who, dear?"

"Sandy and Judy. They tried to save her."

"Save who?" The voice was breaking up. Through the crackle I heard "Molly."

"What's wrong with Molly?" I asked, and then she told me.

It was just as well that I had packed up. I had fifteen miles to hike out, a hundred miles to drive, and a navy dress to change into. Then I had to face them all at once. I wasn't ready yet. For a moment I thought about not going. Molly, poor beautiful Molly.

Then I remembered another call I had to make. There was someone that Frank wouldn't call, hadn't spoken to in years, and she would need to know. Thank goodness it was a name I could remember. It was the hardest call I have ever made.

Sandy's cell phone went off in the middle of the prayer, and she slipped away from the crowd to answer it. A few folks raised their eyes and glared after her. The wind caught the bag tags again, and they clinked together against the casket for a while. Then the gust died and they hung silently.

For some reason Sandy had ended up standing by me and the space she left behind felt good, almost tangible, when she was gone. The sun was low over the trees at the edge of the cemetery and long shadows came toward us from the west. The spectator role was a welcome relief as I stood there letting the preacher take over. The crowd was small. Most of the people who went to the church probably skipped coming out to the graveside since it was nearly rush hour. People had kids to care for, dinner to cook, those sorts of things.

Hazel Hazel sat in the front row, the only person I ever met with the same first and last names. Had they known she would fall in love with Billy Hazel, I suppose they would have named her something else, but even after Billy died, she kept the name.

I had met her a couple of years ago at her home, a worn mobile home in a row of brown and white homes out past Snellville. Pine trees sheltered the narrow, angled lot, and a small, homemade porch hung under her front door, its two-by-four railing stained a deep redwood color. A stack of cinder block steps led to a gravel walk that connected them with the sole parking space at the end of the trailer.

When I pulled into the spot, she came to the door, leaned out over the porch and squinted down toward me with a puzzled look. She had loose skin that suggested she had once been fat and a tired look that dominated her face.

"What d'you want?" she called out cautiously.

"Are you Mrs. Hazel?" I asked her in return. I had started to say Hazel Hazel but it sounded too odd.

"Hazel Hazel, that's me," she said. "And who are you, pray tell? You ain't from the landlord, I hope," she added.

"Molly asked me to bring you this," I said. "She's in bed with the flu."

I held out my hand with an envelope as I went up the steps. The blocks shook a little as I stepped on them, and I grabbed the rail for support. The envelope contained money, I thought, but I didn't know how much.

"Come on in, child. Let me fix up some stuff for you to take her."

I followed her into the dimly lit living room. She stood by the refrigerator to the left in her tiny kitchen and began pulling out containers of what looked like home-cooked vegetables.

"Here, take these to her. I got a bushel of beans and a half bushel of peas at the farmer's market, and she can eat these. I didn't get them all canned yet. She don't get her vitamins regular like and then she gets sick."

There were five containers.

"And I made a cake. The mixes were on special this week."

She handed me a slab of chocolate cake on a thin paper plate that tried to fold up as I held it.

"I was hoping she'd come by," said Hazel. "She don't get out here as much as she used to."

"I know she tries," I said. I didn't know at all, but it sounded like something I should say.

"Frank won't let her, you know. She has to sneak out."

"Oh."

"He don't let her work none, either."

I had guessed that was the case, although Molly had never mentioned it. Then I wondered where the money had come from. Frank was the kind of person to keep track.

"It's her birthday today. Tell her I'm sorry I didn't have money for a present, but maybe she'll like the cake."

"She'll love it," I said.

"She's one special child," Hazel said. "My only daughter. And there weren't no boys."

Sandy slipped back into her seat and whispered, "Jeff's on his way."

The preacher had raised the Bible up from the podium with one hand and with the other was pointing toward the sky. Then he set it down and started talking. His voice was too low to carry well and I hadn't tuned in.

"Wait for him," Sandy implored. "Wait."

I knew the mourners would all leave, and Ellen and Amy had to go home and fix dinner for their husbands, and Lynn had to get her son from the day care center, and maybe that would leave Sandy and me there alone waiting for Jeff. For some reason I knew Sandy would stay. She almost seemed like a friend. I did want to see Jeff, and the neutral, somber ground around us would be an adequate place to start.

How long do they wait, I wondered. How long after the people leave do they wait before they lower her into the ground and take the dirt and put it in on top? Do they shovel it in by hand with tiny thuds or push the whole mound in at once, suffocating her in a single clump with some kind of blade on a small tractor?

432

Do they level it off or leave a hump so when the dirt packs down and settles in over her there won't be a dip? Will they plant grass? Seed or sod? Will they leave the tent up awhile? Who takes the flowers? My mind filled with these tiny questions because the big questions had been there too long and had tangled themselves up in too many corners of my brain. I was pushing out the questions that were bothering me the most, standing there on the surface of the earth that would hold her.

And then there loomed the immediate question. What should I say to Jeff, and why?

And I knew that whatever was said, we would eventually go away and leave all those plastic bag tags, chemically secure for thousands of years, there beneath the ground to guard her body as it slowly melted into the earth and dissolved back into nothing.

O, Georgia!

Southern Comfort
by Regina U. Galloway

B.B., honey, teach me the blues
Lend me a wail from a long trombone
and a wavery scale from a saxophone
Keep playin' and singin' bout things we lose
Come on B.B., I need some blues

Hey, Ray baby, play me some blues
Make that keyboard ring and cry
Start with slow bass and trill to the sky
Sad out some rain on an old tin roof
Ray, get me happy with some lowdown blues

Tone out loving with a broken heart
wrenching with pain that tears it apart
Paint old and smoky in the deep midnight
years of hard times when life's a lost fight

Where'd y'all get those low soul blues?
Down by the river there's a Southern muse
sounds like the ghost of an ole screech owl
or a lonely baby or a coon dog's howl

I never picked cotton or had cardboard shoes
but I grew up hungry for Deep South blues.

O, Georgia!

Biographical Notes

Judges
Fiction and Non-Fiction

Donna Gessell, Ph.D. is an assistant professor of English at North Georgia College & State University, specializing in 18th century British literature. She also teaches rhetorical grammar (the study of how words make meaning), composition (both in practice to freshmen and in theory to secondary education teachers), and Milton (the keystone figure of British literature.)

Eric Clark Link, Ph.D. is an assistant professor of English at North Georgia College & State University. He received his Ph.D. in American literature from Purdue University where he specialized in 19th century American Literature and culture. He has published numerous articles on American literary figures, including Mark Twain, Henry David Thoreau, Robert Frost, Walker Percy, Thomas Pynchon, and others. His first book, *Neutral Ground: The Romance Controversy in American Literary History and Politics*, is scheduled for publication by Louisiana State University Press. He and his wife Tanya live with their two children, Sarah and Nathaniel, in Dahlonega, Georgia.

Alan Jackson is an assistant professor of English at Georgia Perimeter College. After serving on the editorial staff of the Chattahoochee Review for four years, he became editor of Humanities In the South, published by Southern Humanities Council. He is currently working on his doctorate in literature.

437

Judges
Fiction and Non-Fiction

Ethelene Dyer Jones is a retired educator, author, historian poet and speaker. A native of Blairsville, Georgia she has lived since 1960 in Fannin County, Georgia. She was a charter member and president of the Georgia State Poetry Society, now known as Georgia Poetry Society, which was founded in 1979, and she currently serves as editor of its *Reach of Song* anthology. Her books include *The Singing in the Wood: Faith through Flood and Fire; Facets of Fannin: A History of Fannin County, Georgia; One Hundred Years of Heritage and Hope; and Mother and Child Reunion.* She won the 1999 first prize Evelyn Cole Peters American Heritage Poetry Award." She and her retired minister husband, the Rev. Grover D. Jones, live in Epworth. They have two grown children and seven grandchildren.

Margaret Langford has lived in Atlanta all her life. She holds a B.A. degree in English from the University of Georgia and an M.A. degree in English Literature from Georgia State University. She has three children and seven grandchildren. She is married to her husband of 43 years who is a judge in Fulton County. Margaret is a member of the Georgia Poetry Society and has had some of her poetry and articles published in literary journals.

John K. Ottley, Jr. publishes *Midwest Poetry Review* and is executive director of the College of Diplomates of the ABO, an association of board-certified orthodontists. He is a former Army airplane and helicopter pilot. With more than one hundred poems published, he is the only poet to have taken top honors twice in the Byron Herbert Reece International Poetry Awards. A widower, he is an avid hunter and flycast fisherman.

Dorothy W. Worth is a native Georgian who has been widely published in journals, anthologies and collections of poetry around the United States. She teaches Spanish and French at Georgia State University and has won many awards for poetry, including first prize in the International Centennial Olympic Poetry Contest in 1996. Her chapbook, *Desert Places*, was named winner of the Charles Dickson Memorial Chapbook Award in 1996. She teaches poetry courses and workshops around the Southeast and is a member of the Georgia Poetry Society, Atlanta Writers Club, Village Writers, and the Southeastern Writers Association.

O,Georgia!

Authors

Jeff S. Akins received his undergraduate degree with a major in English from Georgia Southern University. He received his law degree from the University of Alabama School of Law, where he graduated *magna cum laude* and was elected to the Order of the Coif. He lives in Statesboro, Georgia, with his wife and three children, and is currently at work on a novel.

Jim Allyn has been a full-time professional writer for 15 years now. HarperCollins released his first book, and he's also had two novels published by Thomas Nelson. As a freelance writer, he's won more than 60 awards—and has written for *The Wall Street Journal*, CNN, Time-Warner, Simon & Schuster/Macmillan Publishing, McGraw-Hill, Coca-Cola, IBM, American Express, Ogilvy & Mather, J. Walter Thompson, and Young & Rubicam, among others. He was born in San Jose, California, and graduated with a Journalism degree from the University of Oregon in 1983. He lives on a lake outside Atlanta with his wife, Kathy, and two daughters, Jenny and Amy.

Roseanna Almaee is an instructor and Director of the Writing Lab at Darton College. A resident of Albany, Georgia for six years, she is an active volunteer in her community serving on the executive board of the local arts council and as president of the Albany Writer's Guild. She is a regular participant in the Americus Poetry Slam and co-editor of three editions of the popular *Flint River Review*, a juried anthology of Georgia writers. Married twenty-eight years and mother of two girls, Ms. Almaee has written for the Albany Herald, Albany Magazine, the Edmond Oklahoma Sun-Times, and educational journals.

Beth Alphin was born in Carmel, California but has lived most of her life in the South except for three years in southern Germany. She has an undergraduate degree in English history and literature from Georgia State University and a Masters Degree from Asbury Theological Seminary in Wilmore, Kentucky. Her father is a born and raised Atlanta native. Her mother was born in Canton but grew up in Atlanta. She has a family heritage in Georgia through the Banks family of Elberton. She has always been involved in some creative endeavor beginning with music and painting. She began writing poetry during her teenage years as a way of expressing her feelings, instead of keeping a journal. She has several children's stories that she is trying to finish.

Farrar Atkinson has written numerous short stories, poems, plays and several novels (as yet unpublished.) She has won awards at writers' conferences and in last year's competition of Georgia writers, her creative nonfiction piece, *A Portrait of Misery*, was published. She's currently working on a collection of 'Southern-flavored' short stories and looking for an agent. A graduate of Mercer University in 1961, she taught biology as a Peace Corps volunteer in the Philippines. She's a realtor with Suwanee Realty, a mother and grandmother.

John Neal Bagwell, the son of a past *O, Georgia!* writer, has traced his family roots in this state back to 1789. He has spent his life in North Georgia, except for a brief period in Saudi Arabia and Kuwait. It was his service in the Gulf War which gave him the insight for *Dream Passin' By*. John is a career lawman, and he and his wife currently live in Gainesville.

Genie Bernstein, an Eatonton, Georgia native, draws upon her rich southern heritage for her writing. She is married to a research professor and enjoys a combined family of six children and seven grandchildren. With a background in commercial property management, she blends real estate intrigue with her love of the

South in a series of mysteries set in middle Georgia. Her first and second novels, *Hatred in Harmony* and *In Dead Harmony* are receiving favorable agent interest. She is fortunate enough to live in Athens, where she is active in the Harriette Austin Writer's Group at the University of Georgia.

Robert Black is a writer and editor with a not-for-profit public health research company in Atlanta. He lives in Lilburn with his wife, Michele Lynberg, stepchildren Shannon and Craig, and two stub-tailed miscreant canines. He has been 'committing' poetry for three decades and sees little prospect of kicking the habit. He is writing a novel that will be finished some day.

Enoch Brown attended Piedmont College and did graduate work at the University of Georgia. He is a World War II veteran and a retired grocer of 35 years in Jefferson, Georgia. His poetry book is titled *Wivern At My WINDOW*. He has had poems published in Calliope, DeKalb Literary Journal and Snake Nation Review. His interests include poetry, painting, minimal found objects and scrapture.

Mary Anna Bryan grew up in Augusta. She received her B.A. degree from Agnes Scott College and her EDS from the University of Georgia. She lives with her husband and cat in Lawrenceville. For the past two years Mary Anna has participated in the Callenwold Fiction Workshop under the leadership of Carol Lee Lorenzo. She is completing her first novel, *A Token Of Grace*.

Born in Chatsworth, Georgia in 1951, *Teresa Linderman Bueno* has lived here all of her life. The oldest of three children of Roy and Virginia Linderman, she has two younger brothers. The first 14 years of her life were spent in northwest Georgia, mainly in the Rossville area. She frequently spent time with her maternal grandmother in Chatsworth. In 1965 her family moved to the Atlanta area, where Teresa lives today. Teresa is married to Othon

Bueno and has two adult sons. She loves the beach; she and her husband spend much of their time at their beach house in the Bahamas.

John Bush teaches English and coaches debate at North Gwinnett High School. He is in his third year of teaching, his second at North Gwinnett. He lives with his wife Dawn and daughter Elizabeth in Cumming, where he has lived for most of his life. As for activities, he likes to trout fish in Hiawassee and to visit the Keys every Christmas—he enjoys fishing there, too. He graduated from U.G.A. and North Georgia College, but says most of his "schooling" comes from family and teaching.

Genevieve P. Nicholson-Butts is a graduate student in English at the State University of West Georgia. Her poetry has appeared in *Eclectic*, the university's literary and art magazine. As an undergraduate at the State University of West Georgia, she worked as a Writing Center consultant, served as contributing editor and editor of *Eclectic*, and helped organize several creative writing workshops. Before completing her B.A. in English at this institution, she attended Emory University, Valdosta State University, and Georgia State University. Born in Decatur, Georgia, she currently resides in Carrollton, Georgia, with her husband.

Jim Connor was born in Detroit, Michigan, and after military service, attended St. John's University earning degrees in English and Special Education. He moved to Atlanta, Georgia in 1972, and presently lives in Marietta with his wife, Judie and their daughter, Susan. He has previously published four short stories in the *O, Georgia!* anthology, among them *The Troll Under the Bridge* and *The Trumpet Man*. He is presently working on a series of short stories about a particular neighborhood and the coming of age of the young persons who live there.

William O. Dekle holds a B.A. in political science from Emory University and a Masters of Fine Arts from the University of Georgia. He served a tour as a Naval Officer, has written songs, plays, feature articles, and been a real estate broker, written music arrangements and sung back up in Nashville, and gotten mugged while walking out of church in Los Angeles. He has lived in Munich, Madrid, Copenhagen, Georgia, Massachusetts, Florida, California, Texas, Tennessee, and, apparently, traveled extensively.

P. Hoover Denson was born in Middletown, Ohio. She was transplanted to Georgia at a tender age and has called Georgia home ever since. She graduated with degrees in History and Public Administration from the University of Georgia, Athens. She is a mother of two incredible children and the wife of "the nicest man on earth." They live it up in Decatur, Georgia. She has worked as a government consultant, a banker, a secretary, and is currently working in the DeKalb county library system. The extent of her writing career has been limited to drafting legislation, authoring a government handbook, and getting a few poems published in a college literary magazine. She has recently completed a mystery which she is currently, lazily trying to market. She is also working on a novel.

Sam Isaac Edwards resides in "the treehouse" in Calhoun, Georgia. He has had numerous occupations, ranging from presidential aide, to soldier, bartender, politican, and farmhand, to name a few. He has previously published short stories, and recently had a memoir, *From Outhouse to Whitehouse to Treehouse* published by Parris Press.

Bonnie Fangmann lives in Lilburn, Georgia with her husband of 34 years. They have three children and two grandchildren, and she works as a kindergarten paraprofessional in Gwinnett County. She believes that children are our greatest gift and considers working with them a joy and a privilege. She writes poetry and is working on a children's book.

April S. Fields writes two monthly columns, *I Was Just Thinking*, for the Buford Free Delivery, and *Making Home*, for the North Georgia Star. Her work appears frequently in several trade newsletters. She also writes, produces and performs puppet shows to benefit local children's charities. Her secret passion, however, is her ongoing work on a collection of short stories, titled *Paper Dolls*. As she writes each story, which focus on women's triumphs over struggles, April finds her own sense of success.

Kimberly C. Fears lives in Lawrenceville, Georgia with her husband Brett and their three children, Austin, Sydni and Kendall. She works as a Kindergarten/First Grade Teacher's Assistant at Beaver Ridge Elementary School in Gwinnett County, where she also serves as the PTA President. Kimberly enjoys writing articles and poetry for their local church newsletter, *Faith In Action*, a publication of Suwanee Parish United Methodist Church. She believes God has given her the gift to write to encourage those who may be getting a little weary from fighting the good fight. Kimberly's philosophy in life is "Put God first in everything and be willing to go wherever He sends you. Love Him and have faith in Him, so you can obey Him; and He will surely bless you!"

Helen Freeman was born into an Air Force family, so spent much of her life crossing continents on a regular basis, from Europe to America. She is bi-lingual, speaking German and French in addition to English. She holds numerous degrees, including a B.A. degree in English, a Master's in English Education, a Master's in Family Counseling, a Master's in School Counseling, a Master's in Gifted English and a Specialists degree in school counseling—she has literally spent her life in school and teaching English continues to be her passion. She is active in various organizations such as Peachtree Presbyterian Church, Scottish Rite Auxiliary and the Georgia Council of Teachers of English. She has had several articles and a poem published in Junior League publications.

Regina Ulmer Galloway lives in Forsyth County and teaches American literature and composition at Duluth High School. Her publications include a collection of Cherokee legends, *Aunt Mary, Tell Me A Story*; a biography, *The Artist and the Storyteller*; and a family history, *Gaineswood and the Whitfields of Demopolis*.

Jennifer Gammage has been writing since she was five years old. At 21, she hopes that she has advanced beyond "Rolly-Polly Kitten" stories, and that she will some day be a respected Southern writer. A graduate of Wesleyan College with a degree in English and a minor in Theater, Jennifer feels that being published in *O, Georgia!* is the beginning of her long-standing dream. Although she has been published in small publications such as the *Flint River Review* in Albany, Georgia, she hopes that this, and continued exposure will give her the lift she needs to publish some of her many other works. A prolific writer with a definite affinity for words, Jennifer has written eight books (all non-published), five of which are still in her head! Because of her love of words and her exceptional memorization skills, Jennifer also enjoys acting and hopes to continue this pursuit. Jennifer has a slavish devotion to her cats: Greymalkin Kinkmeister, M'Cloud, Chance-Man, and Tangelo Tigra.

Holly Barrios-Gayman's poetry has been published in *O, Georgia!* and *The First Anthology of Poetry of the Pick Up Poets Society*. She lives in Alpharetta with her husband, six cats, two dogs and a parrot. When she is not writing poetry you can probably find her in one of her gardens.

Kathleen Gunter is 51 years old and has been married to the same wonderful man for 30 years. Their lives constantly overflow with the excitement and struggles of having six children. Several years ago she answered an ad in the local paper for the unpaid position of community columnist. Encouraged by the response to her columns, she has continued to write, ever expanding her topics and audience via the Internet. She generally writes about the most important things in her life: her faith, her family and her experiences of becoming a good ole' Georgia girl.

Lisa Haman was born in Everett, Washington, but moved here when she was five years old. She says she is now a southern girl, much to her mother's dismay. She lives in Marietta, about three miles from the famous Big Chicken. She has always loved books, so it seemed a natural progression to writing stories and poems. When she was in eighth grade her English teacher, Mrs. Reagin, gave her class a creative writing assignment. She wrote, *How Donkey Got Long Ears* and has been writing ever since.

Maxine Hamm is a native of Alabama, but has lived in north Georgia for the past 36 years. She has taught in public school for the past 29 years. Her hobbies are writing, music, poetry and short stories. She had two short stories published in the 1997 edition of *O, Georgia!*

Virginia (Jenny) Bishop Heaton received a B.F.A. from Auburn University in 1967, and has watched words write themselves into her serigraphs and paintings for years. Recently she read *The Artists Way* by Julia Cameron, and now dares new dreams of creativity via journaling—investigating ways to incorporate visual arts and words and producing writings that stand on their own. When not processing poems and prose, she creates line sculptures that include figures and writings of twisted wire. *O, Georgia!* is her first opportunity to have her work published except for prayers printed in her church's bulletin. She has had poetry selected for oral presentation at Pinckneyville Arts Center's Spring Read.

Terry L. Hensel lives in Alpharetta with his wife Joan. They have two sons in college. Terry and Joan own a mechanical contracting firm that both sons have worked for during the summer. Terry is a member of the Georgia Poetry Society, The Pickup Poets, and the Tri-County Writers. He writes short stories, essays, poems, and an occasional song.

Born as Vicki Lynn Robinson and raised in a small Alabama town, *Vicki Husby* feels gifts of optimism and will power. She is married to Barry Husby, and says he is the most divine combination of all things she wants, and needs, in a life partner. Her marriage has brought the long-sought stability she craved. It has allowed for a complete dedication to the cause she so deeply espouses, the betterment of children's lives. For over ten years she has taken roles such as nanny, governess or teacher, often seeking out troubled kids. Writing has long been her 'salve for the soul.'

T. Kyle King is an alumnus of both the University of Georgia and the Phi Kappa Literary Society, which was founded in 1820 to foster debate and creative writing. He practices law in Jonesboro and resides in Peachtree City with his wife, Susan. He is currently writing a novel.

Linda Stoutenburg Kirkland has a degree in anthropology (she was a professional archeologist and says it's not nearly as exciting as you'd think), a delightful husband, a close family and a good life. She's also taught school, tended bar, run an Olympic volunteer program, managed an Army surplus store, word processed and waited tables for a living. She's been writing since she was ten but this is the first time she's ever had the nerve to enter a contest!

Before *Devaun Kite* began writing fiction, she worked in the accounting profession for twelve years, as a CPA. She earned a Ph.D. and then worked as an Assistant Professor. She has various academic articles and book chapters. *You Get What You Need* is her first published work of fiction. It is a chapter from the novel *An Incomplete Stigmata*, which she plans to complete this year. She lives in Decatur with her husband.

Lisa Kurth is originally from Cajun Louisiana. She has been writing since she was a child. In grade school she wrote for the school newspaper. Lisa attended college at University of Colorado, Boulder. She continued writing, painting and teaching at the college level while living in Colorado. She and her husband moved to Los Angeles, then later settled in Georgia. Lisa now works as a Psychotherapist at her own private practice in Alpharetta. Aside from several clinical publications, she was published in the 1997 *O, Georgia!* anthology. Lisa lives in Cumming with her husband and their three children.

Thomas Lynn was born in St. Louis during the Great Depression and raised in a military family. He later saw combat during the Korean War before serving 40 years as a federal agent and a crime analyst with a county police department. He has since published poetry, fiction, essays and articles in numerous journals and magazines while on the advisory board of the Southern Poetry Association. He currently writes a quarterly column *Eyes Right!* for the National Veterans News Network plus *The View From My Writing Desk* for Sharing & Caring Magazine. He feels his greatest work is yet to come.

Originally from the Northeast, *Dagmar Marshall* received her degree in Journalism at Green Mountain College, Vermont. She moved to the Atlanta area in 1963 when her husband received a job transfer, with a family which included three children. She worked in real estate for 25 years in sales, marketing and management positions, but is happy to finally be pursuing writing full time. Dagmar is now in the editing stages of her first novel, and a children's story she wrote, *A Very Special Christmas Tree*, was recently published.

A native of Washington, *Leona Peffly Martin* earned her B.A. in English at the University of Washington. She also has a Master of Counseling degree from Arizona State University. She retired recently after sixteen years in case management with aging programs in Arizona and Georgia Her book of poetry, *Voices Remembered*, was published in 1994, and her poetry has also appeared in several journals. She has two unpublished novels and one in progress. Her most recent focus has been on writing short stories. She belongs to the Georgia Poetry Society and the Georgia Gerontology Society. She is married with three children and seven grandchildren.

Meryl Larsen Martin has lived in Atlanta since 1972. She holds degrees in nursing and English literature, and has been honored to be an at home mom for 27 years. Before being published in the 1996 and 1997 editions of *O, Georgia!*, her poems could be found on floor cloths and paintings. She just completed a children's story which is currently being illustrated. Her husband, Jay Martin, and their three children are a constant source of joy and inspiration.

Betsy McCall, a graduate of Harvard College and Harvard Law School, "retired" from the pressures of law practice in 1998 to fret over a mostly non-existent career in writing fiction. She lives in Dunwoody, Georgia with her husband and two sons.

Virginia M. McGuffey graduated from the University of Georgia School of Law in 1976. Much of her legal career was spent representing NationsBank and its predecessors, most recently at Troutman Sanders LLP. In May 1996 she left the practice of law to pursue a lifelong interest in writing fiction. Three of her stories have been published to date, including *Cold Front* which won the *Georgia Bar Journal's* annual fiction contest for 1997. She has three children, Mack, Michelle and Jennifer. Her husband, Wade is managing partner of the Atlanta law firm Goodman McGuffey Aust & Lindsey.

Except for a brief stint in Chicago, *Jim McVay* has lived in Cumming, Georgia for the past 15 years. He has an Associate in Arts degree from Jackson Community College in Jackson, Michigan, and a Bachelor of Science in English Language and Literature from Eastern Michigan University in Ypsilanti, Michigan. He and Thercia, married 39 years, have a daughter, two sons and five grandchildren. A recent change in careers has finally provided some time to devote to developing his writing skills.

Jeanne McPherson grew up in North Carolina, and graduated from Duke University. She lived in and taught elementary school for varying periods in Alabama, Delaware, New Hampshire, and North Carolina (again), but Georgia was home base during the nomad years with her engineer husband. Her two sons are native Georgians and live with her in Marietta. In 1977, she began working for a publishing company in Atlanta, compiling trade directories. In May of 1998, she left that job in order to create meaningful works from boxes of notes and ideas collected over the years. She has been a Georgian now for the greater part of her life, and intends to remain so.

Margarita Moldovan is an "almost native Atlantan," having moved here from Cuba when she was only 6 months old. She is a graduate of Georgia State University with a Bachelor of Arts in English. She lives in Alpharetta with her husband, two young daughters, and her dog, Nellie. This is her first attempt at publishing her poetry.

Monica W. Munn is the author of various published short stories, articles and a novel-in-progress, *Signs of Another Season*. After earning degrees in Journalism and German Literature from the University of Georgia, she has spent her time jobbing and continent-hopping, gathering experiences, writing and dabbling in other cultures. Currently living and working in Frankfurt, Germany and travelling Europe, she plans a move back home to Georgia in the near future.

Jessica Nettles lives in Powder Springs, Georgia with her two children. She is a junior at Kennesaw State University, where she is studying English with the hope of being a writer sometime before she grows too old to type. She has written three scripts for the Front Pew Players, a theatre group at the First Christian Church in Marietta, Georgia as well as several inspirational essays for an upcoming devotional book. When she isn't writing late into the night, Jessica enjoys gardening, reading and collecting movie soundtracks. She is currently employed by Starbucks Coffee company as a Master Barista.

Edith Harper Pinson is a native of Ellijay, Georgia and presently resides in Duluth. She is a graduate of Mercer University and Georgia State University. She taught second grade at Big Creek School in Cumming and retired after 25 years in June, 1999. Her love for writing is shown in her poetry. As she writes, she strives to reflect a positive outlook, make memories more memorable, and sentiments more sentimental, as they relate to her own life as a grandmother and a teacher.

Larry G. Rader was born and raised in Ordway, Colorado. After graduation from high school he enlisted in the Army where he spent 20 months in Vietnam. He served 20 years in the army living in 10 different states and residing overseas for seven years. He has lived in Georgia since 1981. After military service he worked as an industrial mechanic for 10 years. At the age of 51, he returned to school as a full time student at Ogeechee Technical Institute in Statesboro, Georgia, and is enrolled in the Computer Information Systems program.

Donna Reames has been writing since she was nine years old, when her story *The Boy With The Golden Nose* was accepted for use in the school library reading program. Since that time, she has written numerous articles for Nursing Magazine, poetry for Blue Mountain Arts, Inc., and The Calligraphy Collection. In addition,

Donna is a newspaper columnist for two weekly papers, the Harris County Journal and the Harris County Herald, where she writes her columns *Down Home Doodles* and *Life According To Zoe*. She is the mother of daughters Zoe, Chloe and Caroline.

Born in Florida, but raised in Georgia, *David Schmidt* has also lived in Arizona, Ohio, and Virginia. He briefly studied philosophy at Georgia State University before pursuing a degree in English at Kennesaw State University. He is currently focused on building a career as a freelance writer and artist. He lives with his wife in Cherokee County, and draws much of his inspiration from the foothills and mountains north of the Etowah River.

Sheri Layne Smith grew up in DeKalb County, Georgia, and now lives in Atlanta where she is a labor and employment law attorney. She appeared on Jeopardy! last year and is worried that life will be downhill from here. Sheri loves to read, especially poetry, and collects teapots and first editions of her favorite books by southern authors. Her story *Summertime* is an excerpt from a novel which she hopes to finish this year. She thanks her mother, friends, and writing instructor for their unfailing support, and Vicki for being the inspiration for Leanne.

Carroll V. Springer is a retired airline pilot living with his wife of thirty-five years in Cumming, Georgia where they have resided since 1972. He is originally from North Carolina, where he graduated from high school in 1960. He attended North Carolina State University in Raleigh, North Carolina. Since then, he has been involved in the aviation industry, primarily with a major airline based in Atlanta. Other interests include oil painting, drawing, and boating—particularly sailing.

Rosemary Colangelo Stewart worked as a school social worker in New York for fifteen years. Since moving to Georgia three years ago, she has been writing full time. Her *O, Georgia!* entry,

Father of the Year, is taken from a coming of age novel she wrote called *The Only Truth*. She has had several poems published and an essay in the *In My Opinion* column of the *Atlanta Journal*. She lives in Snellville with her husband, Alex, and her daughters, Alexandra and Rebecca.

Sean Taylor is a writer living in Alpharetta with his wife, Lisa, three children, Charis, Evan, and Jack, and his cat, Merlin. He is currently the editor of *On Mission* magazine, published by the North American Mission Board of the Southern Baptist Convention.

Kalynn Sharkey Vernick was born in 1954 in Cleveland, Ohio. She graduated with a degree in English Literature from the University of Cincinnati in 1978. Kalynn began writing poems, songs, and short stories at the age of twelve. After the birth of her first son in 1985, her literary urge subsided for many years. She concentrated on raising her two sons and volunteering for school, sports, and church activities. Four years ago, after getting a job as a paraprofessional in an elementary school, she developed a new surge of creativity and started writing a novel. Three years later, her first novel *Where Your Heart Is, Also* was finished. She remains busy with her sons, her job, revising her novel for potential publication, and writing poems and essays.

A fifth generation Atlantan and lifelong Georgia resident, *Anne Webster* is a former nurse who teaches a correspondence course in business writing, as well as creative writing workshops in Atlanta schools. Her poems have been published in the following journals: *New York Quarterly, Southern Poetry Review, DeKalb Literary Arts Journal, The Sunstone Review, 13th Moon, Stoney Lonesome, The Gladstone, Ethnic American Woman*, a textbook anthology, *Full Moon Solana, I Have Marks to Make, Nebo*, and *Explicit Lyrics*. New work will appear in upcoming issues of *Dream International Quarterly, Piedmont Review* and *Atlanta Press*.

O,Georgia!

It has been an improbable journey, over a span of 73 years, from Brooklyn, New York to Decatur, Georgia. With stops along the way in Washington, D.C. and Richmond, Virginia, *Leila Weisberg's* life has been a mirror of the times. Widowed at age 47, with six children to look after, there was no time to try to fulfill the hopes of her eighth grade teacher for a "literary career" for Leila. When she retired she was on a mission to write the stories that she had been storing in her head, for her children and grand-children. *Breast Cancer* was written to alleviate the anguish of her family and friends about her condition. She had to convince them of what she already knew, that SHE IS A SURVIVOR.

Catherine Hunter Wise has published articles and poetry in both regional and national publications. A resident of Blue Ridge, Georgia, Catherine is an Axiatonal Therapist for humans and horses. As a Civil War Reenactor, she portrays one of the over 400 women who are known to have disguised themselves as men and fought in the Civil War. Though *To Promise a Soldier* is a fictional work, it is taken from historical facts. The conditions in the Elmira, New York prison were abominable, just as were most of the prisons during that war. There was a woman imprisoned at Elmira, as well as Andersonville and other prisons.

Paula Woolf has taught elementary school in Illinois, Texas, and Augusta, Georgia. Currently she teaches in the gifted program at Alpharetta Elementary School in Alpharetta, Georgia. Two relo-cations provided unexpected breaks in her teaching career and the opportunity to pursue her dream of writing a children's novel. Her first novel, *Old Ladies With Brooms Aren't Always Witches*, was published in May of 1998. Mrs. Woolf resides in Alpharetta with her husband of twenty-eight years, Steven, and their fifteen-year-old daughter, Lindsay. Their son Kevin is a senior at Oglethorpe University in Atlanta, and their older son Jason is married and lives in Augusta. Paula is very grateful to her wonderful family for their encouragement and support.

Born in Rome, Georgia, *Walton Young* has lived in the metropolitan Atlanta area most of his life. He received a bachelor of arts degree in journalism from Georgia State University, where he also earned a master of arts degree in English. He was the first master's candidate at Georgia State to write a creative thesis, which was a short novel. Currently he works in retail advertising at the *Atlanta Journal and Constitution*, where he's been employed since 1972. In addition, he teaches English part-time at Georgia Perimeter College. He is married and has a son, who attends Duluth High School.

Yuval Zalkow was born in Israel in 1971 to an Israeli mother and a father from small-town Georgia (USA). She inherited neither her father's Southern accent, nor her mother's Israeli accent. Her family moved to Atlanta a year after she was born and though she has left Atlanta for college and other events, she continues to wind up back here. She is a computer programmer and lives in the mid-town area. She enjoys bicycling through town, sleeping in the park, reading and attempting to write fiction!

458

O,Georgia!